MANCHÁN'S TRAVELS:

Manchán Magan is a writer, traveller and television documentary maker. His programmes exploring the people and cultures of China, the Middle East, India, Greenland, South and North America, Ireland and Eastern Europe have been sold around the world. His first book was the acclaimed *Angels and Rabies: A Journey Through the Americas* (Brandon, 2006). He has lived in India, Canada and South America, and when not writing tends his oak wood in County Westmeath, Ireland. More information: www.manchan.com

MANCHÁN'S
TRAVELS

A Journey Through India

MANCHÁN MAGAN

BRANDON

A Brandon Original Paperback

First published in 2007 by Brandon
an imprint of Mount Eagle Publications
Dingle, Co. Kerry, Ireland, and
Unit 3, Olympia Trading Estate, Coburg Road, London N22 6TZ, England

www.brandonbooks.com

Copyright © Manchán Magan 2007

The author has asserted his moral right to be identified as the author of this work.

ISBN 978–086322–368–6

2 4 6 8 10 9 7 5 3 1

Mount Eagle Publications/Sliabh an Fhiolair Teoranta receives support from
the Arts Council/An Chomhairle Ealaíon.

Cover design: Anú Design
Typesetting by Red Barn Publishing, Skeagh, Skibbereen
Printed in the UK

Dedication
For Cróine

Acknowledgements

To Ruán for allowing me mould and meld, assimilate and partially assassinate his character without asking for a veto, or even to read the text.

To Marianne Gunn O'Connor, for giving me all the encouragement I needed at the most important time. And to Pat Lynch – not just the voice but part of the soul of MGOCLA

To Steve MacDonogh, for his continued belief and support. To him and Cleo Murphy for reigning in my bluster and sharpening my thoughts.

To Pembroke and Rathmines libraries for their efforts in keeping me informed and entertained. To Chandana Mathur and Anne Haverty for their help.

To Liam Ó Maonlaí, Eels and Josh Ritter for "Rian", "Blinking Lights" and "The Animal Years" – the soundtrack to my writing.

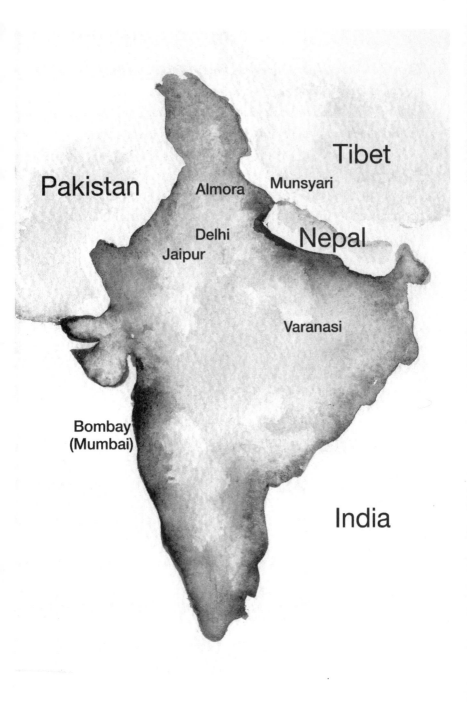

There's a worm addicted to eating grape leaves. Suddenly, he wakes up, call it Grace, whatever, something wakes him and he is no longer a worm. He's the entire vineyard, and the orchard too, the fruit, the trunks, a growing wisdom and joy that doesn't need to devour.

Rumi

(Although this is a true story, certain parts of it have been fictionalised to aid narrative fluency and protect those involved.)

Chapter 1

KHIM SINGH WAS on top of the mountain waving down at me. I felt I ought to wave back.

"Morning, Mocha-ji!" he bellowed down the hillside, and the air was so pure and the wind so still it was as if he were standing right next to me. It was this sense of clarity, of hyper-reality, that had brought me here, halfway up the Himalayas.

"Morning, Khim-ji," I yelled back.

"One of the lepers from Baldoti station wants to talk with you," Khim roared.

"Fine," I replied grudgingly. "So send him down."

I hoped I had masked the annoyance in my voice. It was the same whenever I was rent from my thoughts, the deluded realms of my inner meandering. It was precisely this sort of intrusion I had come here to avoid. You think if you journey to the farthest reaches of the Indo-Gangetic plain and settle in a remote cabin you'll be safe from people. Not so. And it wasn't simply that I was being inhospitable; the truth was that I wasn't in any state to see anyone. I was too far gone. My brain had drifted too far from shore.

Khim made no reply, and I yelled up again, "Send him down! Okay?"

I gave my head a little wiggle to signal my acquiescence, but still he didn't react. Through the trees I saw him standing there, running his fingers through his oily hair, shifting from foot to foot awkwardly. Either he hadn't heard me or he had more to say.

"But, Mocha-ji," he shouted down, "you should know, the boy is a pooftah!"

I paused for a second, trying not to smile.

"Okay," I called up. "That's okay, Khim."

A boy with leprosy was coming to visit me, and all Khim could think of was to warn me he was gay. I loved India more with every day.

I had spent the last five months hiding out in this stone hut in the forest with no running water or electricity, living like a hermit, cowering over a tiny fire in the centre of the room, eating *dhal* and rice. My days were spent hiking in the foothills, meditating and drinking glasses of piss. (My own, of course – I wasn't that far gone.) I believed I could hear voices inside my head. Moreover, I thought they were wise and loving: a choir of angels sent to light my way. At night, I'd leave my body and travel to other places, places beyond. I may well have been losing my mind.

Turning back into the cabin, I went to crouch down by the fire and await the boy. I could feel the usual bothersome strobes of euphoria shooting through my spinal column and onwards towards the firmament. It was getting so that they never went away – a chorus of Pied Pipers coaxing me to their cave. I knew what they wanted. They wanted me to drift out even further, never to come back.

As I say, I wasn't in a fit state to meet anyone. I had been on my own too long. My mind had begun to burrow into places it shouldn't be – places it shouldn't even know about: those shifting, shuffling nano-zones that link different facets of existence; the no man's land connecting grasshoppers to blades of grass to the wind that blows on both; the places where CDs and the laser reading them and the sound circling outwards all meld into one – places our 3-D focus is supposed to keep us safe from. It was my own fault, I know that. The whole *reality set-up* had never been enough for me – it was too stagnant, too limited. I had always wanted more. Somewhere I could breathe, somewhere beyond the claustrophobia. I learnt early on that what I was looking for wasn't here – it wasn't anywhere, or if it was, it was simply *elsewhere*. A place in which you could bypass the safety parameters of the brain and just drift. I suppose I knew that eventually I would end up lost, but I didn't care – in terms of a spiritual appetite, I was bulimic.

While stoking the embers with a branch, I took deep breaths to ground myself as best I could. Meeting anyone, particularly one of the lepers from Baldoti who most likely was looking for something from me, required concentration. I had to focus, to keep it together. It was odd that the boy was gay. A curiosity, certainly. I had known since I was a child, kneeling in my soutane and smock at the altar trying to stay awake through sermons about the Church's acts of mercy, that lepers were a part of India, but I never knew that homosexuals were too. I suppose I had never thought about it one way or another.

I recognised Tara Parbet the minute he stuck his shy, twinkling face in through the door. I knew him from my weekly visits to the leper station. He was one of the better patients, diligently taking the new wonder drugs each week, and with every chance of making a full recovery. He was sixteen now, and if he kept up the treatment for the full ten-month course, he would most likely be cured by his seventeenth birthday. I had been told he was an exceptional student, in line to be the first of the Baldoti boys to receive a scholarship to the local college. For him, there was a definite reason to get well. The promise of a future. It was exactly what most of the rest of them lacked. They didn't even want to be cured, as it would mean an end to the charity and medical care. And, since no drug could cure the stigma, they would always be seen as pariahs whether infectious or not. It was a real struggle to get them to take the drugs. My role, my sole responsibility on the planet for the previous five months, had been to oversee their medication, to watch them swallowing their colourful little beads of rifampicin, clofazimine and dapsone once a week. If they refused, I didn't grab their jaws, didn't hold their noses or ram the stuff down their throats. All I did was note their names down in a ledger and tell the station director next time he was in the area.

I wasn't doing any of this out of goodness or humanitarian concern, but as a favour for an old family friend. I had been fed heroic stories of Wolf's exploits in India by my parents since I was a child. He was a diplomat who had abandoned his distinguished career in the German foreign service to lead a crusade to wipe out leprosy in India through a pioneering new multi-disciplinary approach. Ten years before, he had set up a leper station here in the mountains, and it was he who had introduced me to the area – this idyll high up in the hills where India, Nepal and Tibet met. He had frequently invited me to accompany him on a trip here, and when I finally arrived, I felt completely entranced by the place and couldn't face leaving.

As he was setting off to visit his other stations, he made me promise I would keep an eye on the medical regime at Baldoti – just to oversee that the patients took their medicines once a week. It was a simple request, and he knew I had nothing better to be doing. I had got myself a little cabin in the hills and planned to hide out there, living as anonymously as an Irish boy could among Himalayan hill tribes. Every moment of every day would be entirely my own, to walk and think and dream, to hike down to the spring and soak myself in the pool beneath the pine trees. To be as mad as I wanted to be. I planned to walk to Almora for provisions once a week, and it would be no great sacrifice to stop in at Baldoti station along the way. It was as far as my service to humanity was being asked to stretch, and I knew I couldn't refuse. But believe me, I was no Mother Teresa. I was well aware that the lepers didn't even want my help. For most of them, taking the medication was just another ordeal in a life already full of hardship. They took the drugs because they had to. And they had to because otherwise all the work done by the well-meaning vicars and spinsters who organised fundraising fêtes and cake sales, and that of the International Leprosy Mission pen-pushers who commissioned reports and drew up treatment strategies, would have been in vain. They took the drugs because we wanted them to and because the pen-pushers might otherwise risk losing their pensionable jobs.

Tara didn't look too damaged. There were some lesions on his cheek and forehead, like a blighted potato, but they would soon heal. He had lost half his nose, but once it healed over it would look rather sweet – an elegant little button nose. Admittedly his aquiline profile was ruined for ever, but he was unlikely to have been considering a career in modelling anyway. I threw another cushion on the floor and bade him sit down. He took this as his cue to begin rattling out the same litany of questions that I had been asked a thousand times before. "What country are you from? How many hours by aeroplane? Are you married? Why not?" and so on ad infinitum. This wasn't a conversation. The answers led nowhere. It was a game of squash, and I was the alley.

Finally, he ran out of steam and fell silent. I was glad to have it over with. I had been through the same rigmarole with every one of the few visitors who had dared come near me: the local *sadhu* who came looking for alms; the *lakhri-wallah* selling a cord of fire wood; the pretty nurse from the leper station who had wanted me to meet her family. They all led me through the same steps.

I offered Tara tea – there was just enough milk left in the billycan which the *dudh-wallah* had brought earlier that morning for two cups. Putting the can straight on the fire, I threw in a few spoons of leaf powder, then carved up a pod of cardamom and a stick of cane sugar while it was heating. Tara was quiet now. I knew the battery of questions had been a dynamo to launch him into his topic, and if he hadn't built up enough charge he would stall. I could see he was having doubts about being here at all. Things would drag out for ever unless I helped him.

"So, Tara, how are things at school . . . at the station? How's life?"

"Oh, very good, sir. Thank you, sir."

"Please, call me Mocha," I said.

"Thank you, Mocha-ji," he said, adding the Hindi suffix denoting either honour or affection, it was hard to tell. "I have a problem, Mocha-ji . . ."

He stopped dead, and stared deep into the mud floor.

"You have a problem," I repeated and sat back as the unbearably long pause echoed through the room.

"I like other boys," he finally managed to spit out.

I smiled with as much reassurance as I could, but I needn't have bothered – his eyes were glued to the fire and were blurring over with tears or perhaps the sweat which was pouring off him with the sheer strain of revelation. It was hardly the third secret of Fatima, I thought, yet from his appearance it was clear it had taken enormous gumption. He looked as though it had been extracted on a rack. I was searching for something suitably reassuring to say when all of a sudden he recovered his spirit and looked up at me perkily.

"Do boys like other boys in your country?" he gushed in a rapid torrent of words. "I have seen movie film from your America, and there were many boys kissing other boys. It's good in your country, yes? Not evil, no?"

"Ahhm . . ." I said, desperately trying to think of a suitable reply.

"Am I bad?" he squeaked.

"No, no, of course not, Tara. It's wonderful," I said, casting about for platitudes. "Everyone is different, and . . . I suppose . . . it's kind of like our duty to be true to ourselves, isn't it? It's good to express our feelings."

I thought that would do it, but Tara was still looking up at me like a First Communicant waiting for the host.

"Liking boys is a fine thing, Tara," I said with more conviction and a reassuring finality. "A fine thing. Really. Really and truly."

What else could I say? I felt like the trusted English teacher or drama coach in those American teen series. The smile plastered across Tara's face showed it was precisely what he wanted to hear. I felt good about myself.

"Do you have a boyfriend?" I asked.

His umber skin blushed a tobacco brown, and he nodded.

"His name is Sangev."

"Well, that's great, Tara," I said. "I hope you and Sangev are very happy together."

That was it. Nothing more happened. I think he just wanted to share with someone. I waited a moment in case he had more to say, and then stood up by way of a gentle hint that it was time to go. The need for isolation was rising up in me again like the fevered thirst of a wino. I needed to be alone, and every extra second of this enforced sanity was causing a stress that was almost painful in its intensity. Thank God, he quickly took the hint and got up, *namasted* and shot out the door.

I swear that was it. A boy whom everyone secretly knew was gay came to me to tell me, and I congratulated him. What was wrong with that? How was I to know?

As a Westerner in India, I was constantly misreading situations; walking on eggshells, oblivious to the shards of chaos I left behind. Greeting people in the wrong way and in the wrong order, eating food with the wrong hand, treating women inappropriately, saying stupid things. I was just another bull in the china shop, smashing through cultural sensitivities.

I had no idea why Tara wanted to tell me he was gay, but I thought it was only polite to reassure him when he did. How was I to know that for him I represented a spokesman for the whole world outside his village? Where previously it had been something shameful, best kept quiet, now he felt he had been given the backing of the world. An imprimatur from on high.

Over the following few days, he was seen holding hands in public with Sangev for the first time; and soon after, he began dressing provocatively:

cutting the ends off his trousers to make pedal-pushers and tearing saucy holes in the rear. He figured out how to tie his shirt-tails into a bow to make belly-tops, and Khim Singh even claimed to have seen him wearing *kohl*. It amazed me that he picked up on all these things so quickly; where had he got the ideas from? Were there gay spores in the air that blossomed on fertile soil? Or perhaps a camp aesthetic hardwired into all our psyches ready to be activated when required? He boasted to everyone in the *chai* shop how I had said that in my country homosexuality was admired and respected, that being gay was an honourable thing, something wonderful.

I never did. At least, I don't think so.

The compounder of the local mission hospital came to see me in real concern, and he was soon followed by the matron of the leper station. They both pretended to be concerned for Tara's well-being, but actually they were just furious at me for interfering. I couldn't really blame them. They could clearly see the inevitable repercussions of what I had done, whereas I was only beginning to grasp the trouble that had been set in motion. I had in fact detonated a bomb at the very heart of the community – dropped sarin in the water. Suddenly I understood *Star Trek's* Prime Directive – never to interfere in other planets' cultures. I understood why it was so primary. It wasn't that Captain Kirk or Picard or I, for that matter, felt traditional cultures should remain locked in the past. In fact, one of the things that excited me most was how all over the world cultures were opening up, casting off the old hypocrisies and accepting new thoughts and practices. It was just that I (and, I expect, Kirk and Picard, too) never wanted to be the agent of change. I always kept away from crusades and causes. I was too obsessed with myself to care very much about the concerns of others.

Now suddenly my life had become upended. The sarin gas was spreading. People were beginning to mutter behind my back about Tara, to stare irascibly at me in the market. I tried my best to keep my distance, but Tara insisted on calling around to show me his latest fashions and bore me with love stories about Sangev. I learnt that his family was growing ever more despairing and that the entire community laid the blame on me. Things could only get worse. I tried half-heartedly to encourage him back into the closet, but having tasted freedom he wasn't going back.

"Oh, no, thank you, Mocha. You have been my greatest help. I am now Gay Pride *sahib*. Sangev and I shower you with garlands."

I had detonated a bomb as surely as if I were some enemy agent. I realised that my only option was to flee. What else was there? Anyway, I had grown lazy in my hideaway. Torpid. Not to mention, dangerously near lunacy. What had started as a way of freeing my mind of conditioning had become an obsession in itself. Each morning I found it more and more difficult to coax myself back into my body. My dream life was so much richer, more lucid, than reality that I was finding the body increasingly reluctant to pick up the gauntlet again and carry me through the day. It was definitely time to make tracks.

I had packed up my gear, paid off my tab in the *chai* shop and was just about ready for the nineteen-hour bus ride up to Dharamsala via Simla when Khim Singh screamed down the mountain at me that my brother was on the phone.

My brother?

No one had ever phoned me before. I didn't think anyone even knew exactly where I was. I was afraid someone must have died, and while chasing up to Khim Singh's shop, I went through the list: my mum? sister? friends?

Across the *chai* shop counter, I grabbed hold of the receiver to hear my brother, the Tiger, asking me on a crackling line across half the world, "Have you ever heard of TnaG?"

"What?"

"Tee-na-Gee," he repeated

I never had.

"It's a TV station – Teilifís na Gaeilge. Brand new. The government's setting it up to save the language."

"Great," I panted. Chota Lal, the Nepalese kitchen boy, ran barefoot through the snow with a cup of *chai* for me. "So what?"

Pulling the receiver away, I took a warming sip. It was from Khim-ji's own pot, not the normal dishwater he served his punters. On days like this, with icicles dripping from the eaves, Khim-ji brewed up an especially strong stew with knuckles of ginger and a spoon or two of powdered opium for sustenance.

"We're going to make a TV series on India for them."

"Who is?" I asked.

"You and me, you idiot!"

I reeled against the awning of the tea shack.

"Are you out of your mind?" I yelled to Dublin. "We don't know how to make television."

The Tiger is two years older than me. He is a good laugh, but basically a chancer who believes nothing is beyond him, and always has some mad scheme on the go. Admittedly he had worked on and off in the film business for a few years, but he had never actually held a camera in his life, unless, perhaps, hauling it into the back of a truck.

"Don't worry. We can learn all that," he said breezily, and went on saying something else that I didn't catch; it was drowned out by a dump truck speeding by, spitting slush up at the stools and tables. As the engine roared away, I could hear the Tiger asking, "Are you up for it?"

"No" I said.

"What?"

"No," I said again, louder.

"Are you up for it?" he repeated.

"How the hell would I know?" I said.

What sort of stupid question was that anyway?

"Excellent," he said. "See you in a week."

The line went dead.

He must have lost his mind. I was in no condition to do anything, let alone present a television series, and least of all one on so abstract and contentious a concept as India. Had I had the money, I would have rung him straight back and explained everything. I'd have warned him off; admitted to the bouts of euphoria; the epiphanies of unassailable arrogance, nay, transcendence; the early stirrings of a messianic complex. I would have told him straight out that I was unhinged. But I'd spent my last rupees on an oil lantern to use when transcribing the angelic messages that woke me in the night.

I had no choice but to accept my fate.

Over the next few days, the Tiger wired me some money. I exchanged my bus ticket north for a train ticket south to Delhi, got a haircut and had my ragged clothes washed and ironed. Khim Singh told everyone in the *chai* shop that I was a celebrity now, and they began to forgive me for Tara.

Their new compassion made me better disposed towards the whole project – television clearly had its benefits. I was coming around to the idea of being a presenter, to this surprise soapbox I was being handed. My only cause for concern was that I hadn't seen Tara for a few days and was beginning to worry about him.

Chapter 2

JUST AS I was about to enquire further about Tara, I was distracted by the sudden appearance in the *chai* shop of a Norwegian man who came lurching in one morning while I was having my buttered toast, and proceeded to sit breathlessly down beside me, saying he had walked all night in order to reach me in time. He was stick-thin, with feeble patches of wispy beard scattered across his face and an old aluminium rucksack on his back. He said he lived 2,000 metres higher up on a ridge just below the snowline on Nanda Devi – about 16 kilometres away by goat track. Somehow he had heard I was making a television programme and wanted his story told so badly that he had immediately set out on this journey down to see me. He feared I might already have left, and it was the joy of finding me here that gave him the energy to get his story across.

"It's the immortal *yogis*," he murmured exhaustedly to me, "the immortal *yogis*. These are what the world needs to know about now. It is your destiny – to be the one. It is, like, a duty."

At first I tried to ignore him and went on eating my toast. He wasn't the first crazy Westerner I had come across in the hills. Too often idealistic backpackers smoked too much *charas* and flaked out.

I could see Khim Singh loitering behind the man, wondering whether or not to boot him out. It was hard for him at times to tell normal backpacker eccentricity from psychosis. I'm sure he must have been dubious about my behaviour on occasions also, but I was a good customer and worth indulging. This man was oblivious to all that, busy riffling through his rucksack, taking out reams of foolscap paper covered in a tight, black, spider scrawl and handing them to me.

"Read this," he said. "It'll blow your mind. I've added some notes in the margins to make things clear."

The disconcerting luminance of his eyes and his frantically nodding head should have warned me off. I had enough weirdness in me to sniff it out in others pretty quickly. Bracing myself, I stared coldly back at him and shook my head, shoving the papers back across the table, narrowly missing smearing them with the butter knife. It was then that his face crumpled, revealing the exhaustion of the night's hike, and I couldn't help but feel compassion. His arms were reaching out so pitifully lest the papers be stained, the least I could do was be civil.

I asked him his name.

"Lans," he said. "Lans Okalsom."

"Let's just take things easy here, Lans," I said. "I'm having my breakfast, see?"

"Immortal *yogis*," he said; "you know what I'm on about?"

I shrugged. I wasn't sure I wanted to, but he went on anyway.

"Some people – a rare few – are born without the mix of fear and love. They have just love. It is *karma*, you know? And, because they have no fear, they never get sick and their bodies age only very slowly, if at all. Without fear and sickness and things like that, life gets boring, and they can't relate to us so they live alone. Many move to the Himalayas because of the quartzite and migmatite in the rocks. It boosts their thoughts, a bit like a transceiver."

Lans was staring beadily at me with those pale Scandinavian eyes, beseeching me to understand. I signalled Khim to bring us more *chai* and tried my best to follow his words.

He explained that these people were the *yogis* who lived in the caves above us. They spent their time meditating on behalf of the rest of us, living in a more or less comatose state and rousing themselves only every hundred years or so, to eat and drink and have their hair and nails trimmed. They used the caves to protect them from the snows and otherwise depended entirely on the services of their custodians: a handful of families who protected them generation after generation from wild animals and prepared food and washed them whenever they awoke.

From what I could make out, Lans wasn't one of these custodians. In fact, I don't think he had ever even met an immortal *yogi*, but a few years ago he had become so obsessed by the idea of them that he'd sold his in-car hi-fi business in Oslo and brought his wife and children out to live in a goat-herder's shack beneath a glacier 3,500 metres up the Himalayas. He wanted to help the *yogis* on their central mission to regulate the pulse of the earth. This was a service they had been doing for us for thousands of years, and it was thanks to them that we had never descended into total barbarity and that all our wars tended to peter out eventually. The power of their thought was so strong that they could neutralise, or at least balance, all our negativity.

This was a lot to take on board over breakfast, and I may have got some of the details mixed up, but as far as I could tell that was the gist of it. In fact, it reminded me most of all of a *Star Trek* episode. I was coming to believe that the entire *Star Trek Series One* and *Next Generation* should be required watching before setting foot in India.

What had upset Lans so much was that he had somehow learnt that the *yogis* were preparing to leave their bodies and abandon the earth because they felt we no longer needed them – we were ready to look after ourselves. They were planning to hang around for another ten or fifteen years to balance things in the Middle East and Africa, but after that they would pull the plug and die, leaving the planet completely under our control – trusting in organisations like the UN and EU to mop up any remaining skirmishes that did break out. Lans was convinced that without the *yogis'* help we would plummet back into the Dark Ages, and he had sacrificed everything to come here and beg them to stay. It had cost him dearly. His youngest daughter had nearly died the previous winter when she had crawled out of the cabin into the snow and had almost frozen to death. A few months later, his wife had been badly mauled by a Buddhist monk who had come down from Tibet to trade salt. The monk would have raped her had Lans not come back early from collecting firewood and beaten him senseless. Now he risked penury. The Norwegian embassy, which had been paying his social security benefit until now, was insisting that he start signing on back in Oslo. I didn't have the heart to ask where all the profits from the hi-fi business had gone.

I could see he was laying it on thick to gain my sympathy, but I knew from his eyes that there was no way he was lying. I tried to explain that I wasn't in any position to help get his message across. The television series we were making was only a rough thing for a tiny Irish language station, and we probably wouldn't even be filming very much in the Himalayas, but he just repeated again and again that this was my destiny.

"How else do you think I would have known about you?" he asked. "I live high up on a remote mountain; there is nobody for miles, and yet yesterday the first person I met in a month told me about you and your work. Call that *co*-incidence? Would you dare? Remember the gods are listening!"

Any *so-called* coincidence was down to the proclivity of hill tribes to gossip and the long-acknowledged efficiency of bush-telegraphy, but I said nothing. Instead I agreed to take a look at his notes and meet up with him later on.

They contained details of eight immortal *yogis*, three of whom were over 2,000 years old. The first one was Maha Avatar Baba-ji, who lived across the river from Mount Kailash. He led a simple life as though he weren't the "total master of the universe". Despite the fact that he could manifest anything at will, and irrespective of his glory (which could not be expressed in words), he allowed his neighbours give him money and food and clothing. It was as a favour to them that he did so.

He sounded fascinating, and it would have been great to have him on the programme, but unfortunately we weren't going anywhere near Haldwani; and the rest of the *yogis* mentioned in the notes lived way up in the mountains and would have taken many weeks to reach. If we had the budget for it, I might have considered proposing the idea to my brother. When I met up with Lans later that evening, I explained that our itinerary was more or less planned, and we couldn't start suddenly chasing around after demigods.

"But you're going to Rajasthan, aren't you?" he asked excitedly.

"Yeah, maybe," I admitted.

"Well, what about Bhartrihari?"

"Who?"

"Bhartrihari!" he exclaimed. "Did you not read the notes?" And then he dived back into his rucksack, pulling out more files and scanning through them. "Here it is – Bhartrihari. He lives in Alwar. It's on the road to Jaipur. He's one of the real oldies – been here 2,187 years to be precise. You've got to meet him. I'll give you his address."

Lans tore out a sheet of paper and printed his name and directions.

"Unfortunately, I can't guarantee he'll be in when you call," Lans said. "He doesn't always materialise in physical form for visitors. You just have to hope you catch him on a good day. But I can tell you, every 108 years, as sure as clockwork, he buries himself alive and has concrete poured over him to form a tomb as a demonstration of immortal *yoga*, and since his last event was in 1898, he might easily be around preparing for the next one. I've never been to his place, but I was told that there are seven tombs in it, all intact, as he's been doing the same miracle for the last 753 years."

"Why?" I asked.

Lans just stared at me in wonder.

"Seriously," I said impatiently. "Why bother?"

"That's for each of us to figure out for ourselves," Lans said, as if I were an idiot. "It's actually one of the questions you get to ask if you study under him, but he is a notoriously harsh teacher and insists that you study for at least a few decades, and preferably a century or two, so he doesn't get many takers."

I decided not to continue the conversation. The whole idea of this *yogi* burying himself and then reappearing as if by magic somewhere else reminded me of only one thing: the transporter on the *Enterprise*.

I know I should have advised Lans to get help and left it at that. He was clearly unwell, but somehow I didn't have it in me. His beliefs were no more outlandish than any of the thoughts that had been circling my own head for the previous few months; he just wasn't lucky enough to have a Tiger to steer him clear. I found myself saying to Lans that if we happened to be near Alwar and had time on our hands, we would swing by and see what we could find out. If Bhartrihari was around, well and good, but I was careful not to promise anything. I suppose I was impelled more out of sympathy for his poor wife and nearly dead daughter than anything. They had indulged him so much already, the least I could do was this minor favour.

Chapter 3

THE APPEARANCE OF Lans distracted me for a time from Tara, and when I eventually went to the leper station to say goodbye to them all, I could find no trace of him anywhere. I asked the compounder, and he tried to fob me off, saying that Tara had gone to see his relations. It was only when I pressed him further that he admitted that he was actually in the sanatorium but that under no circumstance was I allowed see him. The compounder claimed that he was infectious. I sensed something was wrong immediately and barged straight in past the matron. And there, lying on a cot with a drip in his arm, I found Tara, his face puffed up and bruised. The poor boy looked in a terrible way. At first he wouldn't talk to me and buried his face in the pillow. It was the matron who finally told me what had happened; how his uncle and some friends had broken in the night before and beaten him senseless. They were out of their minds on moonshine whisky. One or two ribs were broken, and the doctor thought he might have ruptured his spleen.

"My family don't want me back," Tara whispered when he realised I wasn't going to leave. "They say I am evil."

"Oh, God," I cried. "I'm sorry."

He flashed me a flinching smile and turned back to the pillow.

"Maybe things were moving a bit fast," I said. "You could take things slower. Give it time."

"You are not understanding," he said in an anguished pitch. "They say I am evil. They don't want me back."

I wondered was he just being maudlin now, melodramatic, but as I stared at his poor battered body, I couldn't help but be moved. The bruising on his face was the colour of a swell at sea, and up and down his ribs were punch marks red as any scald. This was why the Prime Directive was as it was – Tara's cracked ribs were the consequences of ignoring it.

"What will you do?" I asked.

"I am not knowing," he wheezed. "They say they are only coming to warn me. Some others threaten to do much worse. Uncle says Mother has had breakdown. I will go to Delhi I am thinking. Sangev says there are people there who look after people like us."

"Will Sangev go, too?" I asked.

Tara shook his head sadly.

"He has been sent away. Sent to his *bapu's* house up near Nepali border. A shepherd village – *Bhotiya* people. He will be shepherd there."

"I see," was all I could manage.

In the space of a few minutes, his own family had inflicted more damage on Tara than the leprosy had in a decade. As if being attacked from inside were not enough, they thought he deserved this, too. It was at times like this that I hated traditional cultures with kamikaze passion. I would willingly have joined any crusade against them, gladly casting my self-centric sensibility aside. I would have ridden in bearing the standard of progress aloft, gouging and lacerating all about me. I was angry, really angry, possibly most of all at myself. I should have seen it coming, should have kept my stupid mouth shut.

"You think you'll go to Delhi?" I said eventually. "Have you money?"

It was a stupid question.

"You don't worry about me, Mocha-ji. You have been too kindly already. I shall be very fine; money is not my big need."

"Yeah, right, Tara," I said. I had to admire his pluck, even if he was clearly bluffing. "Look, I'm going to Delhi in a few days. I'll buy you a ticket and you can come with me. We'll find out who these people are who you say can help you. Everything will be grand."

His face broke into a pained smile, and I left him to rest.

Chapter 4

DAWN WAS BREAKING as Tara and I made our way out of Old Delhi station and on to the city's streets a week later. Night watchmen were unravelling their cloaks in deference to the early sun, stretching life back into their crabbed limbs joint by joint. Their braziers were less a source of heat now than a means of warming last night's *chapattis*. Tara was looking around him in wonder; this was not how he had imagined the great city – like a hive fumigated, its drones up and about, but less frantic than usual; its cars and taxis not yet on the streets and the buses still keeping the steady, slow pace of the street sweepers. Servants were scrubbing porches, jewellers dusting their cabinets, peanut-sellers sorting their produce into mounds like croupiers in a casino. The city was slowly winding itself up for another day of mayhem.

Tara handed me the address Sangev had got for the contact it was claimed could help people like him. All it said was "Sri Gupta, beside Water Closet, Beneath Connaught Place". It seemed like nonsense.

Connaught Place was a three-ring bull's eye of grand colonial buildings, opening on to a lush lens of grass. It was a wedding cake of colonnaded arcades and iced façades, built eighty years before as the crowning epicentre of the Raj. Beneath it, as far as I knew, was nothing except rats and sewers. The address was clearly made up. I pointed this out to Tara, but he wouldn't listen. He couldn't countenance the fact that Sangev might have failed him, and he insisted that we go there anyway. We would search and we would find it, he swore.

I wondered who this Sri Gupta figure was anyway, or what he might be able to *do* for gay people. It reminded me of the secret addresses of back-street abortionists in Liverpool or London passed through the hands of anxious girls in Ireland.

Having failed to convince Tara of the futility of our mission, I spent the morning with him, winding our way around each broad crescent, in and out between the grand colonnades, looking for an underground entrance. The buildings were designed to last for ever as symbols of the Empire's omnipotence, but they were already beginning to collapse: the pristine plasterwork now had the look of stale cauliflower, or as though this great wedding cake had been left out in the rain. There were holes and crevices knocked into the walls for storerooms and sewage outlets, but none of them led underground. It struck me how appropriate it was that these buildings which had been designed to last a thousand years and then leave behind a corpse as beautiful as the city's other ancient ruins were fading as fast as the influence of the empire that had built them.

It took an hour of searching before Tara finally began to accept that Sangev might have been wrong. He agreed to head to the central grass circle to rest and get a drink, and it was there that he spotted it: the entrance – a narrow tunnel barred by lozenged gates leading directly underground. Tara turned to me with a proud, joyous smile and ran down the ramp. His way was barred by armed and turbaned guards who subjected us to a full body search before allowing us through, and we made our way downwards, feeling the dead heat and stench of sweat assault our senses. I had to remind myself where I was and why. I wondered whether Lutyens, the architect who had built this monumental dartboard at the axis of India, could ever have envisioned such a seedy warren being dug out beneath it. Here was an underworld of moustached faces in leather jackets lit by eerie strip lighting in nasty shades of amber and indigo. There was bad Hindi pop blaring from ghetto-blasters, and all around us a knot of tunnels, arced out like a triskele, were lined with stalls selling smuggled goods: replica guns, perfume, drink and electrical equipment carried over the mountains from Russia. It was as crowded and chaotic as the bazaars of old town but with an eerie, sleazy feel all its own. Tara asked one of the stall owners if he knew of Sri Gupta, but the man just stared blankly. Everyone there seemed disconcertingly pale, with an un-Indian sense of despondency that made me

shiver. Having trailed through stalls of stolen electronics and bolts of mouldering upholstery, we tracked down the water closet mentioned in the
address, but there was no way of picking out a single individual in the constant stream of hawkers and buyers flowing past. Tara called out his name
a few times but got no reply. Suddenly I felt something pulling at my
trouser leg and, looking down, I found a rake-like figure in a crimson *dhoti*
whom I hadn't even noticed before, smiling up at me. He was crouching
on a footstool, and was now shouting something.

"You are looking for me?" he was saying.

"Sri Gupta?" I yelled back, but he was obliterated again by the press
of bodies around me. All I could see of him when they parted was a bald-
ing pate spalted by dermatitis bobbing about like a cyclopean eye. The
crowd was like a tide, and as it ebbed I noticed that around his feet lay a
semicircle of blades and knives arranged on either side of a well-worn
whetstone. Somehow people knew not to trample on them, although there
was no way one could see them from above. He pointed to a scimitar hanging on the wall behind him which was engraved with his name, and when
I looked down again he had produced two footstools and a kettle from
nowhere and was beckoning us to join him for tea. We crouched down
anxiously, submerging ourselves in the sea of people. They parted for us
easily, although I was still afraid that at any moment they might close in
again and drown us. Tara said straight out that he was gay and needed
help, but Sri Gupta ignored him and stared hard-eyed at me. He kept staring for up to a minute, then made a big show of picking up my sleeve and
sniffing it deeply, then running his fingers around my earlobe like an uncle
preparing the penny from the ear trick.

"You come from sacred Himalaya mountain," he said. "I am feeling
this in you."

He gave a cursory glance at Tara, who was wearing fake designer
shades I had bought for him on the train and smoking a biddie in a flamboyant fashion.

"You, too," the old man said to Tara. "But *you – you* are never going
back."

I was impressed by this. From his eyes I could tell that this was the
desired purpose of the statement. He produced a length of wire hanger
from a fold in his clothes, gesturing that he wanted to stick it into my

head. I looked askance, but his eyes were dancing so brightly and there was so little trace of menace in them that I felt I ought to trust him, for Tara's sake if nothing else. He was smiling so benignly that it was as if by sticking a wire into my head he was doing me a great favour. I glanced over at Tara to see if he knew what was going on, but he was equally lost. So, I just shrugged and nudged my stool in a bit closer through the seaweed of feet. Sri Gupta stroked my head a few times, touching a point on my neck which made it flop prone to one side. Then, with one hand firmly on my crown, he began to wind the length of wire into my ear. It was at least a foot long and as he pushed it ever so gently, deeper and deeper into my head, I slipped into a state of suspended animation. I was conscious, but neither capable of, nor wishing to struggle – like a kitten clasped in its mother's jaw. It was bizarre. My consciousness seemed to follow the tip of the wire as it plunged ever deeper into me, and though it couldn't in truth have gone any more than an inch or two, it felt like it was already in my belly. The whole experience lasted only a few minutes, until he retracted the wire again, which was now coated in the darkest brown wax. This seemed to delight him, and he waved the wire excitedly for my appreciation, wiping the wax on to his finger and bringing it to my nose for me to smell. I looked on blearily, attempting a dazed smile, but all I wanted was the wire to enter me again, to send me back to wherever I had been. Sure enough he did soon start pushing it in again, and instantly I was lulled back to bliss. I think he repeated the whole thing three or four times, each time increasingly excited at the amount of wax he retrieved.

I would have wished for it to go on for ever except that Tara let out an urgent raspy cough which yanked me brutally back to earth, and I was reminded why it was that I was here. With great reluctance, I forced myself to look around me at the hoards passing by and managed to summon the will to pull away from Sri Gupta and sit up straight again.

When I had recovered somewhat, I explained that we needed to talk about Tara. The old man's face immediately turned apathetic, the delight vanishing from his eyes like a child told it's time for bed.

"Yes, yes," he said wearily. "I know what you want."

He picked up the whetstone and ran his thumbnail along it.

"The boy is a pooftah, yes?" he continued. "So, I take him – no problem. I sort him out. For you I do this."

He wasn't even looking at me, but instead was examining the last ball of wax, fixedly, as though trying to find within it all the joy that had so quickly dissipated. The light that had gone dark.

"What do you mean, you *sort* him out?" I queried.

"I *sort* him out!" he said impatiently. "It's a pooftah, yes? I deal with him. I deal with the pooftahs. It is the line on the side."

He picked up a blade and began polishing it wearily on the whetstone.

"Sideline, you mean," I said, tetchy like a spurned lover.

He puckered his lips and shrugged.

"I don't understand," I said. "What do you mean *deal* with him?"

But Sri Gupta just sighed.

"Tara has been disowned by his family," I explained, "and we were told to come here to find help."

"Yes, yes – of course. That is what I am doing. I help, no problem. This is what I am explaining you. You leave him here and all is fine."

He had discarded the whetstone and knife now and started fiddling with his various knives and bits of wire, fidgeting like an addict desperate for his fix. Suddenly he grabbed the wire and began winding it into his own ear until that same blissful feeling that I had felt spread across his features. A stab of jealousy ran through me, and I looked with irritation at Tara. While my eyes were averted, Sri Gupta jerked the wire out again, threw it on the ground and reached out to grab my arm, pulling it towards him. The action was so fast that I had no chance to resist. He twisted my arm upside down, examining my wrist, staring at it obsessively, pulling my hand back to make the veins stand out. I was still a bit bleary from earlier, and it took me a moment to summon the strength to wrench my arm away, but I found I couldn't. His grip was too firm.

"Your watch strap," he said finally. "It's frayed, see?"

Sure enough, the cotton strap was working loose.

"I fix it," he said, pulling out a needle, a hammer and some studs seemingly from nowhere.

He was just beginning to unbuckle the strap when I managed to get my arm away, yanking it full force out of his grip.

"There's no need," I said firmly. "The strap is fine."

I had suffered too often at the heavy-handed hands of well-meaning craftspeople before. Spectacles beaten into shape on an anvil. A sandal stapled with catgut. A paperback rewoven. I used to be impressed by the endless recycling in developing countries, but over time had come to think that maybe when something breaks it wants to let you go. It wasn't healthy to keep on clinging on.

The incident with the strap steeled my resolve and I stood up determinedly, pulling Tara with me and dragging him away out into the sunshine again. There was no way I was entrusting him to that lunatic. I still didn't know what exactly he did for gay people, and I didn't want to find out.

I brought Tara to the Alka Hotel and left him in the lobby while I put a call through to Peadar, my contact in the Irish embassy whom my brother had wanted me to get in touch with regarding the programmes. I figured he might be able to help me find a support organisation for gay people in Delhi.

"There's no point in even bothering your barney," Peadar said with a touch of smug triumphalism.

It turned out he was an expert on the situation. A significant proportion of the diplomatic corps were gay, as tended to be the case until recently, when life for homosexuals became slightly easier at home and they no longer felt the need to live abroad. The embassy had found out long ago that there was little or no gay infrastructure in India, and the only place where there was any type of support network was in Bombay. Peadar said the only help he could offer us was the name of a friend of his, an American ex-Peace Corp worker who had had an article in the *Times of India* a few months back campaigning for gay rights. He said that if there was any sort of network starting up, this man would know about it.

"What sort of television series are you making anyway?" he said. "Gay groups seem like an odd topic to focus on, if you don't mind me saying so."

"This isn't for the television," I clarified. "It's a private matter."

"Oh, of course," he said in hushed consular tones. "I quite understand. It can be very hard when you're away. In fact, if you'd like to . . . ?"

"That's not what I meant, Peadar," I said, but he cut me off with a knowing ho-hum and put me on hold while he found his friend's number. I rang it straightaway. Reg was his name. He agreed to meet us in the burger joint he owned in Paharganj later that afternoon.

Reg was a squirrel-cheeked, blond-tufted man in his forties. He put us sitting at a Formica table on swivelling tractor seats which he claimed were cast from the same mould as Burger King seats. They were the first genuine examples of fast-food seating on the Indian subcontinent.

"Every goddamn *idli-wallah* is copying me now," he said. "It's always the same, the pioneer gets it up the rear. I often wonder why I even bother. I mean, you try and bring a bit of your own culture to a place and they just hijack it. Bastards! It was the same with the Peace Corps – all of it, Shiva-humping hog shit."

I told him about Tara and he said, "The way I see it, it's like this: young Tara here has two hopes – no hope and Bob Hope!"

He paused to snigger, as if this were somehow funny or even original.

"You're not the first boy to like other boys, kid," he went on. "Just look around the walls of any Hindu temple. It'll tell you everything you need to know about sexual degeneracy. But this is India for God's sake, not Malibu! Here you cut it out after adolescence. Where else do you think the expression *gaand-masti mat karo yaar* (Pal, stop your bum-hot-play) comes from? You can't be openly gay in India, so just get that out of your pretty little leper head. Unless you move to Bombay and work in the movies, you don't have a prayer. And trust me, shedding skin isn't highly prized in Bollywood right now.

"I tell you, your best bet is to marry some cousin and not sleep with her. That's what everyone else round here does. That way *Amma* and *Bapu* aren't shamed, and they still get the dowry. Everyone is happy. No one cares if you fuck crocodiles and elephants, as long as you're married, get it? Nothing is worse in India than being a *vamsa mrityu* – a genetic dead-end."

"That's disgusting," Tara said. "I am loving Sangev. I won't live a lie."

"Well, my friend, you've just got to face facts: you were born in the wrong place at the wrong time. If you were rich, there'd be no problem. But something tells me you're not, huh?"

Tara cast his eyes low.

"Look, I don't mean to be crass, I'm just laying it down as it is," Reg said. "It's my way – gets me into a whole heap of trouble here."

He dug out a toothpick from his breast pocket and began opencast mining on his front gums, breaking off finally to ask, "What's with the great English, anyhow? Most mountainy boys I met can't go much beyond 'h'llo-my-nim-is'."

I explained about the leper station and how my friend had set it up and insisted they all learn English as well as some trade to make them more employable once they were cured.

"I am practising all the days with Matron and the most excellent doctors," Tara said.

"He can even read and write," I said. "He was heading for a scholarship."

"Blow me with a feather!" Reg exclaimed. "The genius of us queers never ceases to amaze me. No wonder everyone hates us. If we teamed up with the Jews, we could end up running the entire world. Nevertheless, all that stuff is piss-all use to you now. You could speak better English than Shakespeare and it still wouldn't make a blind bit of difference to your little conundrum. As it is, if you really can't hide what you are, then your only hope is to try the *hijras*. Throw yourself at their mercy – I'd say you have a chance. Beneath all that scaly stuff, you're probably a pretty enough boy. A bit of Nivea can work a charm."

"Oh yes, of course, *sahib*," Tara crooned. "The *hijras*, *sahib*. I will be throwing myself on my knees to them."

Tara had a tendency to notch up his Indianness when being obsequious.

"Whatever," Reg said dismissively. "It's worth a try. But don't let them freak you out – they can be a bit scareapalooza at first. Don't worry, they soon chill. Mention my name, if you want. They come in here the whole time; they know me real well. I'm sort of the go-between for some guys in the States who are helping them. By the way, are you any good at singing? Or dancing? That would go a long way."

Reg didn't wait for an answer – the chip pan caught fire in the kitchen, and flames came licking out through the beaded curtains.

Reg looked back at it, glowering, then turned to me and said, "See! This is what happens. You try and bring a bit of yourself, a bit of ol' Uncle Sam to a place, and the staff, they just shit on you from on high. We're going to need the Peace Corps in that fuckin' kitchen when I've finished with them, the trashy Krishna-kissing scum."

He raced off to sort it out, but stopped before disappearing through the beads to say, "Come back if you need a contact for the *hijras*. And hey, good luck!"

I had only one question for Tara as we left the burger bar.

"Who the hell are the *hijras?*"

And he told me what little he knew about this subculture of eunuchs and sexual outcasts who were principally known for crashing weddings and births, where they danced provocatively or sang raunchy songs until they were asked to leave. If they didn't get paid, they cursed the family and the child, or worse they lifted their skirts and showed their deformed genitals. Their blessings were valued as much as their curses were feared. People said they could bring impotence and financial ruin to a man, or make a woman barren.

"How can they help?" I asked.

"I think they might be being gay also."

"So?" I said.

"I don't know, but if Reg *Sahib* says they can help, I must go to them."

I felt I owed it to Tara to find out a bit more about the *hijras*, and if anyone could fill me in it was Miranda Singh Guli. She was a high queen of Delhi's diplomatic circle, with a finger in every pie and an obsessive interest in the most arcane minutiae of Indian culture. Besides, she was the only person in the city whom I actually knew.

I left Tara to go back and get an address from Reg while I went to the boarding house, dug out my best shirt and trousers, and headed to the elite enclave of Lodi Colony.

I had met Madame Singh Guli two months earlier when she had pulled up in her blacked-out Rolls Royce to pay her yearly visit to Baldoti leper station. I, as the "honoured" foreign supervisor, had been called in for the day and had traipsed along behind the matron, the compounder and the district doctor – in that order – while Mme Singh Guli toured the compound. Later as she was signing a cheque for some obscenely large amount before driving off again, she invited me to call in for sundowners any time I was in Delhi. Now, I was going to take her at her word. The district doctor in Almora had told me that she was one of Delhi's most elegant *memsahib* feminists, a staunch storm-trooper of the high society of Chanakyapuri. No evening went by that she didn't dine or drink for her country in some foreign embassy, consulate or international commission or other. Second only to her social obligations was her commitment to her charities; every lunch was a big *do* in aid of some or other heart-rending Indian problem.

The taxi left me at the foot of her sweeping stone staircase, shadowed by the enormous portico towering above. The house was stark and gaunt: large rooms of white marble with a few judiciously positioned pieces of overly ornate hardwood – thrones, temple panels and divans built for giants. A Punjabi retainer was frying wafer-thin potato chips in the hall, while another circled the guests offering gin-tonic or whisky-soda. Madame Singh Guli was in the drawing room in a lurid peacock-print *sari*. She was deep in shallow conversation with some incredibly elegant-looking Indians, and so I retreated to a bench in a corner where I struck up conversation with someone who said she was a cousin of our hostess' ex-husband. I allowed a reasonable period of small talk to develop before broaching the subject of eunuchs, but I needn't have bothered. The topic didn't phase the woman in the least. I found that Indians would go to any length to explain their culture to *firangi*, foreigners. No topic was too obtuse or banal. I'd lost count of how often people had patiently tried to explain to me the morality of the caste system.

"Oh, yaar, *hijra* culture. Fascinating!" the cousin trumpeted. "You see, they are simply a must at one's son's first birthday party. *Hijras* are the third gender in India. Hermaphrodite children are given to them at birth. They are invaluable, really. When your baby is born with healthy genitalia and you hear the thunderclap of their striking palms in the street, you hurriedly dispatch alms to these unfortunate androgens. Of course, you do, yes?

"It is very simple. They absorb our horror of physical distortions. They release thankfulness in us. We are mutually reliant, are we not?"

"Well . . ." I mumbled, still not adept at handling the Indian use of the rhetorical. "And, are they all hermaphrodites?"

"Oh, goodness gracious, no! Most *hijras* are male, some are gay, others transsexual. They are all in some way deviants, you understand? They don't fit into society. I think most of them . . . if you excuse me . . . are *castrated*. They like dressing up as women, but not like the queens of drag, you know? They don't want to look like beautiful women. No, no, no. They accept their ambiguous role from antiquity.

"I always pay them whatever they ask, so they won't raise their petticoats above their gaudy heads and ruin the kiddies' nursery rhymes or magic show or such like."

Sitting there on the exotic wooden bench soaking all this up and marvelling at her passion, I regretted the fact that I hadn't within me the energy to lob back replies at anywhere near her intensity. I noticed everyone in the room was operating at that same frantic frequency – a boisterous tumult of gushing and thrashing, sending tributes and tirades across each other's bows. The art of conversing with educated Indians was something I would have to practise further.

"Above all, they are performers really," she surged on, "sanctioned by the gods to bless families. I don't like them being called prostitutes, you know? They are artistes – although they do also beg, of course: going around to businessmen, shopkeeps and street-*wallahs* to collect money . . . Extortion would be too strong a word. I like to think of them as auspicious – while also being, of course, loathsome and calamitous. But they are part of us, part of our culture – a million bright, dancing men-women-its. Without them India wouldn't be India, now would it?"

"Eh . . . no," I stuttered.

I hung around for another drink and then went back to the boarding house, feeling somewhat reassured. Tara was sitting up in bed wearing my baseball cap and reading my copy of *Rolling Stone.* I found I was able to be more encouraging to him about the *hijras* now – to consider them as a possible option, with a somewhat clearer conscience. Maybe they would indeed prove to be the answer. It would do no harm to meet them anyhow.

"Who's Lenardo Di Caprio?" Tara asked casually, looking up from the magazine. His head was set at a studied slant so that only one eye was visible below the peaked cap, and he had a coy look about him as though he'd been practising this pose all evening. Suddenly he reached for the cap, twirling it 180 degrees around with a quick backwards swipe. I realised I was seeing his first faltering steps in learning the language of the baseball cap, a complicated grammar and syntax that Americans had developed over decades. He had been studying the photos in the magazine to decipher the meaning of each pose, of each various slant of the visor that signalled different nuances of seduction, intimidation, ennui, sauciness, sassiness and insolence.

"He's an actor," I said. "And what are you doing wearing my hat?"

"He's very pretty."

"*Gaand-masti mat karo yaar,*" I said, quoting Reg's remark about bum-play. "Did you go back to the burger bar? Did you get an address?"

Tara pulled off the cap like a batter after a home run, waving deliriously at the crowd, and then spun it over to me with a debonair flick. He wiggled his head provocatively and explained that Reg had made contact with the *hijras* and they were expecting us. *Us?* I frowned. I had intended simply to accompany Tara to Delhi and leave him here. I didn't have time for any of this. The Tiger would be arriving in two days' time, and he had told me to have bought and read every guidebook I could find, and have visited the Irish embassy to inform them of our plans. Now Tara was telling me the *hijras* could meet us only after the weekend, which didn't suit me at all. I tried to sound happy for him, but all I could think of was that within a few days I would most likely be talking into a camera lens, in Irish – an awkward, inexact, barely fathomable, semi-dead language – about a country that I still found utterly unfathomable. I simply had too much on my plate to nanny Tara any further. I told him straight out that I couldn't stay here holding his hand any longer. I had work to do, and we agreed that I would move to a new hostel in the morning so that I could focus on it. I would meet him somewhere on Tuesday if he still wanted me to accompany him to the *hijras*.

Chapter 5

I SPENT THE WEEKEND chasing back and forth to the embassy and around the bookshops of the various five-star hotels in Delhi, gathering up maps and guidebooks, and by Monday afternoon I was standing in the arrivals hall of Indira Gandhi Airport watching the Tiger coming through the gate, barely holding his own against the current of billowing *saris* and nylon shirts around him. Standing directly between us was a scrum of Punjabi taxi men, wiping their brows with rags as they hauled a mountain of floral-patterned suitcases for an overdressed maharani. We hugged briskly, and I began to feel somewhat better about the whole endeavour. Everything about my brother was reassuring. He radiated opulence and abundance, as though he worked for *Vogue* and not an, as yet non-existent, Irish language channel. He certainly looked the part, wearing a brand new safari suit and carrying those aluminium bricks of luggage used only by the munitions and the film industries. Inside was either camera equipment or a nuclear warhead.

"You really are serious about this?" I asked, steering him through an ochre throng of bickering *sadhus*. "It's not just a joke – a way of scamming a holiday?"

"Of course, I'm serious," he rattled out. "This is our big chance! A brand new channel, with hours and hours of empty television time to fill. We've got to seize this. I've told them there's no need to pay us unless they like what we do."

"You mean we're not being paid?"

The Tiger stopped and stared at me.

"You spend your days squatting alone on the side of a mountain. You do nothing. How can you possibly waste your time any further?"

He had a point. I wasn't even sure I believed in time any more. Instead of answering, I fired more questions at him.

"What about the crew?"

"We're the crew."

"We're the crew! Who's director?"

"Me," he said.

"Who's filming?"

"Me."

"Who's on sound?"

"Me."

"So, what am I?" I asked, suddenly anxious.

"You're the researcher. And writer. And presenter. You can be producer as well if you want."

"*Producer!* What's that? . . . Actually, never mind, I can't do it."

There was only so much responsibility my tender mind could bear.

"Fine, I'll produce," he said. "First, I need coffee."

As we sat in a tea shop, he explained how, a fortnight earlier, in the middle of his Christmas dinner, he had suddenly decided it would be nice to come out to India, and he had struck on the idea of making a series of travel programmes while he was there. On the day after New Year, he had driven across Ireland, through the snow, to Galway, charging into the offices of TnaG, the brand new Irish-language television station, to cajole them into lending him a camera and paying his expenses. "What had they to lose?" was the key to his proposal.

Everything, I would have thought. This was a fledgling channel, which within nine months would be broadcasting eight hours of television a day in a language that was almost dead. Ireland, strutting intrepidly forth into the future, was doing her best to cast off this last vestige of her peasant past. Despite some half-hearted lip service paid to the language, by and large people found it faintly embarrassing, a reminder of darker times. We wanted French, Spanish, Japanese, anything but our own thing-tongued mumble. Yet the government – Fianna Fáil, the *Soldiers of Destiny* – were descendants of the Republican martyrs who had been snipered, hanged, guillotined for *the Cause* – the cause of nationalism – and they couldn't now stand idly by as the language coughed its death rattle. To assuage their guilt, they had paid out £12 million for a brand new TV station. A third national channel – entirely *as Gaeilge*. TnaG was our knight in shining armour. The Future. It alone could make our barbaric, bardic tongue relevant to the modern age. It had to: it was the last chance.

How those staunch custodians of the language – the street-fighting Republican aristocracy and elitist academics mouldering in academies and Gaelic quangos – would shudder to know that the future of their sacred language was being entrusted to the likes of us. That people like my brother were simply walking in off the street and being given commissions.

Although, to be fair to TnaG, the Tiger is the sort of person anyone would trust. Charm and purpose shine from him. In the winter of 1985, he'd been sweeping the streets of Piccadilly for the Greater Metropolitan Council when he collapsed unconscious over his litter cart suffering from bronchitis. My mother couriered money to him for antibiotics and a winter overcoat, which he immediately spent on a top-of-the-line Gaggia espresso maker. Style is *his* Primary Directive. He oozes assurance. At school he used to keep his books in a briefcase, and at the cinema on a date he'd whip out a bottle of chilled white wine and two flutes from the same case. He has an intuitive sense of occasion.

I could imagine him striding into the offices of TnaG in a black Italian jacket and leather trousers, tossing back his tobacco-esque mane and beguiling them with a proposal for the most innovative and exciting travel series ever made.

"It's gonna be incredible – can't you see the potential?" he would have enthused. "It'll run and run. We'll go right around the world with this. This is the big one!"

His energy is meteorological. He would have struck their offices like a bolt of lightning, thundering out his ideas, before sweeping out again. They wouldn't have known what hit them. But at the back of their minds would have been an impression, a conviction even – let's give him a chance. Impulse, energy, spontaneity are his essence. Like the sun, when he shines you can't but glow. And as an extra impetus to them, there was the fact of his bloodline. At the back of their minds, they would have known that the Tiger was the great-grandnephew of The O'Rahilly – the equally preening and passionate founder of the Irish Volunteers, who exactly ninety years before had spearheaded the resurrection of the Irish language, had written a new alphabet for it and convinced banks, businesses and even the Royal Mail to accept it as an official language. There would have been the underlying hope that his vision and resolve might have passed down the line.

I, on the other hand, was a shambles. Some boys are born too sensitive for life, with an overarching tendency towards introspection. Bordering androgyny and autism, these child-men are at home in no land. Previously my type would have entered the priesthood. Nowadays, I was destined to spend my time wandering the world, searching for whatever it was I sensed was missing. I had been roaming the lands of the disconnected for almost a decade, searching for a Utopia that I knew I would never find. Places that hadn't yet plugged into the grid of the West somehow soothed me. I'd travelled through Africa, South America and right up into remote valleys in Canada where New Agers were wiping the slate of development clean and starting over. That I'd end up in the Himalayas sooner or later was inevitable – my sort always does. Fortunately, I hadn't followed the others into an *ashram* or a haze of cannabis. I was of the purest strain: those who find even the company of other outsiders a drain. No one could measure up to the euphoria I felt inside. While in the eyes of the world I was a dreamer, in my own mind I was divine.

The Tiger swallowed back his third cup of bad Nescafé and declared it time to get to work. He wanted me to hail a taxi, but I managed to persuade him that if our budget really was so tight, we'd have to live like Indians and from now on travel by bus. The poor man was too jet-lagged to argue, and he allowed me to steer him out of the air-conditioned airport into the sweltering heat that battered his unacclimatised body like a fly swat. At the bus stop, his precious cases were wrested from him and tied to the timber-framed roof of a Delhi-bound bus while we were crammed through its accordion doors. This was the Tiger's first time to step off the opulent Western stage, and his mind was in overdrive processing the stimuli. He kept up a running commentary of his impressions, and I was amazed how quickly he was able to move through the same stages of adjustment that had taken me months: from disbelief, to horror, to understanding, to acceptance. He has always been able to chew up life faster than anyone I know – as if by immersing himself more deeply in it, he is able to create a vortex around him that intensifies the experience. I watched him now expanding his outlook to accommodate this new world, all in the space of a single bus journey. By the time we had reached the city, he had left his preconceptions far behind and was processing what was around him on its own terms, ready to dive head first into its chaos. His rabid enthusiasm couldn't help but re-ignite my own, which had become dulled by months of familiarity.

I had booked us into the Hindustan Palace, a cheap boarding house in the old city. Again, I was a little over-conscious of our budget when choosing the place. It didn't have any rooms as such, but rented the roof of an X-ray clinic, where it set up awnings and iron beds each night like a field hospital. I loved the cool breeze that blew in over the city, and I slept sounder there than in more expensive places; but nothing could quite make up for the open-drain lavatory in the far corner of the roof. A shower curtain had been strung across it for privacy, but it didn't quite stop the smell from drifting across.

The Tiger was not impressed.

"We're poor, Mocha," he said, "but not this poor. From now I'll make the arrangements. Okay?"

I nodded meekly.

"Now, let's get down to business," he said, unzipping a case full of small bottles of whiskey. "I hadn't time to arrange permits, so if any officials stop us, just hand them one of these and walk away, get it?"

Wrapped up in military-style webbing along with the bottles were two knives: a large-bladed Swiss Army and a tungsten-coated Leatherman.

"These you don't give away," he said. "These you don't touch – they are for my own personal use."

I nodded meekly.

A second case contained things for me: brand new copies of Ó Dónaill's and de Bhaldraithe's Irish-English and English-Irish dictionaries, and the old Christian Brothers' Irish Grammar manual. Unfortunately, the shirts I had asked for had been forgotten, so I would have to present the programmes in my old T-shirts and tracksuit. No matter. The Tiger's designer safari suits behind the camera would be elegant enough for both of us. A third case overflowed with film equipment: cameras, microphones, tapes and the dog-like muffler.

"Keep your grubby fingers away from all this," he barked. "I'll handle the equipment, and you look after your dictionaries, okay?"

Seeing the hurt in my eyes, he added, "Look, if we break the camera, the programmes don't get made. How would you feel if the first Irish channel failed because we had broken their camera?"

I had no reply. Seeing this array of state-of-the-art equipment had shocked me back to my senses. There was no way I could do what was expected of me here. It was simply ludicrous. I had never been near a camera before. The only jobs I'd ever had were as a farm labourer, a shelf-stacker in a German hypermarket, a childminder in Canada and a hostel manager in Ecuador. And it wasn't even as if my brother had that much more experience: it's true he worked in the film industry, but closer to the caterer than the cameraman. He had been a trainee assistant director and location manager for a while, but he'd never actually operated a camera. It was he who arranged to have Tom Cruise's flowers delivered to the cameraman whose helicopter was drowned during the filming of *Far and Away*, and he managed the sets that were built and then blown up for the Easter Rising in the *Michael Collins* movie. By all accounts, he was excellent at this job. People noticed him – Julia Roberts had asked her chauffeur for his number – but he had never actually filmed in his life before, and certainly not made a television programme on his own, without any crew, other than a fragile-minded younger brother.

I hardly slept that night. For once, the cool wind on the roof didn't soothe me. My head began to spin with panic whenever I thought about the aluminium weapons boxes chained to the railings of the bed. The cold, glinting torture implements nestling inside: the titanium-tipped tripod; the chrome lead connectors; the chain-mail microphones. I had hoped that by throwing myself head first into the work it might all just come naturally; that if it was *meant to be* everything would simply flow – like the way I was just able to wake up one morning and suddenly be able to hear the tonal frequencies of each of my *chakra* points, or how I had become aware of the way trees communicated with the world through swaying their branches and dancing their leaves.

Now I was faced with the horrible truth.

Just before dawn, as my inner angelic choir was finally sweeping in to lull me to sleep with assurances that I was on my soul's divine path and that a *way* would be lit before me, a party of Welsh revellers turned up on the roof. They were just off the bus from Goa and intent on reminding themselves of the great time they had had. At first I thought they were hippies from Rishikesh, high on a particularly intense retreat, but then realised that when they said the word *Om* they didn't actually mean it, but were using it as a code for *E*.

"Once the *Om* had centred my soul, man," one said, "my cells just blew wide open, and I was able to dance all night!"

"Yeah, fucking A," a friend replied, high-fiving him.

I wondered how I'd explain *Om* to a television audience. It set me reeling again. I realised that even if the series ran for a thousand episodes, there was no way you could sum up even that single concept, no matter how many pithy sound bites one used. *Om* doesn't just mean God, it *is* God, and Love, and all the energy of the universe. To speak the word is to invoke all of its force, like Thor summoning thunder. How do you sum up all the energy in the universe in a sound bite? Particularly in a language that shuns the very notion of brevity.

It was interesting that the boys were using this term to describe ecstasy. These were the nineties' equivalent of Beatles devotees making pilgrimage to Sai Baba in Rishikesh, and it seemed somehow appropriate in the synthetic nineties that sixties marijuana was being replaced by metyhlenedioxymethamphetamaine. Both drugs opened a door to an element of *Om*, and it would be hard to prove that one was more sacred than the other: the important part of a retreat is the act of retreating, rather than what you retreat to.

The Tiger was awake before me next morning. He had the tripod set up on the ramparts and was filming the city. I gulped hard, threw on a T-shirt and pulled myself out of bed. He took one look at the state of me and winced. A *samosa* hawker was walking between the beds with a tray of fried food on his head, and having bought a few we wound our way down through the stairwell of the X-ray lab and out on to the Delhi street. The minaret in the old town was the best place to start filming, I thought, but in the auto-rickshaw on the way over, the Tiger pulled out the camera and began filming whatever was around: a mint-green Formica bus sidling towards us, an elephant carrying timber, swarms of auto-rickshaws swaying with their crippling payloads and bearing down murderously on a line of school children. Our tiny sofa on wheels acted as a frenzied camera dolly, giving the scene a suitably frantic appearance as the lens lapped up everything it saw. At one point, the Tiger turned the camera on me and, throwing the microphone over, told me to say something into it. I gulped hard and looked into the convex orb of the camera, with its petroleum-black sheen swallowing me, demanding me to perform. Suddenly I was face to face with all that was expected of me, and instantly I knew it was impossible. I could see my fish-eyed face staring back at me like a common carp in an exotic aquarium. I had no idea who this face belonged to, what he stood for, what he wanted to say, what he wanted to do. All I knew for certain was that he didn't want to be there. He wanted to be back in his cabin in the Himalayas drinking his own piss.

The Tiger kept on filming, eventually panning on to the twinkling buckles of the children's natty school bags when he realised I wasn't going to perform. A minute later, he panned back again, hoping that by some miracle I'd suddenly spring into action, splutter into glorious life like a newborn baby. It was pointless. I was stillborn.

The truth began to dawn on my brother gradually, and he laid the camera down with a studied calmness that couldn't quite hide his fury.

"Well?" he said, not at all kindly.

I winced.

"It's not a silent movie, you know," he said in an eerily hushed tone that was far worse than if he'd shouted.

"Huh?" I murmured.

"It's an all-Irish station, remember? They might like to hear some."

"Some?" I said, as a taxi careered menacingly towards us. I was stalling for time.

"IRISH, you fool! Some *Gaeilge*! Your national fucking tongue."

"Okay," I said. "No need to shout."

He sighed.

"Just give me a second," I pleaded.

And as he picked up the camera again and the evil red eye began to flash its menacing command, I tried to pull together the trailing threads of my tattered mind. I breathed in, goading myself just to open my bloody mouth and say something, anything. The silence went on for ever, until finally and mercifully I suddenly chugged into life . . .

"Sometimes when you're feeling the Indian air on your face, maybe it's not actually air but a secret realm communicating the Mughal stories and Bhagavad Gita myths that have gone or become vaporised in dimensions that can't readily be accessed through . . ."

The red light died as my brother turned off the camera and laid it aside.

"Are you on drugs?" he asked. "Are you out of your bloody mind?"

I sank into myself.

"What in the name of God . . . ?" he screamed.

The rickshaw-*wallah* pulled over in fright and cut the engine. The Tiger rewound the tape and stuck the viewfinder into my face. Seeing it back, I could tell it was a bit vague, a bit left field. Gibberish, actually. The Tiger was staring numbly ahead, like a blanket-wrapped crash victim on the roadside. He had charged so confidently ahead with his great plan that he had never actually stopped to think how dependent it was on me. Without me, there were no programmes. It had never dawned on him that I might fail. How could I? All I had to do was talk, for God's sake; to walk and talk.

We sat there for I don't know how long. It killed me to see the despair crawling up through him. He was always so buoyant, so alive, that it was hard to watch the flame flicker, about to snuff out. He had seen to everything – got the commission, got all the equipment, travelled across half the world – and now here I was, flushing it all down the drain.

"Well?" he said at last.

"Em," was all I found to say.

He looked away, breathing deeply to steady himself, and rooted out a Camel from his jacket. I could see his hands quiver as he tapped the cigarette on the box and I feared he might cry. He flicked the lighter, pulling on the butt as though it were a life rope.

"I'm sorry," I whimpered.

He swung back towards me.

"No! There's no blood *sorry*. It's too late for *sorry*. Far too late. I've promised TnaG a travel series, and that's what we're going to give them, even if I have to drag you kicking and screaming around this bloody country, get it? All I need from you is a few simple words. A few coherent, sensible, relevant words!"

I didn't blame my brother for being angry. I could see his point. There must have been hundreds of eager young Irish speakers back home who'd kill for this opportunity. A dream job. He couldn't allow it all to fail simply because he had the bad luck to have me as a brother.

He ordered the auto-rickshaw to start up again, and as we were winding our way back into the traffic, he turned the camera on again and ordered me to say something.

"What?" I said.

"ANYTHING!!" the Tiger roared. "ANY-FUCKING-THING AT ALL! Surely to God you must feel something? Isn't there anything worth conveying? Look around you! This place is incredible. It's alive. It's a dance – a vibrant, chaotic explosion of human expression."

". . . I suppose," I said.

"So . . . ?!"

He pulled focus in close and I began, "This place is incredible. It's alive, a dance – a vibrant . . ."

My syntax was garbled and I was frothing quite a bit, but the words were mostly drowned out by the blaring traffic, and anyway, Gaelic is such an indefinite, colloquial language that one can extract meaning from the roughest mumble. It felt strange to be using this tool, the oldest surviving vernacular language in Europe, to describe the very area where it originated. Gaelic and Sanskrit are the two closest remaining remnants of the original Indo-European language that the first tribes who roamed the Indus valley and central Europe spoke. It was as if I were bringing it back home, like leading the emigrant back to the homeland to die.

By mid-afternoon we had got a lot in the can, and the Tiger said we'd take the rest of the day off. He was exhausted from the flight and our fight, and anyway it was Tuesday, the day I had promised to bring Tara to the *hijras*. I still hadn't mentioned anything about him to my brother, and I felt this wasn't really the time. I told him instead that I was going to a café to write my diary and I'd meet him back at the hotel later.

Chapter 6

I WALKED THE few blocks to Tara's boarding house in Paharganj where I found him lying on his bed leafing through a copy of Armistead Maupin's *Tales of the City* that some backpacker must have left behind. Scattered on the floor were dog-eared spin-offs of *Sweet Valley High* and *Buffy the Vampire Slayer*.

"There's a book exchange downstairs," Tara said when he saw me looking, "and it's free!"

You'd think backpackers in India would favour some more appropriate reading material – Naipaul or Kipling or Rushdie, for example – but it was always pulp teen novels that appeared on hostel shelves. Perhaps it was precisely this tendency towards extended infantilism that gave backpackers the idealism to go off exploring the world in the first place. They were an army of Peter Pans, all hell-bent on adventure, and willing to lose themselves in futile quixotic campaigns such as saving Bengali tigers or Kalahari tribesmen or kidnapped fairies.

"The manager were very happy to get your *Rolling Stone*," Tara continued. "Most very popular newspaper, I see now."

"What have you been up to all weekend?" I asked. "Reading?"

"No, no, not reading, Mocha-ji, but exploring! I've been exploring everywhere!"

He threw aside the Maupin book and jumped up excitedly to give me a big hug. I was taken aback. Indian men don't normally hug; they pat and paw and drape their arms affectionately around you, but they rarely do a full embrace. Tara's hug was a long playful squeeze – I felt sure he had picked it up from *Tales of the City*, which was basically a flamboyant gossip session about gay life in San Francisco.

Stepping back a little, Tara gave a twirl to show off his new jewel-encrusted hipsters and told me that he had been on a shopping spree. I wondered, worried actually, how he had afforded it, but I didn't ask. I didn't dare. He had changed in so many tiny ways from the boy I had first seen in Baldoti station just a few months before that I thought him capable of anything now. He was so much more sure of himself; this despite having lost everything that mattered to him. But I didn't dwell much on it. I was keen to get the *hijra* visit over with and get back to work. Tara wanted to know all about the filming, how it was going, what we had done, but I found it difficult to explain. What was there to say really? My first experiences were too traumatic to think about, and I had no idea where we'd take it from here.

Tara threw on a tasselled suede jacket that looked like it was from one of the American shops on Connaught Place, and we set off straightaway for Nizamuddin, just up from the Chanakya guest house, where the *hijras* lived. He talked non-stop the whole way about the wonders of the city and how he adored every inch of it – except for the Gaylord restaurants which he felt didn't live up to their name.

"Weren't you a bit scared or lonely going around on your own?" I asked.

"Oh, no, Mocha-ji. Not in the least little bit. I made so many nice friends."

"Where? How?" I asked, but he just tapped his nose mischievously. I was almost sure nose-tapping wasn't an Indian gesture either – probably a *Sweet Valley High* influence. "That's for me to know and you to . . ."

He faltered, not remembering the words.

"Find out," I said. "To find out."

"Yes! You to find out," he repeated with a falsetto thrill.

"Whatever," I said. "You seem to be coping pretty well on your own. Maybe you don't need the *hijras*?"

"Of course, I do," he cried. "I must be with my own people. It is all too important, you see? I am not an idiot boy; I know that sooner or later the bones will be beaten out of me again and again if I'm on my own. I see now that India is India, not Beverly Hills 90210."

I stared at him, saying nothing.

The *hijra* house was a white three-storey building no different from the laundry and apartments next door. It looked clean and well built. The young girl who answered the door was suspicious at first, but mentioning Reg reassured her. She led us inside to a small room like a convent vestibule where she told us to sit and wait, then vanished into an open courtyard behind.

The interior was more ostentatious than I had expected, with ornate wooden furniture painted gilt, and drapes on the walls. Although I knew that *hijras* had once had power and status, I had presumed they were little more than outcasts and beggars now. Surely the pittance they got from dancing at weddings and alms couldn't pay for all this?

It was a few minutes later that we heard the approaching commotion of shrieks and sighs, and a gravelly voice calling out in Hindi coming down the stairs. Suddenly a tall, gaunt, middle-aged man dressed in a flowered *sari* and heavy make-up appeared. I didn't know where to look, or even what to do or say. I blushed. Of course, I had seen transvestites before, but this was something else entirely. I was reminded of the first time I had seen a dame at a Christmas pantomime and had clung to my grandmother in fright. The figure was similar, but not quite the same. He/she reminded me most of a man dressed as a woman at the end of a long night's fancy-dress party. She looked weary and somewhat dishevelled, and her make-up was bordering on the grotesque. But her hair was beautiful – rich and lustrous and heavily hennaed. She seemed to have well-proportioned breasts, and her legs were shapely and marble smooth.

She bowed an elegant *namaste* to us, and both Tara and I shot to our feet and *namasted* back.

"You must forgive me, I was taking a nap," she said in her throaty voice, and I found myself aroused, to my great surprise. I certainly wasn't attracted to her in the least; it was like the way you get goose pimples before a thunderstorm or the feeling when the strings rush in in *The Sorcerer's Apprentice*. She clapped her heavily lined hands at the young servant girl standing behind her and called for tea. (The servant also seemed to have been a boy originally, but it was difficult to tell.)

"I am Jemdanee, mother of the house, and you?"

We introduced ourselves.

"And this is the little boy who has run away, yes?" she pointed her long varnished nail at Tara, with an exaggerated flourish, and began talking to him in Hindi.

He answered her in his mountain dialect, but halfway through switched back into English for my benefit. ". . . it is not necessarily that I am wanting to be woman; I am wanting to be free to be who I am."

"Look, petal," Jemdanee replied. "India is 70 *crore* [1 *crore* = 10 million] Hindu and 8 *crore* Muslim; 40 *crore* men and 35 *crore* women. You're either one or the other. It's that simple. If not, you're one of us. You look fine to me, or at least you will when we clean you up – wipe away the rest of that skin rot. A bit of face paint masks a lot, am I right? Just ask your foreign friend here: his countrywomen know about plastering it on."

She looked questioningly at me, and I nodded automatically. I could see how the *hijras* could extort money from people. There was a barely concealed air of menace that elicited compliance. A hint of sorcery.

Looking over at Tara, I could see he wasn't in the least intimidated. In fact, sitting upright on a divan with his arms stretched out like buttresses behind him and one ankle resting on the opposite knee, he might have been posing for a photo. Now that I thought of it, it was remarkably similar to a pose Leonardo Di Caprio had struck in the *Rolling Stone* shoot.

Jemdanee was staring at him, her eyes ranging up and down his strong but blighted body in total silence. She looked away somewhere above her head and began to frown as though she were making calculations. Finally she turned back to him, saying, "Yes, we will have you."

I was taken aback. He hadn't even been offered yet. I could see Tara wagging and wiggling like a dog's tail. He looked delighted, but just a little anxious, too.

"You may join us now straightaway," she said. "But only for a try-out – four months, let's agree – then *we* decide."

Tara's whole body was wobbling back and forth now. I couldn't be totally sure if it was with joy or fear. I didn't know whether to congratulate him or not.

"It's that simple?" I couldn't help asking.

Jemdanee eyed me up and down with a disparaging gaze, before finally letting out a decompressing airbrake of a sigh. She mumbled something to her servant who was sitting at her feet, and then said to me, "Look, kitten, we're not being the choosy ones here. As you may notice, none of us is going to be giving birth any day soon. There is no natural process of *prajanan kriya*, how do you say it . . . re-gen-er-ation. Despite this, our culture survives thousands of years. We take what we get.

"Some say there are a million of us now – rubbish!" she continued.

She spat dismissively before going on, "In my opinion, there are no more than 10 *lakh* [1 *lakh* = 10,000], but until they include a third gender box on the census, how can we know? All we need is for Tara to be able to sing and dance – badly, preferably. We don't want any Twinkle Khannas here. We'll teach him the rest. What I need to know from him is – and this is the most vital thing – is he sure and surely sure that he stays and sticks it out?"

She turned to him and spoke with a steely glint.

"You're in or you're out, child. There's no running home to Mama, and no friends beyond these doors. We are your family now. And let me say this much: when I say family, this is what I am meaning. We are the only true community left, outside of Gandhi-ji's *ashrams*. We look after you for life, you see? Sharing all the things. This house, it belongs to all of us; and you are always sure of a welcome in every other *hijra* house in India. We are all family, yes? My house is your house and all like that. If you are liking, you can be a little Kim-boy and take to the Grand Trunk Road, wandering from house to house for ever, dancing at the festivals and holy gatherings for many months, if that is what you are liking."

"O, Devi, my Goddess," Tara implored. "I am liking very much. I love dancing. You are being so much generous and kind."

Again, Tara had reverted to pidgin English through obsequiousness. I noticed him screwing up his face, wanting to say more.

"But also I can meet my old good friends from time to time, yes?" he enquired anxiously.

Jemdanee ignored the question and turned to a sweeper who suddenly drifted in through a shaft of sunlight in the courtyard. This boy was younger than Tara, and I would have sworn he was a girl had he not had such impossibly slender hips. A diaphanous fuchsia bodice clung tightly to him, rippled only by a lime scarf that wound itself around him like a

ribbon on a maypole. Jemdanee frowned, clicking her fingers, and suddenly the youth was gone, and she carried on talking.

"You'll have a home and someone to look after you. You'll have family who love you, who'll never shun you like your own family did. Here,
every day is party day. Every day we put on our best dress and we enter-
tain. You'll be happy, I promise you that. We're good, good people."

Jemdanee bent forward in a confiding gesture, and continued, "I will
tell you this also: when my parents sent me here first, I hated every
moment of it. I wanted to die. But I hated myself even more. I did too
much suffering for too long, then I just gave up, and instead I realise I am
who I am and I revel. I am beautiful. I am *Me*. So what if my genitals are
mushed? I am not perfect, but then, who is? Everything possible exists in
nature, and I am proof. I wish I realise earlier. I wish I save myself the
pain. If you love yourself, and are proud of who you are, no one can make
you miserable. This is my *mantra* now. All of us are beautiful works of art,
each one different, and the differences are the beauty.

"So, come on, join us. Who else gives a bugger about your limp wrists,
anyway!"

Jemdanee's words worked like a charm on Tara. I could see he was
entranced, but they seemed to have left her completely exhausted. She
sank back into the divan and called out petulantly for lime soda, which the
young *chela* sprang up to fetch. Tara barely had time to follow her pert little bum out the door before Jemdanee piped up again.

"Well, come on, Tara girl. Are you staying or going?"

He opened his mouth to reply, but no words came out. I think he was
in awe of this powerful chatelaine; his earlier poise had now deserted him.
Jemdanee looked at me and with snide sincerity said, "So, *sahib*, are we
good enough for your little mountain boy? Yes, no?"

My reply was drowned out by the arrival in through the door of the
rest of the family back from their day's work. Five *hijras* came tumbling
into the room in high spirits and laughing raucously. On seeing
strangers, they froze, huddling up together and peeking out at us shyly
from their veils. They were younger, but no more beautiful than
Jemdanee, with dark, opium-bleary eyes and skin a jarring red-brown
tone – like gargoyles in terracotta. Their *saris* were even more lurid than
the usual Indian examples, and each had the same exaggerated gestures

and camp mannerisms as their chatelaine, who was explaining our presence to them in some dialect before switching to English to introduce us formally.

"This is Marat Khan," she said, pointing to a tall, well-built woman with flowers in her hair and a ring through her nose. "She will be the mountain boy's *guru*, if he stays. He will be her *chela*, her disciple. She will take everything he earns, and she will look after him in every way."

Marat Khan had high cheekbones and the saddest smile I'd ever seen. She nodded formally to Tara, who cast his eyes low in deference. Once Jemdanee had introduced us, the eunuchs grew more emboldened and came closer, staring at us as though we were animals – strange, exotic species from abroad – and sniggering and jostling each other. Once their curiosity had been sated, they each went over to Jemdanee, took out a purse of money and laid it at her feet. Marat Khan meanwhile had sat down and was running her fingers along Tara's face, staring in wonderment at his little nose. She pulled up his shirt to check for breasts and seemed disappointed.

"You are not hermaphrodite?" she said sadly.

"I am gay," Tara answered meekly.

"No matter. Next goodest thing. We will take care of the rest."

I thought it beholden on me to ask the vital question. The one unmentioned issue. The very thing that permeated everything – the *raison d'être* of this strange place. I steeled myself and began.

"When you say *the rest*, what do you mean by that?" I enquired. "What is *the rest*? What are you planning to *do* to him?"

There was silence as a dozen sour faces stared at me in disdain.

"*Do?*" cried Marat Khan in a high-pitched squeal, but Jemdanee silenced her with the merest twitch of a finger, and it was she who answered instead, in a syrupy sweet tone that belied the chill in her eyes.

"What will we *do* to him, my Irish *sahib*?" she repeated, raising her voice to a crescendo. "What is it you are really asking? . . . I ask *you*, what will *you* do for him? Will you bring him back to your country with you? Will you get him an MBA from Harvard? Teach him computer system automatic programming? Yes? Make him Wall Street *rupee-wallah* or distinguished gentleman doctor?"

I sank back.

"*We,* my foreign friend, we will make him one of us. Isn't that what you want? Isn't that what he came here for?"

Tara looked at me urgently, signalling, imploring me to say no more. But this was no time for silence. Someone had to speak up. Someone had to acknowledge the truth bearing down on the room around us – hanging heavily, or more accurately, not hanging – the gap between their thighs. Tara's entire future lay in the balance. The word *hijra* could mean only one thing. For Tara to become a *hijra* presumably required him to have something removed. Something important. What I needed to know was would it be lopped off? It was that simple. It was I who had led him here and it was up to me to find out.

"Just answer the question," I said. "Will you operate on Tara? Is that what you plan to do?"

It was as if a shower of hailstones had suddenly come crashing down on the room. The *hijras'* faces froze in frigid grimaces. Tara shrank back into himself, into the poor leper figure I had first known in Baldoti station. From the side of my eye I could see him signalling me, for God's sake, to keep quiet.

"How dare you!" Jemdanee cried. "You filthy *gora,* how dare you? Get out! Leave us and take your diseased runt with you. Take him back to the mountains to his people so they can belt him some more. Take him with you to your country. Make him a rich little *sahib* boy. But leave us in peace!"

"Please . . . !" Tara cried. "My friend does not understand! Jemdanee, please! Mataji, mother of all the *hijras,* most splendid of all Mata Bahuchara's daughters, please! Don't take notice of Mocha-ji. He is *gora* . . . *firangi.* He does not know. He does not see the great honour you are offering. He is, after all, but the poor misunderstanding *gora.*"

Tara's face lit up in supplication. His body crumpled in conciliation. His eyes sparkled with adulation. It was quite a performance. I had to hand it to him, the boy could radiate like plutonium when necessary. He reminded me of a dervish in the throes of religious ecstasy, tossing and turning on the divan as though possessed.

Jemdanee couldn't help but be moved. The bitter, shocked expression on the faces of the others gave way now as they waited on Jemdanee's verdict. They would either attack, beating and scratching as they barrelled us towards the door, or else all would be forgiven and Tara would get a second chance.

Jemdanee breathed in laboriously, rising like a peacock to issue her promulgation.

"It will be the boy's own choice entirely," she said to me. "Of course, it will. He, and he alone, will decide whether to cut or not."

I nodded somewhat demurely, only half believing her, but she made no effort to convince me any further. My expression mustn't have been grateful or servile enough as she lashed out again.

"You stupid *gora*!" she cried. "The cut is beautiful. It brings peace, transcendence. It brings . . ."

"I'm sorry," I cried. "I didn't mean to offend."

"But you did," she said again, sniffing haughtily and waving her fan as though I were a bad smell. She reached down to sip her lime soda, and I thought the matter had been put aside, until she swung back at me.

"You foreign people, you are all the same. Transfixed by your genitals. You will never understand."

"I'm sorry," I repeated, but she seemed unable to rein herself in now.

"It is such a beautiful thing," she exclaimed, genuinely moved by the thought. "We dress him like a bride for his bath, and he prays to the Goddess Mata Bahuchara, and we make offerings of flowers and sweets. Then we undress him and we hold him close. We have a bridle with polished buckles and soft rich leather. It is very old, very beautiful. Then the cutting is only so quickly, one slash. Then it is all over and we spend the night awake – all of us, we . . ."

Tara interrupted, "Please Jemdanee, please don't be offended. Mocha does not mean any rudeness. He is just looking out for me. I am very much appreciating him and you."

"Of course, you are," Marat Khan cooed.

But Jemdanee seemed unwilling to let it go. There was a rabid expression in her eyes, and suddenly it struck me that she was barely conscious of where she was. She was off her head on opium.

"The wound is permitted to bleed as much as it needs," she went on, oblivious to anyone else. "It's a sacred act, can't you see?"

"Please, Jemdanee! Don't be concerned," Tara tried again.

But she ploughed on, "No, next day we pour the hot sesame on, to clean and cure the area. From then on he is a she and eats only *ghee* and mutton and fresh vegetables. These have very much good fats in them and vitamins, too, and proteins that help her be strong. And she drinks also so much good black tea with *ghee* because it helps make the urine pour. Pure, too, it helps make the urine pure. Then forty days later we throw the greatest party to celebrate, and we give her *saris* and gold and silver jewels – most beautiful like a wedding – and we sing and dance all the night until the morning."

My legs were tightly crossed at this stage, and I was visibly blanching, but Tara didn't seem in the least phased. He was staring at Marat Khan in awe while the prettiest of the *hijras*, a young girl who looked half his age, was sitting on his lap running her fingers through his hair. I leaned across and asked the girl what she thought of Tara, but either she had no English or was too shy to answer.

We must have been there over an hour at this stage. I was thinking of the Tiger and that I had to get back. Tara was still not saying much – he was just staring. I asked Jemdanee could I have a moment in private with Tara, and she clicked her fingers at her *chela*.

"Bring them to the veranda," she said.

We were ushered out into a neat enclosed courtyard with cactuses in glazed pots. I crouched down on an upturned pot and looked questioningly at Tara. His mind was elsewhere.

"Well?" I said.

It was only the second time I had ever seen him stuck for words.

"She is so beautiful," he finally managed.

"Who?" I asked

"Marat Khan, my *guru*, of course!"

"I see," I said hesitantly. "I have to say, I'm a little concerned, Tara."

"Oh, please, don't be. There is no need for concerning. It is only that you are not understanding so much. My country is not Sunnydale or San Francisco. Things are very much different here."

"What are you going to do?" I asked

"You know!" he replied passionately. "You know already."

I do? In truth I didn't want to know. I had serious doubts about the whole thing, but I knew I wasn't in any position to say so. I wasn't prepared to offer him anything better. I was out of my depth. All this was hurtling around my mind when suddenly I looked up and saw *her* staring at me. A girl so beautiful I felt my breath fail.

Oh, my God, was all I could think. I could have cried right there and then, like when you see something so perfect your mind can't process it in its entirety – like the first time I saw the aurora borealis at the Arctic Circle or the time a whale rose up out of the ocean right beside me.

Oh, my God!

Her hair was very short. It was black and somewhat feathery, and her cheeks so long and deep they were more like slaloms. She had the palest, most perfect skin, like a child's freshly shaven head. And her eyes were black, luminously black, dancing inside their pools like oil on the sea. When I looked at them, I wasn't aware of anything else. In fact, it took enormous effort just to get my focus back.

She proceeded down the remaining steps and across the room towards the courtyard where we were. First, she came to Tara and then to me, extending a pale, thin hand to each of us in turn. This was a rarity in a country which favoured the slight bow and raised hands of *namaste*.

"I apologise," she said in a shy, breathless voice. "I apologise. I was upstairs resting. I am Niishraah . . . Has Jemdanee taken care of you?"

Her face bloomed in concern, and we both nodded eagerly, desperate to reassure her, to make her existence on this planet any little bit happier.

"He . . ," I began, before catching myself just in time, "*She* has been most considerate."

"Of course," she purred. "Yes, of course. Jemdanee is *most* considerate."

There was no way one could confuse this girl for anything other than female. She had that beauty that comes from creating life, from the biological bond that ensures our continuance. She reminded me of a doll, but with mischievous eyes and graceful as any dancer.

"And, who . . . who are you?" I asked quietly.

"I am Niishraah," she said again, proclaiming it with infectious joy. "If Jemdanee is the queen, it could be said that I am . . . I am the princess!"

She chuckled, and both Tara and I joined in, genuinely and joyfully, although we had no idea why.

Suddenly a pout of concern passed across her face again, as irresistible as before, and she asked, "Am I interrupting you? Were you talking with each other? I do not mean to disturb your good selves."

"No, no. Not in the least," I cried. "Please, sit down."

I jumped up off the pot to offer it, but she dropped on to her hunkers instead and stared up at us with her chin in her palm and the expression of a ballerina accepting a bouquet at a curtain call.

I was riffling my mind, desperately thinking of a topic worthy of her, when Jemdanee and her retinue came shuffling into the courtyard.

"Well?" she demanded.

The three of us looked up at her. I had forgotten what I was even doing there.

"Well, Tara?" she repeated. "What is it to be?"

There was a long pause. Everyone was staring at Tara, not sure whether he was making up his mind or just enjoying the drama.

"I am yours, Mother," he exclaimed with finality. "For ever and always, yours, and your great *guru* Marat Khan's. Of course, I am."

"Yes," she chimed.

I had lost the will to resist. These people, whoever they were, were beyond me. They were as irresistible as they were off-putting. Any group good enough for Niishraah was good enough for me. No sooner had Jemdanee got Tara's pledge than she returned to her peremptory manner.

"You understand there will be no more contact with your previous life," she said with a touch of menace. "I trust you understand this."

Tara gazed solemnly.

"You have welcomed me into your hearts," he said, with the brightest smile breaking across his leprosy-dappled cheek. "All of you, thank you."

What more could I do? This was India and I was not of it. I had no idea of its currents, its inner workings. Tara had made up his mind, and that was that. Niishraah had reduced me to a state incapable of rational thought. All I could think of was that I wouldn't ever see her again. I couldn't bear that. I would gladly have cut off my own stupid slug if that's what it took.

Chapter 7

THE TIGER WAS asleep when I got back that night, and I thought it best not to mention anything about it the following day. We spent two more days in Delhi, and the work became somewhat less tortuous each day. Basically, my brother arranged that I would appear on camera as little as possible. The series might have my name in the title, but there would be an admirable shift of focus away from the presenter and on to the local people themselves. Later we would win praise for precisely this pragmatic and unavoidable decision.

From Delhi we headed on west into the Rajasthan desert with our driver, Salim-bi, a cross-eyed Muslim who had recently put himself in hock for life by buying the shell of an old '65 Ambassador and a '95 Toyota engine to make it go. Already the repayments were crippling him, and he was only too keen to bring us as far out into the desert as we wanted to go and to make whatever other sacrifices were necessary. Absolute devotion, he proclaimed, was the hallmark of his work. He made a point of describing how he had kissed his wife and children goodbye that morning, warning them that he might never see them again if his new masters demanded the ultimate sacrifice of him. He wanted us to regard him not just as our driver but our nourishment, our oxygen. This was why his wife had rushed out and bought him kebabs and lamb shanks before the trip, so that he would have the strength to serve us unequivocally. All of this was explained as we crawled out past the suburbs of pokey concrete homes and Marxist office blocks speckled with limpet-like air-conditioners, and on through shanty towns and sackcloth shacks into the wilderness beyond.

His car was like something out of a child's storybook, with flaring wheel arches and wing mirrors so tiny they were more to ward off evil than for vision. The countryside, with its browns and ambers radiating off smoky fields, was a wonderful contrast to the lush foothills I was used to. This was semi-desert with hardly a bush or shrub for miles except for the regular colonnade of neem trees lining the road. Efflorescent dust-devils rose up here and there in orange and grey where some farmer who was hoping to coax a crop from the arid land had set a buffalo to plough the dust.

Rajasthan is a sterile desert state still keening its buccaneering past of wealth and valour which flourished for centuries inside the cosy cocoon woven from the unseemly wealth of its megalomaniac maharajas. It was always the most exotic, flamboyant state. Its princes were akin to medieval knights, known for their passion and bloodlust. War was their sport, and over time they amassed huge wealth by plundering and taxing the lands they conquered. After independence, the maharajas found themselves pulled to earth by the new government, and with them fell their subjects. I was keen to see what remained and to document on film the culture's death rattle, the last tiger hunts, the last purdahhed women and fading princes. I thought it would be of interest to an Irish-speaking audience who had also once been participants in a golden age of culture and power that had now been brought to heel.

We were driving along the narrow tarmac strip from Delhi to Jaipur with Salim-bi at the wheel playing chicken with bullock carts and monster trucks that glistened with fairy lights and Hindu paraphernalia, swerving every now and then to avoid the rolled trucks that lay like upturned cockroaches, their guts spilling from exploded bellies, their drive-shafts prone like severed spinal cords, when suddenly I caught sight of a sign for Alwar pointing east. I shouted at Salim-bi to pull over, and he swerved the car into the ditch obligingly. The Tiger looked at me with a raised eye.

Alwar was the town where Bhartrihari, the immortal *yogi*, was supposed to live. In the same way that I hadn't got around to mentioning anything about Tara to the Tiger yet, I hadn't brought up the issue of Lans either. He wouldn't have understood. I hardly did myself. But, crazy or not, Lans had walked all night to see me; for him this was deadly serious, and I had given him my word.

I took a deep breath and hurriedly explained the situation to the Tiger, pointing out to him how Lans had heard that the *yogis* were so impressed by how we had wrapped up the Second World War relatively quickly and implemented the ensuing peace plan (and then later shown our restraint during the Cold War) that they were now convinced it was time to leave us to our own devices. I told him I had promised Lans I would try to relay his concerns to Bhartrihari.

He reacted just as I had expected, as any sane man would, I suppose. But since everyone was indulging everyone in this sad folly, he agreed to let me look into it at least. Alwar was only twenty-five miles off the main road, and we weren't in any great hurry to reach Jaipur. He told Salim-bi to turn around, and we headed down the track. I have to admit I was more than a little excited. It was just possible that a living god lay at the end of this road. If so, the experience of a lifetime might lie ahead. God forbid, if we managed to find him, or even film him doing his resurrection trick – who knew how valuable the footage might be? Every Hindu on earth would pay to watch; not to mention the buyouts by all those freak-show channels on satellite. We would be rich. I could buy a forest in the mountains and build a meditation centre there with ecological accommodation for hundreds of people.

I went over in my mind what I should say to Bhartrihari when we met. It was no time to be tongue-tied; this could be the making of me as a presenter. I'd make sure the Tiger was filming from the get-go – we didn't want to miss anything. If Bhartrihari was able to appear at will, it was likely he could vanish just as easily. I decided that, before anything else, I should pass on Lans' message to him – it was only fair. Then maybe I could ask him about Jesus: it was said that they had been friends during Jesus' supposed missing years in India. If he had some really good insights into Christ, some really juicy anecdotes, the footage would be priceless. We would be rich men. Very rich men.

About ten miles along the track, we came to a crossroads with a Hindu shrine at its centre, and I asked directions from a skinny cyclist in skimpy rags and flip-flops, but he just frowned, shook his head and went on. Alwar was most likely straight ahead, but we didn't want to risk it, and so Salim-bi got out and wandered off into a field to see if he could find someone to ask. He was gone awhile, and by the time he got back, I had worked out precisely the first question to ask Bhatrihari. I was pulling out a pen to jot it down when I caught sight of Salim-bi approaching the car, dark red with anger. He ran over, pounding from foot to foot like a midge-bitten buffalo. I could practically see the air snorting from his nostrils.

"Bhartrihari is fraud!" he screamed, sticking his head in the window at me.

I pulled back to avoid the spittle.

"Just other filthy Hindu idol-worshipper," he continued. "I did not know, but now I do. In the name of Allah and his Prophet Mohammed, I not drive you. We agree go to Jaipur, not to dirty cow-worshipping thieves! With these lips I kissed my wife and babies bye-bye this morning, so now you think I turn round and breathe the same air as a rotten Hindu god through same lips also! *Hamda'illah*! I not human, too? I not deserving respecting? If you want you get rid of me, you find Shiva-monkey driver, but I not drive, not one more *KM*, not one *tisidel*, towards the infidel."

Since we were stranded in the centre of the desert, Salim-bi knew it was unlikely that we would be dismissing him just yet, and the Tiger assured him that we had no intention of doing so, and that, by all means, we could turn back and head for Jaipur as agreed if it made him feel better. I shot a wounded look at my brother, imploring him to hold strong, to stand firm against this bigot.

"What about Lans?" I whispered, but the Tiger just cast his eyes to heaven.

"I Mussulman. I very holy man," Salim-bi preened as soon as he knew he was getting his way.

"Of course, you are," the Tiger purred. "Of course."

Salim-bi got back behind the wheel, huffing petulantly as he swung the car around, stuffing his mouth with betel nut for reassurance. He flurried and wheezed awhile before eventually settling down.

"Muhammad-blooding Hindus and their million gods," he muttered. "They are everywhere, like rats in a slum. All the Prophet ever wanted was for we know only one true god – *ALL-AH* his name. Is too much to ask? I very lucky man: I ask Muslim brother in field who say me all about

Bhartrihari and his stinking lies. He is big lie. Is only in minds of fools –
some poor farmer every hundred year buries alive hisself to keep his lie
alive. And man's body never get reborn, no, no – it rots in the sand."

To signal his disgust, Salim-bi consciously stepped on the accelerator
just as a school bus was bearing down on us and then had to swerve madly
towards the ditch to miss it, the car tilting sharply as he did so. Salim-bi
swung the steering wheel erratically to regain control, but suddenly out of
nowhere a bridge appeared, even narrower than the road, while the car was
still wobbling. We regained control only seconds before slamming into the
guardrail, whereupon Salim-bi looked back with a huge smile upon his
face as though he had done us an enormous favour.

"Always I work so hard for you, my Irish friends. I keep you safe.
Always, yes?"

That was that. Within twenty minutes we were back on the main road
to Jaipur, and all I could think of was how I had failed Lans. Granted, it
was unlikely we would have met Bhartrihari, but I was disappointed
nevertheless. A 2,000-year-old immortal man would have been such a
coup for the series, and even if it turned out he hadn't known Jesus, the
Irish speakers would have lapped him up. The whole notion of the wisdom of elders and the unbroken line stretching back through time was
still really strong among them.

A few miles further on, we passed a family of goatherds camping on
the side of the road, their red and white tent glistening with mirrored
stars embroidered into its sides to scare off tigers. Docile goats scratched
against a tent pole and a few mangy camels stared toward the horizon.
There were women everywhere, busy grinding, brushing, sewing, but I
could see no men. The young ones were dressed like troubadours in long
black and red dresses with pixelated lozenges and sun patterns embroidered in gold. The older ones were more muted, but their teeth and
anklets flashed silver in the sun, and the copper pots on their heads
glowed lusciously. We stopped the car to take a shot, and as I looked at my
brother bent over the tripod, framing the scene, I couldn't help but smile.
The whole situation was so unlikely.

Catching sight of me, he shot a grimace back. Who could have
guessed that the Irish language would bring us together here on the side
of a road in Rajasthan? Although as children we had been close enough in

that instinctive unquestioning way of siblings, as adults we had drifted apart. I assumed I would see him again only at weddings and funerals. It wasn't that there was any great animosity between us, but we just had little in common any more. To him I was a terminal fantasist, an overly sensitive shambles; while to me he was a fake – an empty vessel, lacking in stability. He was too fast, too busy for me ever to want to catch up with him. I imagined my grandmother now looking down on us. It was she who had taught us Irish – bribed us with sweets and money to learn a new word or phrase each day. The more Irish we spoke, the more we earned. It was a currency, plain and simple. It's not that we were so terribly avaricious or that the language was so odious to us that we needed to be paid for speaking it, just that we needed some form of compensation to endure the teasing at school.

Now, the tables were turned. This once shameful language was rising Lazarus-like from the grave in a whole new incarnation and bringing us along with it on an adventure to who knew where. Although the television station might turn out to be a complete disaster, it might also just work, propelling us and the language in a whole new direction. Either TnaG was the nail in the language's coffin or it was its saviour. The launch date was still nine months away, and despite the forewarnings of the usual detractors, it was too early to tell for sure. Ours was the first ever series to be made. On it and the others was dependent so much – whether after 200 years of decline during which the language was outlawed, its utterance punishable by flogging in schools, it could now be resurrected. And the notion that we were now in this position was even odder than the fact that my brother and I found ourselves standing side by side filming nomads in the Rajasthan desert.

As the camera panned across the empty landscape, I noticed a telegraph pole a short distance away with a laminated poster on it. The words, "DANCE YOUR TITS OFF", were spelled out in fluorescent green and orange. Beneath it was written:

Do you want to go to bed with me?
Put on your dancing shoes, juice up your hormones and get set to party
for not one, two, 20, 40 . . . but 50 non-stop hours
of Mega-mother-funking groove.

India was hoping to enter the *Guinness Book of Records* for the world's longest dance party, which was being sponsored by a deodorant manufacturer. I had seen numerous posters advertising this on the neem trees along the road, but none was quite as explicit as this one. I wondered whether the nomads could read and what they made of it if they could.

The poster boasted of,

10 MTV VJs
12 World Class DJs
50,000 Watts of Sound & Light
50 Non-Stop Bangle-jiving Hours of Dance Action
and
ONE WORLD RECORD

Salim-bi said his wife was needling him to allow his daughter to wear lipstick to it, but he was doubtful if he should even let her go at all. She claimed it was a matter of national pride for the country to win; the eyes of the world would be on India, and it was important that they looked their best; that they looked as sexy as other nations. Some of her friends were planning to wear belly-tops to be truly patriotic. Salim-bi had promised to ask his imam's advice.

Chapter 8

WE DROVE ON to Jaipur and spent a few days filming the ostentatious remnants of maharajan excess: the marble-paved galleries, rose-hued façades and the thousand hand-carved windows of the honeycombed Palace of the Winds. It struck me that just as the maharajas had found immortality through their architecture, their essence captured in bricks and mortar, maybe that was what TnaG was about, too: trapping our bardic tongue on tape, so that when it did finally splutter and die, they would be able to root out the tapes again and show people how this awkward old matrix of sounds and syntax had once been used to communicate – actually to talk and joke and sing in, and make quixotic television programmes in faraway places.

I was finding the journey a bit overwhelming, but this was mainly because I wasn't sleeping well. The spectre of Tara was haunting me. Whenever I closed my eyes, I saw him – as though he were right there in the room with me – being pinned down on the divan with a baton placed between his teeth to bite on and the bridle across his thighs. That was always how I saw him – never singing or dancing or having fun with Marat Khan and the others. It was always the operation. I was regretting ever having got involved. But worse, how could I have left him there? Just walked away. I saw now that there was so much more I could have done. Whenever I had seen the lepers suffering in Baldoti, I had always been able to console myself that this was simply the way of the world. It had nothing to do with me. But with Tara it was different; it had everything to do with me. The least I hoped for was that they would use a new blade, but even that was doubtful. From what I had seen at the leper clinic, supplies were scarce even there, and that was a fully functional missionary hospital. The truth was that Tara was going to be sliced open with a blunt razor and his testicles torn from him. That was the bare truth of it. The *blunt* truth.

Imagine if the roles were reversed; if, for example, it were I in some west of Ireland village eighty years ago, encouraged by the gallant talk of a European anthropologist, there to study my primitive language, to admit my love for another boy, and as a result found myself expelled from that community and forced to become a rent boy in Dublin, where I was whipped by jarvies and beaten by self-loathing members of the aristocratic underbelly. Imagine if this anthropologist – who claimed to be my friend – had stood by and let it happen. That was what was really going on. Both Tara and I knew it was in my power to save him. I was the only one who could.

Every night these same thoughts came railing through my mind, and no matter how much I buried my head under the pillow, I could still see the blood seeping out from between his legs; the wads of muslin pressed hard to stem the flow. I could see the red stain across the divan, smearing the pristine tiled floors and running out into that pretty little courtyard with the cactus pots. I could hear the screaming echoing up the stairwell and out into Nizamuddin. Screams of pain and terror before he passed out.

After our first day's filming in Jaipur, I decided I had to go back. There was no other way. I had to try to talk him out of it, or at least to pay to have it done properly, in a clinic with an anaesthetic and sterilised equipment. Needles. It shouldn't cost all that much; a few hundred rupees would cover it. TnaG would be happy to fund it if they ever knew. The race memory of our own castration by the British Penal Laws was still too strong in us to allow it to happen to someone else.

At breakfast on our second day in Jaipur, I told the Tiger about Tara. I explained the whole story to him and why I had to go back, and to his credit he understood. He accepted it. My brother had always had a great sense of compassion, of social conscience. Far greater than mine. A drawback of focusing too much on the inner realms is that you become inured to reality – immune to the pain and joy of others. We agreed that I would take the train up to Delhi straightaway; meanwhile he could go on filming. He was becoming ever more entranced by the people: their inscrutable gaze and harlequin clothing; their voluminous *saris* sensuous and alive like rivers of cotton swirling down the contours of their bodies. He would savour the chance to drink all of this in at his leisure, to have the time to compose his shots without me lurking behind him wondering when it was time for tea and biscuits.

I promised I'd be back within twenty-four hours.

By mid-afternoon that day I found myself back sitting in the lobby in Nizamuddin, amidst the same gaudy furniture and eerie sense of an enclosed order. This time I was aware of something else – a cloying sense of sterility, the suffocating, fetid smell of life without rejuvenation, of seasons without the rebirth of spring. I crossed my legs anxiously, agitated, until I heard the familiar clatter and saw Jemdanee approaching me with an ill-disposed air. There was none of the false graciousness of last time. She looked ratty and strung out.

"What exactly did you not understand?" she said, striding towards me. "Didn't I say no visits? You think I was joking? Big funny laugh? . . . You go now, leave."

"I know what you said, Jemdanee; it's just not that simple. I need to talk to Tara."

She clucked her tongue threateningly, but I held my ground.

"There is no talking to Tara," she snarled. "Her new name is Colora, and there is certainly no talking to Colora. Go now. If after the months she is not happy here and we are not happy with her, you come back and then you talk."

Jemdanee snapped her fingers, prompting her *chela* to advance and raise my arm gently, assisting me to the door.

"Jemdanee, I demand to see him," I said, the shame of my previous neglect of Tara emboldening me. I was prepared if necessary to attack her, this mongrel, this half sprite. "I know your reputation, but you can't threaten me . . . I am asking you a favour. Give me one hour with him. As you said, I am a *gora* – your powers don't affect me. And anyway, I have my own powers – my embassy – and if I have to, I'll use them."

"You threaten me?" Jemdanee cried.

"No," I said. "All I want is a favour, that's all . . . Tara is very grateful to you; we both are. Please, Jemdanee?"

I like to think that it was my concern for Tara that made me stand up to Jemdanee, who, after all, according to Madame Singh Guli's cousin, made her living out of harassment and racketeering. But in truth, if she had been a *real* man, I might not have shown such courage. Shameful as it is to admit, I regarded her as less than me. I couldn't help feeling that the *hijras* were like capons – emasculated cocks castrated and fattened up for eating: plucked, trussed and stuffed with their own giblets, sitting pretty on styrofoam trays. This was in contrast to me, who was something whole – authentic. I'm not proud of that thought, but it was just what I felt.

Jemdanee stared at me for a long time. She may as well have been chewing lemons for the way her face was screwed up in disdain, and my resolve did indeed begin to weaken, but not before she had clucked derisively and shouted something upstairs in Hindi which brought forth Tara, wearing a length of white cotton over simple pants in place of the jewelled hipsters he had arrived in. I wasn't sure if it was a *dhoti* or a *sari* he was wearing, male or female, but other than that he looked no different. It appeared as though his lesions were continuing to improve, or at least they had got no worse over the few days. He ran to me and clung on breathlessly, digging his fingers into my back while I tried to grip his shoulders formally.

"You okay?" I asked.

He looked up, nodding a high-amp smile.

"You haven't been . . . em," I grappled for the word.

He kept smiling.

"Em . . ." I said, motioning with my finger.

"Oh, no, Mocha-ji."

"That's great, Tara," I said. "That's great to hear."

He hugged me again.

"No, Mocha-ji – no cutting or bleeding. No hot *ghee* poultice."

"Good," I said.

"Have you heard my new name?" he cried. "Colora – isn't it so beautiful!"

I nodded absentmindedly.

"And what about your good self?" he asked. "You must tell me all the things."

Jemdanee was watching us, her eyes beetling with indignation. I asked her could I bring him out to the courtyard with me, and she clucked again, which I took for a yes. As we walked out, Tara slipped his hand into mine and said in an excited whisper, "I am not gay boy!"

I turned to him. "Sorry?"

"I am not gay boy!" he said again. "Isn't it great?"

"You're not gay, not homosexual?"

"Yes."

"Yes, what?"

"Yes, exactly, Mocha-ji," he said. "Not even a little bit pooftah."

"What about Sangev?" I asked.

"Oh, yes, I am loving Sangev," he said wistfully. "I am loving him very much. More than ever now."

"But, you're not gay?"

"No! This is what I am telling to you!"

"You do know what the word means, Tara?" I said. "What being *gay* is?"

"I would hate to be sticking my thingy in him, Mocha-ji!" Tara exclaimed. "Never ever!"

"I see," I managed.

"You see? Yes! I did not understand before, too," he clarified.

"Right."

"Yes, yes. We see now. We are both seeing everything."

I was baffled.

"Well, can you go home in that case?" I asked.

He burst out laughing. "No, no, you are not seeing yet," he chuckled. "I am not gay. I am woman."

"You're what?"

"Woman – opposite to man, like boy/girl."

"I know what a woman is, Tara, and you certainly are not one."

"Most certainly, yes, I am," he said. "Certainly, very much woman. I am wanting Sangev to stick his thingy in me. In my holey bum."

"That doesn't make you a woman," I said.

"Maybe yes, maybe no, but what about this?"

Tara undid his *dhoti* and pulled down his pants.

"Look!" he said. "Look here."

I took a quick glance down and did a fast double take. Grabbing his elbows, I looked up into his eyes, exclaiming, "Did they do this to you?"

"Do what?" he laughed, looking down between his legs. "What is it they have been doing?"

In between his legs was the usual forest of shiny hair, but without any sign of a phallus. I looked down again searching for signs of a wound, but there were none. There was nothing there at all, or if there was, it was too overgrown to see.

"This," I said, pointing awkwardly down.

He looked puzzled, and bent forward to stare, then reaching down to part the curls, he revealed a tiny penis, no bigger than a baby toe and with no visible testicles in evidence. He flicked his member jauntily.

"This is just me," he laughed. "Me being me. It is how I am always being me."

My first thought was that the organ had dropped off with the leprosy, but I knew that was ridiculous. The body doesn't crumble with leprosy; it erodes like the freeze-thaw action on a rock in the desert. Anyway, from my cursory glance down, it seemed the leprosy was confined to his upper torso and showed no signs of having spread.

I took another gaze down. There was definitely no visible wound or signs of bleeding. Either the *hijras* were uncannily good surgeons or else he was telling the truth. His hair was so thick it was hard to see anything, but as he combed his fingers through it, I was able to make out the vague contours of two lumps which must have been the testicles. They were almost fully embedded beneath the pelvic bone and set unnaturally high in the body. Taking a deep breath and summoning my resolve, I tentatively reached down to explore the area with my fingers, but it didn't help very much. I still wasn't sure whether the swollen mounds were embedded testicles or undeveloped labia. Sensing the bile rising in my throat, I withdrew my hand quickly.

No wonder the poor lad had been sexually confused. What the hell was he? I wondered if his family knew the situation, or his doctors in the clinic, or anyone.

Tara seemed tickled pink by the attention.

"Such a hoot, yes?" he said. "Such a laughing matter. A real mickey-tease."

"Not a mickey-tease, Tara," I snapped. "Certainly not that."

"No mickey-tease?" he said, wobbling his little pecker.

"That's something else."

"A striptease?" he said.

"Tara!" I cried. "Where are you getting all this from?"

I crouched down on one of the patio pots, trying to make sense of it all as he retied his *dhoti*. Gradually, I was beginning to piece the situation together. Tara, it seemed, wasn't quite a boy, but nor was he a girl either. And if this was the case, then it was true that you couldn't really say he was gay.

"Does Sangev know?" I asked, inclining my head towards his groin.

"Of course," he said.

"So you never had sex with him?"

"I would never want to do the poking in: I'm girl. That is his part."

"Why didn't you tell me before?"

"I didn't know. I didn't know I was girl."

"You're not a girl," I said.

"In *Sunnydale High*, Miss Latimore tells Buffy and her friends all things about sex-ed. And also Buffy and Willow get to watch the *gross-out* puberty movie in body-health class. In Almora we do not have these things. We do not have vampire slayers or hellmoths either."

"Who the hell is Miss Latimore?" I cried.

"Like Dr Ruth, but for high school. She teaches the *Oops, it's a Baby* programme in Sunnydale."

"Where did you hear about Dr Ruth?" I cried. "No, don't tell me. I don't want to know."

"Xander says Miss Latimore is a muscle dyke, but Willow said that he was a wastoid for even thinking it," Tara went on, ignoring me.

"Leave the bloody vampire slayer out of it," I snapped, and Tara recoiled, making me regret my tone instantly. "I'm sorry, but we're talking about you now. Jemdanee has given us only an hour, and anyway I have a train to catch."

"But it is so good and funny," Tara said. "And it makes me hopeful."

"It's great that you're reading, Tara. I'm delighted, and I'll get you some more books, nice books – more appropriate ones – but please let's stick to the point now."

"My family always say I am boy, so I am boy," he said soberly. "I am always thinking, Sangev, he is the one with the big problems. His big diddly problem, so big like elephant. But Marat Khan, she has now been telling me all the things. She says problem is all with my diddly – it is teenie-weenie, yellow poker-dot bikini. Because I am only girl. Always being girl. And Sangev's diddly isn't so big after all."

I was beginning to realise that Tara was perhaps transgender. Intersexed. His "diddly" was possibly an enlarged clitoris. In the old terminology, he was a hermaphrodite. He actually was a real-life *hijra*.

"Tara, you're a *hijra!*" I exclaimed.

"No, I am girl."

"Tara, You have male organs. Admittedly, they're not very apparent, but they're there."

"This is being very confusing for me," he said, shaking his head mournfully. "On the one hand, it is one thing and . . ."

Suddenly I caught sight of the time and jumped to my feet.

"Tara, I'm really sorry," I interrupted. "I don't have time for this now – there's only about twenty minutes before I have to go."

The train was leaving in two hours, and with Delhi traffic being what it was, it would take almost that long to get to the station and buy a ticket.

"We've got to think fast," I said. "If you're really not gay, then you can go back home, can't you?"

"As woman?" he asked hopefully. "You think I can go home as woman?"

"You're not a woman, Tara."

"Yes, woman, like Miss Latimore."

"No, of course you can't go back to Almora as a woman, not if you insist on dressing like Miss Latimore. You saw how they reacted to your pedal-pushers. Why can't you just go back and be Tara? You can be Miss Latimore inside if you really want, but just be Tara for everyone else. I can get the nurses in Baldoti to watch over you if you're worried."

He swung his head back and forth determinedly.

"What other choice have you got?" I asked.

He remained silent, looking absently around him like Harold Lloyd doing his lost waif routine. I didn't have time for this.

"What are you going to do?" I said. "Are you going to stay?"

He nodded almost imperceptibly. I was desperately trying to work out the implications of all this. For him, for Jemdanee, for me.

"Well, at least you won't have to be cut . . ." I suggested.

"Oh, yes," Tara interrupted. "I will still have the ceremony."

"You'll have the ceremony, fine. But not the operation."

"No, no, that too."

"What?" I cried.

"Yes, yes, the snip and cut."

"But there's nothing there to remove!" I squealed.

I was pointing down at his *dhoti*-wrapped crotch.

"It's testicles they are not liking, Mocha-ji. Penis is no problem. You can have big swinging snake hanging down – no problem – but no balls. Definitively, no balls allowed."

I sighed wearily. This was madness.

"What are we going to do, Tara? You tell me. Tell me what you're thinking . . . What do you want? How do you feel?"

"Confused, a little," he murmured.

"Join the club," I said.

We were getting nowhere.

I could sense Jemdanee circling and could picture the teeming crowds in the ticket office, all wrestling to get on that same train that I had to be on. And I did really have to be on it. The Tiger would indulge me only so far. I daren't push my luck.

"Talk to me, Tara! Are you happy here?" I asked.

"There are so many new things," he said. "It is so many new changes all at once. Confused, a little."

"Why did Marat Khan say you were a girl, anyway?" I asked.

"Because it is what I am . . . I think I was always knowing at the back of my minds, but always everyone say . . ."

"Tara, I'm really sorry, but I just don't have the time now."

"Yes, yes," he said, "no talking just listening."

And he fell silent, staring at me, waiting for me to say something. To set it right. I was the one who had got him into this mess, and he was certain that I would lead him out the other side. He wasn't to know it was beyond me, that I was in way over my head. If only the Tiger had been there; he was the pragmatic one, the decision maker. He would have known what to do. All I could think about was sitting in my hovel in the mountains and how I should never have let Khim Singh send Tara down to me that morning. I remembered how Khim for his part had tried to warn me. All this would never have happened if only I hadn't been so damned accommodating.

Finally I just had to leave him. I couldn't miss the train. I grabbed my bag and fled. Jemdanee had watched my turmoil with indecent delight, and I could hear her triumphal harrumphing echoing in my ears as I ran across the road to a waiting rickshaw.

As the rickshaw-*wallah* dragged me back across the city to the train station, I couldn't help reflecting on what a mess it all was, but at least I was sure Tara would be taken care of. Marat Khan would be certain to keep up the medical treatment, if only out of self-interest. A leper eunuch was no good to anyone. As it was, they would probably have to keep him inside for a few months until his lesions cleared up. And, certainly, his family couldn't get at him there. There would be no more beatings. He'd have time to work out who or what he was exactly.

I sat back in the chariot spellbound by the Herculean feat of the cyclist shackled to his daily grind, straining and grunting over the handlebars like a bullock in harness, and tried consoling myself with the thought that maybe, quite by accident, I had stumbled upon a peculiarly Indian solution to an Indian problem.

When I reached for my wallet at the train station to pay the rickshaw, I found it empty, and it was further consolation to remember that as I had dashed out the door I had upended its contents into Tara's lap. There was the guts of a hundred dollars there. I tried not to think what the Tiger would say when he heard. It could hardly be said to be furthering the cause of the Irish language, but I knew how useful it would prove to Tara. At least I hadn't handed over my traveller's cheques too.

Of more immediate concern at the time was how to pay for my train passage to Jaipur since the ticket office refused to accept the cheques. I tried explaining to a railway official that I was making a travel programme on the splendours of India and needed to get to Jaipur straightaway, and while this impressed him, he insisted that he would have to see my letter of introduction from the Tourism Development Ministry in Delhi before he could issue me with a ticket. I made a mental note to get one at the first opportunity and in the meantime tried asking various backpackers for a loan of a few rupees. They all refused, presuming I was just another drugged-up Western waster, like the ones begging in Connaught Place beside the legless, leprous local beggars.

A dreadlocked English man, tucking into a plate of chicken *korma* and buttered *naan*, put his hand around my neck, pulling me down so that we locked foreheads and said into my ear, "I would, man. I really would if I could. I'm feeling for you. Just go with the soul, yeah? *It* knows. The whole thing is just a journey, right? All of it, just a big trip. Yeah?"

He widened his lips, breathing out and placing an inordinate stress on the word *yeah*, which sent a back-draft of *korma* shooting up my nose that made me hungrier than ever.

The price of his meal alone would have got me a second-class ticket to anywhere for hundreds of miles around. In the end, it was a cosmetics salesman from Udaipur who came to my aid. He had been reading his paper and watching as I went around the various Lowe Alpines, Jack Wolfskins and North Faces until finally he beckoned me over to ask what was wrong. No sooner were the words out of my mouth than he was up and buying me a ticket.

"No! No thanking me," he exclaimed afterwards. "It is Indian way. Gandhi-ji tell us it is the only way so many *lakh* of people can live well together, if all is helping all. One big *masala*. Especially the travelling people – our honoured guests on the Grand Trunk, travelling through our country – we must help them even more . . . Come now – train is boarding."

And he paid off the rickshaw *wallah*, who was still loitering near by, and led me to the third-class carriage where we notched ourselves on to a bench groaning with amply proportioned Sikhs, whose bodies acted like an overstuffed armchair.

"You will be filming in all the big palaces around Jaipur, may I presume?" the cosmetics salesman asked when I told him what we were up to.

I nodded self-consciously – aware of the Sikhs, spellbound by my every action.

"In truth, we should not be so proud of these things," he went on.

"Gaudy showpieces left by the maharajas after they had spent all our money and abandoned us. What good are they to us now, but as sad remainders of our former gullibility? Our former pride and profligacy? If you don't mind my saying so, my friend, may I suggest instead you look at the Janta Mantar, the astronomical observatory which the Maharaja Jai Singh built 300 years ago. It is looking not backwards at our bloodlust and sad *kismet*, nor forwards at the unknown, but outwards at the cosmos. It's about knowledge and learning."

Chapter 9

WHEN I FINALLY got back to the hotel that night, the Tiger didn't want to hear anything about my day. He had had a good time filming and was feeling mellow. Since I could see that my activities would have just annoyed him, I decided to keep them to myself.

"I'm really getting a sense of this place," he said, ordering me a whisky sour on the hotel veranda. "We can do serious work here. I got some great close-ups of the people and some good GVs (general views) of the town. The expressions on some of those old warriors are incredible. What we need now is content: stories to make the whole thing come alive. Have you some good ones lined up? What did you find in your research?"

Research?

When the hell was I meant to have got research done? My brother always expected so much of me. It's what I hated most. It had always been the same; no matter how often I explained to him when we were kids that I couldn't run because of my asthma, he used to keep after me. I used to beg him not to pick me on his team for matches, but he knew the other side never would, and I was needed to make up the numbers. It was the same now. If he could have presented the programmes on his own as well as directing, filming and recording sound, he would have; but as it was, I was needed to make up the numbers. What he needed were stories, and somehow he just expected me to magic them up out of nowhere.

"In four days we have a train to catch to Varanasi," he pointed out on seeing my irritation. "In the meantime, we've somehow got to pull four minutes of television out of this place. Now unless you're going to drink your own piss live on television for an hour, we'd better find some stories."

I decided that now wasn't a good time to mention the fact that drinking my own piss was in fact one of the topics I was keen to cover at some stage, and perhaps now was as good a time as any. I strongly believed the urine therapy was misunderstood in the developed world, and I wanted to set the record straight.

"I gave you a fantastic story in Alwar, and you didn't even bother going there," I whined.

"You mean the *yogi*! The bloke burying himself in concrete?" the Tiger snorted. "You call that . . ."

Ignoring him, I began leafing through the few scant notes I had managed to jot down from guidebooks in the days before his arrival. I had some great stuff about dowry-killings and spurned lovers cooked in tandoor ovens, but nothing at all on Jaipur. Not one note. I had presumed there would be plenty of time during the trip to keep a few pages ahead of him in the guidebook. I hadn't counted on Tara. I noticed my brother getting up to look over my shoulder at my paltry notes, and more to forestall him than anything, I blurted out, "The Janta Mantar!"

Snapping the notebook shut before he could see, I went on, "It's the ultimate location, the ultimate story! An astronomical observatory hundreds of years old, capable of calculating the altitudes of celestial objects and the positions of the constellations with astounding accuracy. It reveals a whole new side to India – not just warfare and poverty, but genuine pioneering science."

"Huh?" the Tiger said.

Desperation gave me focus, and I was able to piece together everything the cosmetics man had told me.

"The Janta Mantar – one of the true wonders of the world," I gushed. "A tool built to shatter the superstitions of the religious elite. By calculating celestial positions accurately, the Maharaja Jai Singh was able to attack the stranglehold that religious belief had on his people. It was like a missile aimed at heaven."

"Mmn," my brother said, trying to hide his surprise. "Sounds like it might be worth looking at."

I told him everything I knew and could see he was impressed. He adopted the indulgent manner he uses whenever he is about to give me brotherly advice or praise – like some preening Dickensian benefactor addressing an orphaned waif.

"You know," he said sonorously, "I always knew you were the man for this job; that there was more to you than met the eye . . . I'm serious! Some of my friends thought I was crazy when I told them I was using you, but I set them right. I told the people in TnaG that until they met my brother they could have no idea how incredible you were. You'd light up the screen, I said. You'd become their *big name* sensation! That's what I told them straight out, that you'd blow their minds."

The spark of confidence that had arisen in me with the earlier compliment was extinguished as the implications of his words sank in – quenched by the backdraft of their expectation. A *big name* sensation? Was he serious! I hadn't stopped to think about how exactly he'd managed to convince TnaG to allow me to present the programmes. I could understand why they might have been willing to take a chance on him, what with his movie experience and all – he had been touched by Hollywood, and in the eyes of lowly television commissioners this sanctified him – but what on earth had convinced them about me? What had he told them to make them believe I was up to the job? Even the thought of it made me shudder . . . The next big name sensation? Oh God!

"This is just what we need," the Tiger was saying, "stories that give a new angle, that cast new light. I need you to find more of these, to root them out. If these programmes work out, we can go round the world with this series, you know that?"

He rose his glass to mine, and somehow I managed to join him in the toast and clink merrily, but I found it hard to swallow. He refilled his glass and got me to order another bottle, saying, "Why not? Let's make a night of it. It's not every day the brothers take on the world!"

But there was no way I could face drinking now. I was too messed up. This was all a big misunderstanding. It was like the time I had tripped over my laces when I was ten, knocking the opposition striker off balance just as he was about to score the winning goal, and my brother had misread the situation, thinking it was all planned, and he got the team to carry me off the pitch in triumph, lauding my skill and prowess.

We got to the maharaja's observatory for dawn the next day as the Tiger wanted to film the instruments in that magical hour when everything is first touched by the sun. He set up the tripod and began reeling the scene into the camera while I skulked about behind him, minding the camera bag and looking around the large stone forms. Running my fingers along the lines and notches that were etched into the mortar and marble, I marvelled at the process by which the sun, by simply shining, could transmute these inanimate objects into complex computers capable of calculating altitudes, azimuths and distances with astonishing accuracy. At one point, I walked into shot by accident, and the Tiger cursed so loudly that other tourists looked over. He was unduly tetchy from the drink the night before, but I admit, I should have been more careful. Half of me was back in Nizamuddin, and he could tell.

"What's up?" he said a moment later, when I failed to pass him the right camera lens that he had asked for.

I shrugged, keeping my eyes low. I could tell he was in quarrelsome form.

"In case you hadn't noticed, directing isn't something I have much experience in," he spat. "For you, it's easy – all you have to do is talk shite at the camera now and then – but I'm under enough pressure here without you screwing up every shot."

I backed away, walking over to the gnomon of the enormous sundial, grumbling to myself about the injustice of it all, but in my heart I knew that he was right – I had to try to be more helpful. When he'd finished the shot, I went over to him.

"Look," I said. "You're right. I'm sorry."

"Yeah, well . . ." he said, snatching the wide-angle lens from me and using it to frame a shot of two giant marble bowls that were designed to confirm the location of constellations.

I could tell he was chewing over something.

"What do you think you are up to with this *hijra* shit anyway?" he said finally, straightening up from behind the viewfinder. "Is it some type of Mother Teresa fixation?"

I shrugged again. I couldn't expect him to understand.

"In case you hadn't noticed, India isn't Ireland. You can't waltz in and set it all to right, you know, like little Miss Pollyanna."

"Fuck off," I said, stung by the accuracy of his observation.

A puckish old woman with the faint tracings of a moustache approached us, and possibly sensing the tension in the air, said, *"Wunderbar! Na? Ist es nicht fabelhaft?"*

She was pointing at the conch-like surface of the marble bowl. She had seen my Birkenstock sandals and presumed I was a fellow German – being gangly and pasty-faced I was often mistaken for one. The Tiger took one look at her, picked up his tripod and moved off to film somewhere else.

I smiled to make up for his rudeness and told her I wasn't German but Irish.

"Ah!" she said. "Your people were still consulting stone circles when this place was built, *nicht wahr?* Still stuck in the past. It was different in Germany, of course – we were using optics – far more sophisticated! But the maharaja had no time for these things, you see? He wanted his calculations based on what he could see with the naked eye, not the manipulated version seen through a lens. You boys should take note. Nothing you see through that little camera of yours is truth. It's just a version in zeros and ones. A version, but not necessarily a true one, yes? I tell my students this the whole time: not to always trust the digital readings, but do they listen?"

Frau Doktor Lieberman was an astrophysicist from a particle physics laboratory in Geneva. She had come away with her husband to take her mind off work, having suffered a breakdown the previous semester. She was still fragile, her husband told me the next morning in the lobby of the hotel we shared. After only two days of sightseeing in Delhi, she had insisted they come here, and her mind had been firing on all cylinders ever since.

Her husband now tactfully tried to steer her away from us over to a postcard rack, but she was in full flow. I was just conscious of keeping her away from the Tiger. I couldn't be responsible for his actions if another of his shots were ruined.

"To you the instruments look dead, *na?*" she went on. "Lumps of mortar, *korrekt?... Korrekt!* They *are* dead! Full marks!... It is the shadows that are alive – it is they that tell us what we need to know – the zenith distances, the meridian passes and so on. People forget that. Shadows have substance. Yes! They are physical reality seen through another dimension. Am I right or wrong?"

I tried backing away, luring her further from the Tiger, but she just went on louder.

"Right or wrong?!" she demanded

"What about?" I said

"The shadows!"

I really don't know," I pleaded.

"Wrong!" she roared. "Of course, wrong. They are not. Not in this dimension anyway. They need to be seen from another place to become alive. Everything has multiple facets, depending on how you look at it. Like a cowpat is different for a human than a beetle. A stone wall is a stone wall, but throw a ray of light at it and it turns into a shadow that can tell the time to an accuracy of three seconds. This is what I'm talking about, yes?"

It was the wrong time to be goading me into this sort of stuff. I had always had a weakness for dodgy quantum hypotheses and the like. Especially when I got stressed. A yearning to lose myself in the most fuzzy realms of thought would gnaw at me – to binge on the furthest-out theories, heady cocktails of quantum and metaphysics. Even as a child I had an obsessive side which sought to lose itself in arcane minutiae. At first it was dinosaurs: I could name the bone structure and scatological category of every genus and suborder of reptile from the late Triassic to the Cretaceous periods. As I got older, I switched to frontier logic, anti-matter anomalies, illogical constants, nebulous voids – all that borderline crazy stuff. It was an addiction really, and I was doing my best to over-come it. Taking it one day at a time. The Tiger had made it clear that now was a time for the nitty-gritty, the hard and fast, buckles and braces. More than ever, it was vital I remain focused on the three grounding principles I had set myself: stick to the 3D dimension, India's place in it and the Irish language as a medium to communicate the first two. That was all. Simple as that.

"What this place really proves," Frau Doktor Lieberman goaded, "is that light is more than just for lighting stuff. It's information – that is, if we have the tools to decipher it. *Licht und Liechtenstein. Na? Ein Witz, heurst du, ein Witz!*"

What the hell, I thought, a quick cup of tea with her would do no harm. The Tiger was busy filming anyway and didn't need me. I followed Frau Doktor Lieberman over to a *chai*-stand and ordered three *chai* and an apple fritter, which I thought I could bring over to my brother later as a peace offering.

As we waited for the tea, Herr Lieberman asked me what else we were filming in Rajasthan, and, in passing, I happened to mention Bhartrihari. I know now it was a mistake. In fact, even as I was saying it, I could feel Frau Doktor Lieberman's interest prickle, the mind bridle. I had been so careful up until then to avoid thinking too much about him.

"Immortal *yogi*, you say!" she said, although I had already moved on to talking about Salim-bi's atrocious driving. "Very interesting. Very, very interesting. *Nicht so, Klaus?*"

She looked to her husband, who was shaking his head anxiously. I could see he was as keen to steer her away from the topic as I was.

"Of course, in science this makes a degree of sense, yes?" Frau Doktor trumpeted as a shot across the bows. "Immortal *yogis* – yes, yes. Very interesting!"

As the *chai-wallah* set out tea for us, I tried to switch the topic to the MTV dance party and Salim-bi's concerns for his daughter, but Frau Doktor would not be thwarted.

"Answer me one thing," she said, stabbing at the jugular. "Tell me what it is you consist of?"

Her fingers were dancing nervously on the edge of her cup. Behind her back her husband was shaking his head plaintively, pleading with me not to continue.

"Well? . . . Well?" she insisted.

I ignored her and went on discussing the dance party and how it struck me that, this being India, the real achievement was not so much to get 10,000 people dancing for fifty hours non-stop in the desert, but to guarantee a continuous supply of power for the huge wattage of sound and light it took to power it.

"Atoms!" Frau Doktor interrupted. "You're made of atoms, stupid."

I nodded, raising my hands in capitulation, but she wasn't finished.

"And what's in an atom?"

I shook my head in desperation. "A nucleus?"

"*Korrekt!* Now, what's in the nucleus?"

I could see there was no going back.

"Protons," I murmured in a jaded, defeated tone.

"What else? What else? What's inside a proton? A quark, of course! And what is a quark? *Three quarks for Muster Mark.* Come on, what's a quark? No, not low-fat cheese! No, not the squawk of a crow. Quark! Quark is energy – invisible, unobservable, but definitely present. Energy – an electronic charge. How much charge? Well, if you unfurl an atom at its nucleus level, you have an atomic bomb. How much charge is in one of those? Huh?"

"A lot," I said.

"A lot – indeed. So let's say – let's just hypothesise, shall we? – that you could access this energy. Suddenly you, *mein Freund*, have gone quantum, ballistic, atomic, fathomless – whatever you are fancying yourself. You're beyond time, beyond space."

She sipped her tea, delighted with the progress so far.

"Now, if by some chance you could bring a thread of consciousness with you," she went on, licking her lips in anticipation, "then you, basically, you are divine – you can do whatever the hell you want! All that is necessary is to focus one's attention inside the atom. Am I right?"

I said nothing.

"Well?" she repeated.

I shrugged.

"Ah-ha, yes, now you are seeing!" she crowed triumphantly. "Who's to say that isn't exactly what old Bhartrihari has been up to?"

She was in a complete froth by now. Her husband was riffling through her bag, desperately looking for her pills, as I got up and ran to the Tiger, who was calling out for me to bring the camera bag. The synapses of my brain were already sparking in many directions, although I tried my best to dampen them, to corral the brave new potentials and possibilities that were breaking loose.

In fact, from the first moment Lans had mentioned his immortal *yogis*, my mind had begun sending up flares – postulating possible hypotheses – but I had managed to keep it in check. Could these *yogis* be real, be some form of meta-human, of evolved consciousness? I chased the thought away at the time, determined to stay focused on my brother's imminent arrival and the work that lay ahead. Now, as though my brain had found a comfort blanket, I sensed it itching to retreat into its chaotic meandering, to burrow down avenues of conjecture and speculation. I sensed the familiar vertiginous sensation as the walls of reality wobbled, and I was off . . .

What if the answer to the *yogis* lay in their DNA? Science claims that 97 per cent of our DNA is junk. As proof, they point to the onion and how it has twelve times more superfluous DNA coding than the human genome, and since onions are obviously not as complex as us, they deduce that most of it must be junk. Fools! How can they be certain that an onion is less complex than us? Do onions make war? How do we know that every onion isn't in constant communication with every other onion – and shallot and garlic clove – on this planet, and on every other planet for that matter? Wouldn't that require a fair amount of processing ability? Or DNA? Maybe every single allium shares the pain when we crush a clove of garlic. Maybe that's why they make us cry. We cry their tears for them. Who knows for sure? Onions may in fact be sleeping *yogis,* and we may be their disciples, planting, feeding and harvesting them generation after generation. I accept that it isn't probable, but it's possible. It can't be dismissed. It's the pure stupid arrogance of scientists that always gets to me. They aren't interested in true science at all, only in whatever predictable data could corroborate what they already know – or what they *think* they know. Idiots. No wonder Frau Doktor Lieberman was going insane.

If the 97 per cent of junk DNA had any use at all, then the *yogis* were probably the ones who knew how to use it, and I thought the least we should do was give them the benefit of the doubt. I wondered should I ask the Tiger to return to Alwar so we could track down Bhartrihari once and for all. The more I thought about it, Frau Doktor's theory about the answers being inside the atom made some sense. If consciousness could, by some dimensional anomaly, switch focus internally – inwards towards the atom rather than outwards – then the outcome could easily appear like a divine human. This atomic anomaly would need to happen only a handful of times, and when you considered how many atoms there were in the universe, the likelihood of its having happened at some point was almost certain.

I tried to work out how many atoms there actually were in existence.

I knew that there were 300,000 million stars in the galaxy and another hundred million galaxies within photographicable range of us; that's 30 million, million, million stars visible from here. Overall, it's accepted that there are around 170 octillion in existence in total. Take every grain of sand on every beach, multiply it by ten, and that number was still only one one-hundredth the number of stars in the universe. Consciousness would have to exist in only one atom in any one of those stars for Bhartrihari to exist. Against odds like those, I wouldn't be betting very heavily. In fact, it was surely a dead cert, especially when you considered how many atoms must be in each star. From somewhere in the recesses of my mind, I recalled that the ratio of my thumb to an atom was the same as that of the planet earth to my thumb. Suddenly the likelihood of immortal *yogis* took on a whole new slant. Indeed, the odds for them seemed higher than for human evolution. In theory, it would be no surprise if we saw them crawling out of the woodwork.

"What's wrong?" my brother said, seeing my dazed expression.

"Nothing," I managed. "I got you an apple fritter."

"Just get me the lens wipe from the camera bag."

"Sure," I said, scuttling off out of range to give myself a chance to recover, but he sensed that something was up.

"What's up with you anyway?" he said. "You look all weird."

"Nothing," I gasped. "It's just the sun."

"Don't go getting sunstroke," he called. "I need a PTC [piece to camera] from you in a minute. Something short and snappy to sum up this place. Okay?"

I nodded dazedly.

"And make sure you keep your bloody hat on and stay out of the sun. You know how feverish you get."

"Sure," I said.

At times it was like having your mother away with you. He had always bossed me, always thought he knew best, and I hated having to admit that most of the time he did. From the time when I was five and he had found me collapsed on the strand speaking in tongues, after I had spent all day under the blazing sun building a sand tyrannosaurus, he had developed a tendency to nanny me. He had brought me home that day and put me to bed and spent the night dabbing yoghurt on my burns until my granny came home and unlocked the medicine closet where the lotion was kept. The burns were pretty severe, and when, a few years later, he read somewhere that burnt skin never fully recovered, he felt guilty that he was responsible for the malignant tumours that would eventually assail me – as though he should have done more to protect me, and that it would be entirely his fault if my wife and children were left widowed and orphaned after my slow and painful death in later life. He worried too much. Before I got the phone call saying he was coming out to India, he had been letting me know by way of letters from my mother his concerns about my dropping out and losing myself in the Himalayas. I wondered whether his whole reason for coming out and making the series was simply to rescue me from myself. Could he have dreamt up the whole plan just to lure me back to reality?

Chapter 10

MY SENSE OF guilt about Tara grew worse as we began filming the old maharaja monuments. I knew how much he'd love to have been here, gaping slack-jawed at the ostentatious relics and rummaging through the jewel-plastered inner sanctums of the palaces while the Tiger went about his business siphoning it all on to digital cassettes. It was Tara after all who had turned me on to this story in the first place on our train ride down to Delhi by regaling me with the excesses of the maharajas. These kings and princes of Rajasthan had become so fabulously wealthy by the beginning of the twentieth century that many of them literally went insane.

The Maharaja of Patiala was his favourite. This twenty-stone glutton spent most of the 1920s and 1930s lounging in his ice-chilled pool, occasionally paddling to the side to sip whisky and fondle the bare breast of one of the his 350-strong harem, each of whom was selected for her sexual prowess and made ravishing by a team of plastic surgeons from Europe who were on hand at all times to make alterations in case the maharaja's tastes changed, or he saw a particularly nice face or body in a foreign fashion magazines. He had a laboratory built to formulate new cosmetics and lotions for them, and kept sex therapists busy inventing new sexual positions for them, as well as training them in the classic positions of the Kama Sutra.

With uncanny media savvy, Tara pointed out that the audience at home was bound to be intrigued by this particular aspect of Indian culture. I dismissed the idea at first, thinking an Irish-speaking audience wouldn't need to be enticed into watching cultural documentaries by stories of sordid excesses, but Tara just waggled his head and giggled.

"It is the tits and bums the men all are loving, Mocha-ji. All the men – in Baldoti leper station and even in Highness Queen's grand Buckingham, too. The Himalaya bumps, little foothills or big Nandu Devi peaks. The boys, they love them all. Same, too, for girls – for them, you must tell in your programme about the diddlies. They are so loving it. The girls in Baldoti were so jealous that Sangev loved only me – he had prettiest diddly in all India.

"You must tell about this maharaja I am explaining you – Maharaja of Patiala – and his great parade every year with no clothes on, but a necklace of three thousands of diamonds and his diddly standing up so proud like a cannon of the Gurkha Rifles. Every year is this parade happening, so that his people know he very rich man and very fertile man, too, you see? Fertile like the Ganges floodplain."

The sing-song element of Tara's talk was so inveigling that at times I lost track of what he was saying.

"The Kama and the Sutra is what I am talking about, Mocha-ji," he added, seeing I hadn't kept up.

He explained that after the maharaja had tired of his whole harem, he employed a team of doctors to concoct new aphrodisiacs for him. They tried gold, spices, iron, herbs and pearls, until eventually they found success with a mix of shredded carrot and sparrow brains. It struck me that we were looking for an equivalent for the Irish language – something to give it back its spunk.

When I said this to Tara, he said, "Yes – mickey teasers."

It turned out that the carrot cure didn't really work very well, and as a last resort doctors were summoned from France to irradiate his testicles. Perhaps this was closer to what we were doing: administering radium treatment that would eat away the most malignant rot on the language and keep it alive for another few years.

If so, the example of the Maharaja of Patiala did not make for an optimistic precedent. The treatment had had no effect on him, and he had died soon after, probably because lack of virility was not what ailed him at all, but chronic lassitude. He had indulged himself too much for too long and simply grown bored. Fatally so. The same could be said of the language. As one of the oldest surviving languages on earth, it had simply grown exhausted – to the point of morbidity. Having served us well for thousands of years, it wanted, needed, to be let go. To be replaced by something younger and more suitable. With great selflessness, it had sent us a sprightly upstart in the form of English, and a country of zealot Redcoats who would bribe and threaten and coerce us into speaking it.

Tara had gone on to say that to understand the maharajas I had to keep in mind the diddlies. Just as in early Celtic societies the king's power stemmed from his virility – his ability to make the land fertile – so too was it in India. The most common symbol of this virility were elephants, because, as Tara mimed for me, of their trunks and tusks.

"Big diddlies on legs is what they are," he told me. "If maharaja has many, he can fucky many acres of land and many *lakh* people."

One maharaja had a thousand elephants, all with gold and rubies and diamonds dripping from their ears. Another had a 100-year-old bull who had killed scores of other bulls and had his own harem of hundreds of females. As the century rolled on, Rolls Royces took the place of elephants.

"Like Madam Singh Guli's, only shinier," Tara said. "Elephants with engines. Diddlies that go *vroom*."

The maharajas would usually buy one of each model of Rolls Royce and customise them. Some were converted into off-road hunting vehicles with full camouflage. The Maharaja of Patiala had twenty-seven cars, some gold-plated inside and out, with ivory steering wheels and gold-brocaded upholstery. Yet, eventually, Rolls Royces became passé and were replaced by trains and planes, which were in fact just bigger elephants, only more powerful and more phallic.

A madness, whether in the form of lust or bloodlust or avarice, spread through the kings and princes of India at the time. As usual, it was the British who were the cause. The stability that they had brought to India put an end to the inter-tribal fighting that had occupied the maharajas for centuries, and suddenly they found themselves with vast amounts of unspent wealth which they lavished on themselves. They built thousand-room palaces plastered with gems, carpeted in tiger skins and crammed with dead elephants and panthers. They bought so many diamonds and so much rare treasure that they had to have hills hollowed out to store them all in. And the real rot set in once they got a taste for the delights of Europe and New York at the end of nineteenth century. Rather than filling their ships with vessels of Ganges water as protection against the impurity of the West as they had done, they now filled them with crates of champagne to bring back home with them.

It was the prodigality of the maharajas rather than their indolence that most disgusted Salim-bi, our driver, and it was only with great reluctance that he consented to drive us around the old palaces. He regarded them as tyrants, drunk on the banality of excess. The only character he had any time for was the Nizam de Hyderbad, the richest man in the world in the 1920s, who showed his excesses through his miserliness and lived in a slum-like bedroom in an enormous mansion – the walls dripping with filth, the ceiling with cobwebs, the ground overflowing with ashtrays and a wastebasket he emptied once a year on his birthday. He wore the same greasy pyjamas day and night, and the same dandruff-caked cap for thirty years. In his filthy, mud-filled gardens, he stored trucks full of gold ingots, and his cellars were heaped with sapphires, emeralds, rubies and diamonds piled in mounds like coal. It was estimated that around £10 million worth of rupees were scattered on his floor with rats gnawing through them. The few visitors he allowed in were given one cup of tea with a biscuit and cigarette on the side, which he would finish himself if there was anything left in the butt.

Hearing all the details of the old regime made Salim-bi's skin crawl, and he usually remained at the entrance, polishing his car and trying not to listen to the gatekeepers and retainers telling their old stories. The fact that the maharajas had overthrown the Muslim Moguls was what annoyed him most. His life was defined by Islam, and even the name of his taxi, "Wimpy Cars", boldly emblazoned on his front door, was a subtle jibe at Hindus: reminding them of that ultimate indignity when the burger chain first appeared in Delhi and dared to serve the garrotted carcass of sacred cows in limp baps with fake cheese. The thought of the minced cow flesh moulded into dung cakes and served in public in their sacred city was enough to ignite fury in any zealous Hindu.

In spite of myself, I liked all the stories about the maharajas. Kipling said that God created them to offer us a spectacle; and certainly they never disappointed. They were semi-mythic hedonists whose lives outshone anything Hollywood or Bollywood have managed since. In fact, their excesses make modern celebrities seem gauche in comparison. Tying one's subjects up and using them as live bait in tiger hunts, as one maharaja did, was on a whole different par from throwing TVs out of windows.

It struck me that excessive displays of opulence were something that cultures in their death throes were prone to. After all, it was Ireland's new-found riches that were paying for this series, our windmill jousting trip through India. I suspected that the whole notion of *Teilifís na Gaeilge* might turn out to be a counter-intuitive, pie-in-the-sky folly that would never have been countenanced in leaner times.

Chapter 11

"IN TWO DAYS we have to be on that train to Varanasi," the Tiger announced at breakfast. "First we've got to find some stories. The Janta Manta might fill ninety seconds at a stretch, but what we need now is meat. We need an adventure."

"Ninety seconds!" I said. "Are you kidding?"

"It was a bunch of stones, for God's sake! In truth, I should leave it at forty seconds and then cut to something meaty."

"But it was fascinating," I protested.

"Maybe to you, but I doubt any of the fishermen, farmers and grant administrators will give a damn. Who do think your audience is?"

"We could interview Frau Doktor Lieberman . . ." I suggested.

"Her!" he cried. "You're not serious?"

I laughed it off. I didn't have the will to argue.

"Look, Mocha," the Tiger began, his voice patronisingly slow and soothing, "television is a visual medium – it's fast, it's exciting, it's not radio. What we need here is action. Let's get out into that desert and taste it, you know? Feel it. See what it's made of."

I nodded sullenly.

"Can you do that for me?" he asked brightly. "Can you get us out there – like, far out. I want to feel the wilderness."

I kept my eyes down, rummaging through my notebook, which he took for consent.

"Good man," he said. "I'm going to spend the morning checking the shot tapes, going through them and marking them up. You go and see what you can sort out. Meet back here for lunch – is that a plan?"

I didn't dare reply. I got up from the table with my bag and books, stumbling out into the lobby, my head reeling with this new demand. He wanted to "feel the wilderness" – how the hell was I going to manage that? I knew that Salim-bi would be no help. His car was already showing signs of demise, its post-WWII body panels crumbling under the strain of the massive Japanese engine. The slightest crease in the tarmac set the chassis shuddering. There was no way it could bring us where we needed to go.

I was curled into the perspex phone booth in the lobby searching through my notebook for the number of Peadar, my contact in the Irish embassy, and watching jealously as a waiter brought the Tiger a fresh cappuccino in the morning room, when I noticed Frau Doktor Lieberman making her way down the stairs. I slunk deeper into the phone booth, burying my head into the wall, and fortunately she didn't spot me.

Peadar proved no help at all in offering advice about how to go about "feeling the wilderness", but he did say that he had been on to Reg, the burger man, who had told him that he had heard that Tara had grown withdrawn and listless since my departure. Peadar reassured me, saying that it had been exactly the same at his nephew's boarding school; the headmaster had advised parents to keep away for the first few months to give the boys a chance to settle in. By the second term, they were always having a mighty time, and frequently cried when it was time to go home for Christmas. But I still felt bad and put a call through to the house in Nizamuddin just to check on him.

It was Marat Khan who answered.

"*Namaste*," I said. "*Mocha* here."

"You know there is no contact," she spat.

"I want to talk to Tara for just a second."

She slammed the phone down. When I went to dial again, I saw Salim-bi shuffling through the lobby, beckoning to me, and I replaced the receiver. Curling out from under the telephone booth, I went over to him. His back was bent convex and he was massaging his ribs tenderly with a pained expression.

"It is so good of you and your brother to be paying for my little, little room," he said. "And you are not to be worrying about it is like pig barn and so hard on my sore back. Otherwise, I gladly sleep in Wimpy Car."

"I'm making some calls now," I pointed out.

"Yes," he agreed. "Then we go? I waiting."

"Go where?" I asked.

"My cousin's carpet shop," he said innocently.

"But I never asked to go there."

"Yes, yes, I see; but your brother, he wanting traditional woven carpet very much."

"No, he doesn't!"

"Yes, handcrafted and all very best quality factory dyes."

"No, he doesn't!"

"Oh . . . !" he said, feigning genuine shock.

He sat down with a groan on one of the lion-claw armchairs and said, "Big misunderstanding. I thought you were wanting . . ."

"What we do want," I said, "is to get out into the desert – far out. Can you get us there?"

"Maybe you like bring your ladies nice wall hanging from India?"

"The desert," I said, ignoring him.

"Out into there with sand and nothing?" he cried.

"Exactly."

"No one, not even great Muhammad's stallions of paradise riding the wind can do this thing," Salim-bi declared, his face pink with excitement. "And it is this the reason – the *dacoits*! They are killing and maiming and the goats are slaughtering and the peoples too."

Salim-bi's eyes sparkled beatifically, and his mouth was plastered across his face like the pre-orgasmic characters in the Kama Sutra. I had seen the movie *Bandit Queen* about the woman *dacoit* (desert pirate) who had rampaged through this region for years and was later raped as revenge, but I presumed she was out of action by now; in fact I had heard that she had been freed from prison and was running for office.

"Ten hundred of kidnapping all this year," Salim-bi gushed. "Men, women, children, even everything. Raiding all the peoples – farmers and doctors and government peoples. Even the shepherds they are robbing. If you want to have slickety-slick you go there."

He mimed having his throat slit.

"I see," I said.

He flashed his crossed eyes at me and marched off delirious. I tried phoning the *hijras* again.

When I heard the voice on the other end, my stomach flipped – my mouth actually dropping open like those characters in the cartoons whose jaws hit the ground drooling.

It was Niishraah, the princess.

"Hell – ooo?" she said, with that same shy breathlessness as before, and I was right back in the courtyard with her. Her oil-well eyes and slalom cheeks.

"It's Mocha," I managed.

"Hey! How are you?" she said with effortless enthusiasm. I now noticed the slightest tinge of an American accent; New York, as far as I could tell, but it may have been my imagination.

"Good," I said.

"This is good. Yes, very good to hear."

There followed a long silence as we both contemplated this. I wanted to run away and live with her in the desert. We could fend off the *dacoits* together. I just knew she would be kind and fun and fascinating – how could someone that beautiful not be? I imagined her belly, soft, shapely, with a light fur extending from below.

"Niishraah . . . ?" I said eventually.

"Yes?" she replied with a voice full of wonder and surprise, as though she couldn't imagine what I might be about to ask.

"I'm looking for Tara."

"Oh," she breathed. "Of course."

"Yes!" I found myself agreeing. I couldn't imagine ever disagreeing with her.

"This is such a pity," she said, her voice breaking with empathy. "You know Tara prefers not to talk to anyone now."

"Just a quick word," I pleaded.

"Yes, you want just a quick word," she repeated in a tone resonating with the reasonableness of my request and the intolerability that it could not be fulfilled. "At this time there are no quick words. There can be none, because you see, Tara is out. I am so sorry."

"No problem at all," I found myself assuring her. "Please don't worry. It's not all that important anyhow."

"All that important?"

"Yes. It's not all that . . ."

"Was it important?"

"No," I said.

"Good!" she chimed.

"We're going out into the desert," I said, for no reason other than to continue the conversation. I couldn't face putting the phone down just yet. "To see what we find there. We want adventure. I'm a very adventurous person."

"Oh, yes!" she said.

"I'm told there are *dacoits* out there who will slit our throats . . ."

"Oh, no!" she cried.

"Yes," I assured her.

"Be trusting everyone," she counselled. "Be trusting everywhere."

We went on like that for a while until I suddenly remembered about the work I was supposed to be doing. Reluctantly I put the phone down and went out into the city determined to find what the Tiger was looking for. I wouldn't let him down. First off, I tried the tourist office, but they were worse than useless. All they would talk about was special offers on buffet lunches with free welcoming marigold wreaths for all the guests. Then I tried the local government offices, and asked them to tell me about the most interesting artefacts, animals, geological features and villages in the desert. They sent me to the university, who in turn sent me to one of the development NGOs.

When I got back for lunch two hours later, I was really excited. I knew that the Tiger would be, too. Having rejected numerous offers of jeep rides to dreary old forts and walking tours of interesting-shaped stones, I had found an old man willing to bring us out on camels into the desert to a genuine nomad camp about half a day's ride away. We could even stay there overnight, camping with the nomads, if we were prepared to pay him extra. This was just the sort of genuine off-the-beaten-track experience the Tiger was looking for. I knew he would be pleased.

But when I sat down and tried telling him, he wouldn't let me even open my mouth.

"Why did you never tell me about *sati*?" he asked as I came through the door.

I had no idea what he was on about. I had heard the term before, of course, but I couldn't imagine what it had to do with us. It was the Hindi term for self-immolation – wives throwing themselves on their husbands' funeral pyres.

"It's just what we need," he said. "To find a real family who has actually gone through it, experienced the whole thing. We can interview them, find out about all the whys and hows."

"But I've got you a story, a really good one . . ." I began.

"Great!" he said. "Now, forget it and find this family. Ask around – try the tourist office."

"But *sati* is ancient history," I protested. "It doesn't happen any . . ."

"Ramakant here," he said, pointing to the barman; "Ramakant says it's hushed up now, but it's still going on. This place is a real hotspot. We're in luck!"

Ramakant had a wide smile on his face, and I could just imagine the overgenerous tips the Tiger had been giving him all morning for coffees.

"But I have camels!" I tried again.

"Forget the fucking camels," the Tiger said acidly. "*Sati* is where it's at, all right? Anyway, I need another few hours to catalogue these tapes – I don't ever again want to have to watch back over you twittering on about maharajas and astrological sites again. I'm hoping to log the exact times of each take you manage without screwing it up, and then I'll leave it to the editor to somehow weave something sensible out of the mess. So why don't you head back into town and make some enquiries; see what turns up. We can skip lunch – who needs it anyway in this heat?"

I was back on the streets again heading for the tourist office before I'd even had a chance to taste one of the pastries that he had been gorging on all morning. Of course, the tourist people were no help whatsoever; all they would talk about was their buffet lunches in lovely maharaja palaces that had been converted into hotels. They said I should do a piece on the gyms and conference facilities that many of them were now equipped with. Eventually, I got so frustrated I told them that if they didn't help me I'd do a feature on the 1,000 kidnappings in the area in the past year. That spurred them into calling their supervisor, who came out of a back office with the address of a friend of a friend who had studied gender studies in Delhi and might be able to help.

This woman, Mina was her name, was a real find. Coincidentally, I had read an article by her in the *Hindustan Times* about a case of tandoor-oven killing, and when I told her how excellent it was she blushed. Straight off, she confirmed what I thought: that indeed *sati* was no longer practised and that there had been no documented case of it in the region for years. It had been banned in the nineteenth century and then banned again in 1956 after a renewed spate. A new law was brought in in the 1980s when an eighteen-year-old widow threw herself on her husband's flames, although many claimed that this wasn't a genuine case as she had been forced to jump in by her in-laws who didn't want her inheriting the farm. Ramakant was right that most of the forty or so cases since independence had been in Rajasthan, but as far as Mira knew there were no families living near by with any direct experience, although there were some extremists in Udaipur who wanted the practice reintroduced as a way to discourage wives from poisoning their husbands and then marrying their lovers.

Mina explained that her studies suggested the practice was never a willing one and that the women were often drugged by their in-laws beforehand. In some cases, they were even tied to their husbands' bodies or to a log before being thrown in. The family would chant loudly so that the woman's cries were drowned out.

She confirmed that, whether the practice was voluntary or not, there was no way I was going to find a family in the area with any direct experience of it, or at least one willing to talk about it, and I was able to head back to the hotel with a clear conscience, knowing that I had done my best. The Tiger was still comfortably ensconced in his armchair when I got back, with Ramakant, the meddling barman, still hovering obsequiously near by. I was starving and ordered a plate of masala dosas, but Ramakant ignored me and listened instead to the Tiger, who was slipping him some more loose change and telling him that he doubted he would ever find such great coffee again in all India.

"So, what you got for me?" the Tiger asked.

I tried to hide my annoyance at his smugness. He had clearly had a wonderfully restful day.

"Nothing!," I announced, somewhat too triumphantly. "It was a complete waste of an afternoon."

"You couldn't find a family?" he said jauntily.

"There's no such thing as *sati*," I shot back impatiently. "It died out long ago. It's a non-story! Just give it up. I told you already, I have a great story for you. A story about nomads."

"Ramakant!" the Tiger called out, ignoring me completely. "Oh Ramakant, my friend, please would you mind coming over here and telling Mocha what you were telling me earlier."

It turned out that Ramakant had made some enquiries of his own while I was out and had turned up a partial case of *sati* that had happened in a neighbouring village just a year before. The woman was pulled out of the flames in time and brought to hospital, and although she suffered some bad burns, she had recovered well. She had since moved back to her parents' family and was goatherding out in the desert somewhere. The Tiger suggested we try and track her down.

"But we need to get a vehicle," he said, "ideally a good jeep."

This was typical of the Tiger. He was always blessed with this type of luck. I would struggle and strain for something for ages, and he'd just be handed it on a plate. I could spend an hour trying to find parking in town, and he'd arrive late and pull up right outside. He knew how to sit still and let the world come to him. It was down to his ability to burn more brightly, to chew up life so intensely: somehow the world responded in kind.

"Wow!" he exclaimed out of the blue. "Of course, I should have thought about it before! I've just had a eureka moment – let's not use a jeep; let's find camels! Mocha, can we find camels? Can you go and find me some, do you think?"

I gaped open-mouthed.

"What do you reckon?" he said. "Isn't it a great idea? Trekking through the desert on camels – like Lawrence of Arabia."

I breathed to calm the anger rising inside me. When I was sure I could talk calmly again, I said, "Did you not hear me earlier? I told you I found a man with camels."

"You told me?" he said. "I don't think so. You should have told me, Mocha. That sort of thing is important!"

Chapter 12

OUTSIDE THE HOTEL at dawn the following day stood Ramchand, a swarthy boy with slightly bandy legs, who had with him three skeletal camels dressed in heavily decorated blankets and throne saddles that failed to hide the chronic mange on their flanks. Each was spancelled with a rope tied to its hocks and looped over the shoulder. The Tiger chose the one that slavered the least, Ramchand's bag was slung over the second, and I was left with the bucking, spitting runt. Once Ramchand had spat the remainder of his betel-nut breakfast out on the pavement in imitation of his camels and carefully wrapped his brown scarf into the undulations of his cotton shirt and pyjama bottoms, he led us out into the empty streets. We trekked though the morning smog to the outskirts of Jaipur with him explaining to us that the goatherds Ramakant had talked of lived deep in the desert, and it would take the best part of a day to reach them. We would have no option but to spend the night there and agree to pay him considerably more. We agreed on condition that he didn't complain whenever we stopped to do some filming.

It took an hour before the last signs of habitation and tarred road petered out and we found ourselves in a vacuum of panoramic nothingness, like the burning white-out that represented heaven in movies. The camels' rolling, pitching, bumping motion took some getting used to, but it wasn't long before we began to feel at ease and rather good about ourselves. I thought about the extra depth and resonance there was to things because of sharing them with one's brother. It struck me that I was really lucky, although it was hard to remain conscious of it all the time. I was lucky he chose me. He could have found some TV bimbo instead, and I would be back in my hovel or in the hypermarket in Germany stacking shelves for some dimwit boss.

As the sun rose higher in the sky and the desert opened out into an eerie landscape of dirty swathes of meringue running towards the horizon, the Tiger said he wanted to capture it on film, and we pulled up to allow him to dismount.

"See that rock over there?" he said to me after assessing the scene. "Head over there and wait till I call you, then walk straight to camera, okay?"

"Uh-huh," I sighed, pulling at the reins to get the camel to drop to its knees.

I didn't feel good about it, and, as though sensing my unease, the camel let out a dinosaurian whine and locked its knees until Ramchand beat it into relenting. Walking shots were never easy. I had got a handle on the rest of the stuff – the long, wistful stares into the middle distance; the interviews with locals; the dramatic close-ups of my eyes ranging over the landscape. Even talking to the convex void of the camera lens was becoming easier. In fact, I actually enjoyed that now – I loved how it never interrupted or lost interest. It allowed me to explain myself without judging. Walking was the only thing I still couldn't get my head around.

Like everyone else, I had learnt as a toddler to coordinate my arms and legs to enable movement, and as far as I was concerned, I had been managing adequately ever since. But the moment the Tiger pointed a camera at me, it all went wrong. It was as if the puppeteer had suddenly got drunk and was sending Pinocchio careering around the stage. My arms began to flap, and the slight slouch that had developed when I had shot up in adolescence now became Quasimodo-like. The Tiger would scream at me in impatience, which only made things worse. I'd become self-conscious then and rigor mortis would set in, as though the puppet had got wet and its limbs had seized. Some days when I was feeling really relaxed and confident, I could pull it off, but today I was saddle-sore and weary, and I knew things wouldn't go well.

The Tiger walked me through what he wanted. All I had to do was head straight for the camera and pass it on the left without knocking into the tripod. He got me to practise a few times while he tried out different lenses. I did my best to stay relaxed, but the minute the camera was turned on, I found myself counting every footfall and jerking my neck frantically from side to side, trying to decide how my facial expression would look normally and in which direction I would be looking.

We did the shot four or five times, with the Tiger growing more impatient each time. I could see it was hard on him. The sun had risen higher and was bearing down tyrannously on us, making it feel as though we were wading through freshly poured tar. And while the little camera was enjoying the honeyed, sepia glow that the light gave everything, poor Tiger was sweating heavily. The rivulets of his sweat were, most likely, working their way into the camera, bringing with them the film of dust that cloaked everything and caking the insides until eventually the whole thing would seize and it would be all my fault. The worry of it made my walking even stiffer.

Finally, he lost patience and turned the camera off and told me to run around a while to relax.

"And while you're at it," he said, "pull that bloody broom pole out of your ass."

I was determined to get it right for him, and after I had jumped up and down a bit and shaken my arms, I told him I was ready. I had wasted five minutes of tape already.

"Rolling," he announced, and I set off from the stone, humming quietly to myself to distract my mind.

"Stop," he cried. "What's up with your mouth?"

"Nothing."

"You're doing something."

"No, nothing."

"Well, stop it."

I tried again, but I was so conscious of not humming that I tripped over. The Tiger let out a cry and kicked the tripod.

"Christ!"

A child could have done what he wanted. A chimpanzee. A well-trained rabbit.

"What the hell has walking got to do with India anyway?" I lashed out. "We're meant to be looking at the people and culture, not me."

I stormed off.

"Where are you going?" he roared.

"Back on the camel."

"No, you're not! Get back here and walk."

I ignored him and reached for the camel.

"I'm warning you! Don't touch that camel. Get over here and do the fucking shot."

Ramchand was looking on embarrassed. I glowered at him, and he turned away and walked off a few paces.

I looked hard between the Tiger and the camel, weighing up my options. In the end it was dogged frustration that made me go back to the rock, to try one last time. I was so angry by then that there was no way I could have walked nonchalantly. I came storming at the camera as though leading a charge.

The Tiger cut the camera.

"You moron!" he screamed. "I mean, for God . . ."

I could see he was angry. Really angry. So angry he was frightened of what he might do or say. He walked away a few steps, making a long loop around the camels, tearing at his hair as he went.

"Okay, here is what we're going to do," he said. "From now on I'm going to film only your eyes and your feet. I'll film them separately, and we can edit them later to make it look like you're walking. No one will ever know . . . it'll work, believe me."

"Thanks," I said, sulking.

"Yeah," he repeated through a tight mouth. "I'm going to set the camera really low, and you're to walk straight towards it, okay? It doesn't matter what your arms and face are doing; I'll see only the sandals."

He lowered the tripod and lay down in the sand. I was looking at him as he knelt and swept the stones from under him. I don't remember why I was looking, but I was. I think I was trying to decide whether he really meant it or not. Was he going to film all of me, and was this just a ploy to make me relax?

Whatever the reason, I was watching him, and I saw the thing come crawling out from underneath the rock. A shiny brown body and twelve eyes casting wildly about in all directions, adjusting itself to the unwelcome light. I could see its armoured segments reaching back from the two pinchers which were open and snapping at the empty air. The segments on the abdomen led back to a tail which was now curling up, brandishing its stinger, a hollow needle primed with poison. It was raising itself to striking height, whipping the stinger back and forth with cruel precision. I tried to call out to my brother, to warn him, but before I had even summoned the words, his hand came down on the ground right on top of it.

He jumped back up as though electrocuted, and for a split second I could see the two surfaces, his fingertip and the scorpion's stinger, tugging apart – the barbed point extracting itself from his skin, from the grooves of his fingerprint. There was resistance, like between a meniscus and the glass. I was aware of the crab-like pinchers grappling with the ground trying to pull itself free. The Tiger let out a shattering scream, and the scorpion managed to cut loose and dashed across the sand. It must have been a female, as clinging to her back were a dozen babies, whipping back and forth as she ploughed through the sand. I stood frozen in pure fear for a second until I heard him call out and then I came running. He was collapsed on the ground, curled into a foetal position, shuddering.

I looked to Ramchand in panic, but he hadn't noticed a thing and was still staring discreetly away, trying not to notice that our argument had escalated to violence.

"Ramchand!" I screamed.

He looked around, took in the situation and came sprinting over. The Tiger's eyes were darting about every direction in confusion; his brain trying to work out where he was, who he was. He had grown very pale, and his facial muscles were twitching as though he really had been electrocuted. I knelt over him and held him, feeling the spasms running through his body. The blood in his veins felt like rivers thrashing in a storm. He reminded me of a live power cable.

"Ramchand!" I cried again, this time in real despair. Tears were running down my cheeks.

"What was it?" he said. He was looking at the sand all around him.

"Scorpion," I said.

"Scorpion?" he repeated.

"Yes!"

"You sure it was scorpion?"

"Yes," I shouted.

"Then, no problem," he laughed merrily. "Scorpion is no problem. I thought it was *hamsha* ant. Good it's not *hamsha*. *Hamsha* is painful as a bullet and sends out a love smell attracting all other *hamshas* . . . I don't see any more ants coming. I think it was not *hamsha*. Scorpion is just like big bee. Sore for a while."

I pointed at the Tiger who was still curled over, too traumatised to hear.

"His face is twitching," I said.

"Yes, yes. Face twitches, tummy vomits, but no dying. Believe me, I am often stung. It's like piece of prickles. Give him water."

I dug out my water bottle and held it to his lips. I noticed his hand was beginning to swell and turn somewhat blue, but no worse than a bad wasp sting.

"Should I suck it?" I asked.

"Just water is fine," Ramchand said.

But I sucked his finger a few times anyway and spat it out. His eyes were closed. I thought back to the time when I was eight years old and he had kicked me down the stairs, and I pretended I was dead, breathing a few final, rasping breaths before falling completely limp. He had let out a cry of panic, grasping me to him and cradling me on his lap, just as I was doing now, and crying hoarsely for my parents to come and help. I stayed dead for a cruel length of time before opening an eye and grinning up at him. He had looked so relieved at that moment, whimpering in consternation, before wandering off to deal with the shock. Looking down at him now, all I could hope for was the same, that he'd open one eye.

"What the hell?" he said finally, stirring himself and looking around.

"Scorpion," I said.

"Jesus!"

"Are you okay?"

"Did you kill it?" he asked.

"No," I said, "I was more worried about you. Ramchand says you'll be fine."

"You should have killed it."

"Sorry," I said, and put the water to his lips again. He fell into a reverie, and I thought I should say something, just to keep him awake or conscious or whatever.

"Look," I began hesitantly, "I'm sorry."

"Huh?" he said, opening his eyes and becoming aware of me again.

"For screwing it up. For making things so difficult."

"Forget it," he said and lay back to rest. His body seemed to have got over the worst and he was no longer shaking.

"No, really," I said.

"You're not screwing anything up," he said, opening his eyes again. "You're just being you – there's nothing wrong with that . . . It's why I wanted you in the first place."

"Huh?"

He lay back again and the tension eased from his eyes. He flexed his hand a few times, testing it. The swelling was already going down. A wave of relief washed over the two of us, and I could see him grow elated.

"It's why I wanted you in the programme, you fool," he said. "So people could see you. It's why I came the whole way out here."

"Yeah, right," I said, thinking he was being sarcastic.

"Just 'cause you can't walk doesn't make you crap," he said. "In fact, it's what I love about you. There's no pretence. There's a million bloody show-offs I could have got who could have juggled plates as they walked if that was what I wanted. But I wanted you. I wanted people to get to know you, hear what you have to say. You're weird, but I'm proud of you. You do your own thing."

"Oh," I managed. I feared I might cry.

"Just do me one favour."

"Sure," I said.

"Get the scorpion for me."

"It's too late," I said. "It's gone."

"Just get it and kill it," he said in a calm, weary voice. "Just do that."

"How?"

"I don't know," he said, slightly impatiently. "Find it. We might need to know what type it is, for an anti-serum or whatever."

"But you're fine," I said.

"Just . . ." he ordered, his neck tensing.

"Okay, okay," I said, backing away.

"Take the tripod with you," he said. "Or, better still, you can have my Leatherman."

He reached into his pocket and dug out his precious multi-tool penknife. It was the first time he had allowed me to touch it. I knew I couldn't refuse.

I set out in the direction I had last seen her go, flicking stones over with the tripod as I went. I had thought of telling the Tiger about the babies on her back, but decided he didn't want to know. I put the fact out of my mind, as I scanned every square centimetre of desert within the immediate vicinity, then slowly and meticulously spread out like a tracker in a manhunt. It took only ten minutes before I found her. She was cowering beneath a large slab of sandstone, curled up beside a centipede. Her tail was slower to rise this time, her reactions less aggressive. She was obviously worn out and made no attempt to run or hide, but instead tried spreading herself flatter against the ground. I considered smashing her with the tripod right away, but remembering the Leatherman, I pulled it out of its pouch and opened the pliers. She tried bravely to sting the stainless steel pinchers and even flipped herself over to attack them with her own frail pinchers, but she was completely outclassed. I closed the pliers on her until I heard her exoskeleton crack. Her eight legs were still beating through the air as I picked her up, rowing like a sculling boat over a waterfall, her twelve eyes darting frantically around. She jerked and flailed the whole way back to the Tiger, her babies clinging on for dear life.

My brother had his Swiss Army knife ready and waiting, and I held her down with the Leatherman while he inspected her.

"Yeah, that's her all right," he said. "We won't be seeing her again."

He ran the Swiss Army knife back and forth over her tail a few times, until it slid between the armour and sliced right through. He flicked the tail away a few feet, as if there were some chance of its reconnecting with the body and coming after him again.

"That's grand," he said, collapsing back on the sand. "You can do the rest."

He handed me the Swiss Army.

"What rest?" I asked.

"The babies."

I hesitated, about to argue, but he gave me such a look that I realised this was about more than just the babies. It was a test. I took a firm hold of the knife and proceeded to pick off each squirming insect. I killed them one by one. The mother's torso was still moving; her right pincher had fallen off, but her left one was still opening and closing automatically.

"Now the legs," Ramchand said when I had got through them all.

"What?" I said.

"The legs," he said. "Cut her legs off."

"Isn't it a bit much?" I said.

"Much?" Ramchand chortled. "Not compared to what she did."

"It was self-defence," I said.

"No, not that," Ramchand said. "Where is the father?"

"There was no father. Only her," I said.

"Yes, I know," he said.

"So why ask?" I snapped.

"I'm not asking. I'm telling. Father is not here – he is in there."

"What?"

"Father," Ramchand repeated. "Father of babies, he is inside."

"What are you on about?" I said.

"You do not know?" he said. "Scorpion ladies, they eat their men after sex. Fucking and then eating. Yum-yum. It is always like this."

"You're saying she ate her mate?"

"Yes, chewed him up limb by limb, but not the shell perhaps. Now she is learning what it feels like."

Chapter 13

WE RESTED FOR an hour until the Tiger got his strength back, and then we headed on, finally reaching the goatherds at dusk. It was too late to film anything, but there would be plenty of time in the morning, and it was good to have a chance to get to know them beforehand. It was the children who spotted us first, rushing out of the camp to greet us, surrounding me, notching into one another like crows on a carcass. I sat down on a rock so as not to be looming over them, and they closed in tighter, peering on tiptoes and craning their necks. They weren't looking at me so much as staring entranced, hypnotised by my features, my glasses, my hands, as if I were an entirely different species: a grotesque alien, larval and beanpole tall.

One boy pulled at my glasses, and when his mother noticed, she ran shyly forward and gave him a slap. She wore a black veil picked out in red dots and had a child strapped in a papoose on her back. She asked Ramchand what we were doing here, so far from anywhere, and he explained that we wanted to learn about *sati*. Her mother and aunts came up behind her, all dressed in black and wearing the family's wealth in the form of heavy bands of silver around their ankles and bangles of cheaper silver up their elbows. Behind them were more young girls with silver stitched into the seams of their printed cotton dresses and hanging in rings from their blouses.

There was only one man in the camp, a frail figure with a deformed spine and a wiry grey moustache like dead reeds on the shore. He came limping towards us, greeting us in the traditional way with his hands clasped to his heart and gesturing for us to join him at the hammered-out bonnet that served as his workshop. He showed us the tiny flowers and insects of tin that he was making and explained through Ramchand that he was in training now to be a great tinsmith in his next life. The women came and sat around us with their sewing materials and listened quietly to the man as they sewed patches of broken mirror into an embroidered cloak.

We asked him about the tradition of *sati*, and he said it was just one of many old customs that were important to his people at one time. If this were a settled person's house, he said, seemingly as a non sequitur, and not a nomadic camp, the women would be holed up in a back kitchen and would never get to see a male visitor, and certainly not share tea around the fire with them. Openness and equality was another old tradition that was important to them, he clarified. The women burst into embarrassed giggles at this, hiding their gold teeth with their hands. The mother who had slapped her child seemed somewhat bolder than the rest and said that she pitied settled women, and that as long as she had her water and fire-wood collected and food prepared, she could do as she wished. The hunchbacked man went on to explain that *sati* was about ultimate sacrifice, and that the rest of the world had forgotten what that meant. We were too self-absorbed to imagine true love.

"In the West you believe too much in life," he said. "You forget it's an illusion. *Sati* isn't painful; pain is just a figment of the mind. With a little practice of *yoga* or meditation, we can turn it on and off."

He explained that until you actually saw a widow's eyes glazing over with ecstasy as the flames enveloped her, you wouldn't understand. You had actually to be there to see the honour in the faces of her family, who in turn would be blessed with fortune for seven generations, to appreciate the ritual fully.

Ramchand said that in his own mother's village the police had tried to stop an old widow from sitting on the flames of her husband's pyre, until her sons and the neighbours attacked them with stones, and they had ended up arresting fifteen people in the ensuing mêleé. There had been another case before that where a widow wanted to commit *sati* and the local government had tried to stop her. Her neighbours had paid for a continuous supply of *ghee*, coconuts and wood to keep her husband's funeral pyre burning until the matter was resolved.

Our host insisted that it was a failure in us if we couldn't appreciate it. For centuries his people had been practised the tradition of *jauhur*, in which, in the face of certain defeat, the men would ride out to battle to be slaughtered by their enemy while their wives and children threw themselves on giant pyres back home. For them *jauhur* was a matter of great pride and honour. It was our loss if we couldn't see that. Normally I found it easy to accept the practices of foreign cultures, but *sati* and *jauhur* seemed a step too gruesome. Ramchand tried to insist that it wasn't cruel. It was done out of compassion for the women and children, who wouldn't have survived long in any event without their men. But I just couldn't see past the vision of the children being led by their mothers into the flames.

We went on talking until the rest of the men came trickling home with their animals around nightfall and the women began to busy themselves preparing rice and vegetables. The women were more reluctant to talk to us now and wanted to wait until their leader, Samshul, got back. He was off scouting for fresh grazing and arrived home only an hour or so later. He sat down on a *charpoy* beside us, lifting a bandoleer of bullets from around his chest and smiling with his wide, bulbous lips, which reminded me of two rain-engorged slugs. A woman infested with lice and fleas and with a beautiful gold brooch in her hair offered him *chai* and a bunch of coriander, which he proceeded to chew on while assuring us that he was happy to talk about anything we wished once he had had his dinner. He said that his people would love to learn more about us and where we came from, too. A scrawny goat covered in sores ambled over to chew at the coriander and rub itself against my thigh. The Tiger was desperate to film it all, but there was so little light. The camera was a first-generation digital Sony without enough processing power to handle low levels. Besides, Ramchand pointed out, there was no point in filming me having dinner as I wouldn't be eating with them. They preferred if we ate separately, away from the fire, so as not to contaminate their food.

I was a bit anxious about how we would present the tribe on film. I didn't want it to appear as though we were focusing on *sati* for any sensationalistic reason. The act of filming a tribe, particularly an isolated, nomadic one whom we could never truly understand, was fraught with possible misunderstandings. I didn't want our preconceptions to get in the way. And what Frau Doktor Lieberman had said about the trust-worthiness of the camera lens made me question the intentions of the camera, its motivations. I know this might sound crazy, but I worried that the microchip inside the unit might have its own agenda. At the back of my mind was the memory of the distrust with which cameras were regard-ed by most primitive societies, who feared that they had harmful powers. Our one-chip Sony xcl certainly was able to see and hear, and even think to a degree. How could we be sure its awareness didn't go further than that? I suppose, what I'm saying is that I had always believed that all life was imbued with consciousness, and that by extension I was the creator of my own reality, and if this were the case, was my consciousness infusing the reality that the camera saw? Or if not, whose consciousness was?

It was a valid concern, particularly in light of the fact that the camera was already showing preferences for certain light and landscapes. Certain sequences of motion appealed to it more than others, and its commitment to recording sound was at best idiosyncratic – reducing some of my words to indecipherable squeaks while capturing others with faultless precision. Its choices at times were suspiciously partisan. For example, to capture the scene of a buffalo cart passing through a Hindu temple, it had strained to Olympian levels of photometry to overcome the low-light conditions, yet it hadn't even bothered acknowledging my presence standing behind the cart talking directly to the lens at the time. It was things like this that first aroused my suspicions, and I began to suspect that if the camera did have a mind of its own, it was clearly biased against me.

Don't get me wrong, I'm not making any outlandish claims here; it's just that the microprocessor inside the camera could think only in simple dualistic terms. Its awareness was confined to a crude reality of zeros and ones, and so it was feasible that it might have got confused at times when faced with the infinite dimensions of Indian daily existence. To put it sim-ply, I wanted to find out if the camera was a bee or a scorpion: was it dili-gently serving its queen and nourishing us all with its honey, or was it a post-coital cannibal that poisoned everyone it touched?

It was the first in a whole new generation of digital video cameras which had never been exposed to places like this before, and it had been programmed in some lab in Okinawa or California where the anomalies and conundrums that are a daily part of Indian life had never before been contemplated. I felt it was important that we remained aware of this, that we took it into account. That's all I'm saying.

As the dishes were being taken away that evening after dinner and washed in the sand by the women, the Tiger was setting up his microphones, hoping to record at least a few songs from the group on to a minidisk. He was having great difficulty explaining to one of the men, who the leader had said was a great singer, that all he needed to do was sing into the tiny foam ball clipped to his tunic. The man couldn't accept the idea that his voice would travel across space through radio waves and into the minidisk. The Tiger had laid out the transceiver and receiver on the sand and was demonstrating with his packet of cigarettes how the voice would enter the tiny holes in the foam microphone muffler and travel down the wire into the transceiver and from there through space to the other. To be honest, I was pretty impressed by the radio microphones myself. They were like audio versions of Bhartrihari. I was constantly causing my brother anguish in the first few days by leaving them switched on when clearing my throat or going to the lavatory. I'd sometimes be off muttering to myself about the injustice of it all and would suddenly hear the Tiger shouting across at me that he could hear every word I was saying. The singer was just coming to terms with the recording equipment when a rider came galloping into the camp, beckoning to the leader, who led him off to one side. We all waited as they talked, and when the leader came back he let out a loud call. Immediately everyone stood up and began dismantling the camp around us, leaving us simply looking around in bafflement. The timber crane over the fire was kicked apart, the tents were taken down and their burlap sides folded into long rolls, the fencing for the goat pens was snapped in pieces and tied to the saddles along with the pans and jugs. Kettles were emptied and bundled up in blankets. Rugs were tied with twine. We looked to Ramchand in concern, but he had no idea what was going on.

I got him to approach the leader, who explained that a sudden rainstorm had struck in the hills far away, where some of their goats were grazing. If they didn't set off right away, the goats would be washed away once the river flooded.

"But what about us?" I cried.

Ramchand translated for me, but the leader didn't have time to discuss it and was already off supervising the fettering of some frisky goats. Within minutes, the site was almost bare, and the tent poles which had seemed so fixed and solid were now hanging from the camels' shanks, wrapped in flour sacks to stop them chaffing. The woman with the golden brooch was going around checking things, and once she was sure everything was packed, she kicked sand on to the fire, plunging us into darkness. A loud call went up that spurred the camels and goats into movement, and they began to file out into the abyss.

The Tiger was making a last-ditch effort to wrest the microphone from the singer. He had just got his mind around the potential uses it could be put to and wasn't keen to let it go. But this was state-of-the-art Sennheiser equipment, more expensive even than the camera, which TnaG had only reluctantly forked out for because the Tiger was going to be doing everything himself – sound, camera, directing. There was no way we could let him keep it. I think the resentment he felt over this might have been the reason the others were happy to ignore the plight we were being left in. Ramchand tried to speak to them, but they were reluctant to offer us any advice.

We were just left there, watching the herd filing off, the laden camels lolloping slowly across the sand, listing precariously from side to side with their heavy loads. I was sure that at any moment they would keel over, but they kept going, gradually getting further away until all we could hear was the cowry shell bells on the girls' ankles and the odd groan of a disgruntled animal. We found ourselves completely alone in the desert in the dead of night.

Ramchand glanced around in a mixture of bemusement and concern; he pulled out a hip-flask and offered us some. We looked at each other speechlessly. I took the flask. There was no argument really. We had forced ourselves upon these people who were so connected with their surroundings that they had to follow its every whim. Unlike settled people, they had never tamed the land and instead lived from day to day reacting to whatever nature brought. Today was a threat of flood in some far-off valley, and they had had to respond. It was a matter of life or death. They had to rescue the goats. If it could be said that meetings with tribal people anywhere were a bit like a trip to the zoo, then this time the animals had got out of the cage and left us in their place.

All I could think about were the *dacoits*, the gangs of desert pirates who sought out the vulnerable. Of more pressing concern, however, was how to get home. While Ramchand knew his way in daylight, he was a city boy at heart and had no idea how to read the stars. In reality, he was as lost as we were. We tried rousing our camels, but they were reluctant to leave the fading sanctuary of the embers. When we did eventually get them up, they wanted only to follow the other animals deeper into the desert, and it took tremendous effort to turn them around. We pulled and pushed until finally we got them to set off more or less in the direction of home.

We hadn't gone far before we began having serious doubts about where we were headed. It was impossible to know if we were drifting off course, but none of us dared to put this into words. I was about to say something when I heard a noise up ahead. It was coming from the ground and sounded suspiciously like some form of reptile, not that I would really know the sounds of many reptiles. I was surprised that one would be out at night – I presumed cold-blooded animals needed sun. As long as we stayed on the camels, we were safe enough, I thought – although presumably if it were a snake, it could bite the camels just as easily. Ramchand shouted to scare it off, but the Tiger hushed him and dug his arm into the camera bag, throwing me a floodlight and signalling me to light it as soon as the camera was ready. It was a battery-operated one with enough power for only a few minutes of intense light, and we had never actually used it before. At his signal, I switched it on and the desert suddenly lit up, blinding us all. By the time my eyes had accustomed themselves, I could see no sign of the snake, but I found my brother dismounted and walking around with the camera, shooting the emptiness around him. Within minutes, the battery died and we were plunged back into darkness again. The Tiger had to fumble his way back to the camel and pack up the gear in the dark. He was annoyed at our run of bad look, first missing the *sati* story and now the snake. He had barely got enough shots out of the day to string even a short sequence together. I thought now wasn't the time to mention the fact that we had no idea where we were headed; better just to keep moving.

"*Táimid chun caint as Gaeilge as seo amach,*" the Tiger said determinedly.

"What?" I asked.

"From now on, let's use only Irish," he said again (in Irish).

"Why?" I said.

"Isn't it obvious?" he said (still speaking Irish). "It's why everything is going against us. 'Cause of the hypocrisy. We're making a series trying to help the language, and yet we're not speaking a word of it."

Or at least, that's what he tried to say. The Tiger's Irish was a bit rusty. He found it hard to convey complex ideas. He certainly didn't know the word for hypocrisy. I pointed out to him that it was hypocritical even to pretend we were doing any of this for the sake of the language. It was becoming clear to me that he might have been using the trip just as a stepping stone in his career. He had always loved film and television, but had never managed to get his hands on a camera until now. For him it was a timely opportunity.

"Let's not dress it up in any false heroics," I said. "You're here for the experience, and me? I don't know why I'm here. I seem to be the lead player in a myth about the language being still a viable organism, still in use in odd corners of the world. My role is as the last dodo, speaking Irish to the camera in odd locations. I'm happy to do it, but it would feel really odd talking Irish to you."

"*Cúpla focail anois agus arís*," he cajoled. "That's all I'm saying."

"It would just feel odd," I repeated. "The last time we spoke Irish was when we were kids."

"*Ach, cad mar gheall ar shochraid Síghle* [my grandmother]?" he reminded me.

"Okay, so maybe at her funeral," I agreed, "but . . ."

"Look, we've been given this opportunity," he said, turning back to English, "and whatever you think about the language, without it you and I wouldn't be here – so can't you just do this one thing?"

"Fine," I said. "You really think the gods will smile on us? I'm not even sure they want the language to survive. They haven't been showing it any favours. Stopping the British outlawing it in schools a century ago would have helped a lot, don't you think? Maybe they actually wanted it to die. Maybe *it* wants to die, and we're just pulling it back from the . . ."

"All I'm asking is that we use a few words now and again: simple things like *rolling*, and *do it again*, and *come forward on the count of five*, okay?"

"But there's always someone else with us," I pointed out. "A driver or guide or whatever. They'll need to understand, too."

"So? We'll teach them – just a few words. They'll love it."

"Umh," I said.

We continued on for another mile or so, slowly introducing Ramchand to the rudiments of Irish filming vocabulary. *Táimid ag scannánaíocht* – we're filming. *Déan arís é* – do it again. *Stad, a amadán* – stop, you fool. Until we were suddenly stopped in our tracks by another noise, a roar pounding down from the sky, riding the air like ripples. The camels grew nervous and bayed back up at it. The Tiger and I were too weary at this stage to know what was happening. Suddenly above us three huge blue-tinged balls of light appeared. Two of them swivelled like insect eyes, while the third bore straight down upon us. The beams lit up an uneven patch around us, and we stopped dead, reining the camels hard as they tried cowering towards the ground as though in a sandstorm. I had visions of gods and aliens as an operatic rhapsody of light and sound bore down on us like the *Titanic* sinking. It was only when the sands began to rise around me that I realised it must be a helicopter. It landed barely ten feet away. When the skids hit the sand, two men got out and ran towards us. They were from the Indian Police Force – anti-*daalit* section, searching for a gang of goat rustlers. They had got reports of our floodlight, mistaken it for flares and come searching immediately. It was a huge disappointment for them to find only us. They were hoping for smugglers – international ones preferably, bringing guns from China to Pakistan – which would have brought them accolades and bonuses. As it was, they lost interest in us fast.

"We're not sure where we are," the Tiger told them. "We're trying to get back to the city."

Something about this they found very amusing, and they sniggered into their police-issue moustaches.

"There is very little we can do," one of them said. "The helicopter is too small for all of you. A few miles ahead you should find a settlement or something. You can rest there. If you like, we can radio ahead to them."

"That would be great."

"Yes, yes," the man agreed, and with that, the pilot accelerated the rotors and the helicopter began to lift off again.

We just had time to wave before they were up and away, leaving us there hoping that there really was a settlement ahead and that he had been able to contact them. It was about fifteen minutes later, just when our eyes were becoming accustomed to the darkness again, that an enormous Land Cruiser came bounding across the sand. Two men in white *dhotis* and puffer jackets got out, one taking hold of the camel reins and leading them off into the darkness while the other instructed us to sit into the jeep and drove off in the direction of the settlement. He didn't say a word, just drove straight towards a long line of wall that rose up out of the sand.

Ramchand tried asking where we were going, but the driver just cleared his throat gruffly, which Ramchand translated for us as "safe place".

At the settlement we were shown into a simple mud room lined with hand-stitched quilts and a black-roped *charpoy*, and told that the owner would see us in the morning. I fell asleep on the earth floor rolled up in a grand appliquéd quilt.

In the morning, I looked out and saw that we were in the gate lodge of a reasonably elegant stone house with a broad tower on its side. The driver came in with buckets of water and led me to a corner of the yard behind the lodge, where he said I could wash. A nylon sheet hung across one side. The rest was fully open, visible for at least 120 degrees of the 360, mostly the house side. I was shielded from the wilderness and laid bare to the house. I washed as best I could, trying to scrub the stink of camel sweat from my skin, and had just dried myself when the man came back with the Tiger and Ramchand and told us that once we'd washed he'd bring us to meet the master.

We were led through the well-maintained gardens, which were kept lush by a complex network of irrigation channels. Neat allotments of millet and cabbage framed the pathway. On a bench outside the grand hallway, which looked cavernous and austere, sat a frail old man in a silk dressing gown, with a nurse. The driver introduced him as Prahlad Jolly Kakkar. He said that he had been a minor maharaja until the government finally outlawed all titles in the 1970s. He asked us what we were doing here, but when we tried to tell him, his mind wandered and he couldn't quite keep up. A servant came out with a pitcher of lime juice and a tin of Fortnum and Mason biscuits, and set up a table in front of us.

Jolly Kakkar chewed on a Viennese whirl and, in a beautifully crisp Oxford accent, asked his nurse repeatedly if his guests had slept well that night. He ignored my efforts to reassure him that we had, and instead rambled on about various topics, at one point looking the Tiger straight in the eye and saying, "You remind me of somebody, but I can't for the blazes . . ."

He drifted off and his nurse adjusted his pillow.

I told him that we had been filming around Jaipur, naming some of the forts and palaces we'd visited.

"Nobody knows how difficult it was," he replied. "At one time we ruled the world – now look. We sacrificed everything for Mother India. Committed mass *jauhur* one last time. Yet still they sneer."

He found this funny and burst into peals of laughter, then suddenly stopped, transferring his gaze to a glass-eyed tiger standing just inside the door. It was moulting badly and had signs of maggot damage. As though he were talking directly to it, he said, "I admit we may have been passion-ate, excessive even, but remember, most of us were small fry – we had tiny patches, a few fields at most. We were doing no harm."

I couldn't imagine this twinkle-eyed man as ever being excessively priapic or grossly indulgent, and yet his driver had implied that he had been one of the really wild ones. You just never could tell. It was as if a bout of lunacy had struck all the maharajas during those years, like a buf-falo stampede or a whale beaching. It was inexplicable and illogical. They became drunk on gold like late-season wasps. Prahlad Jolly Kakkar began to shiver, and his nurse wrapped a cape around his shoulders, helped him to his feet and led him indoors. We watched him shuffling off down a long corridor of polo trophies and panther skins.

I realised that I was watching an evolutionary dead end taking its leave. Not all species require a comet or a global catastrophe to become extinct; some are wiped out simply because they're the wrong idea to begin with. The era of the maharajas had much in common with other pivotal periods of excess, like the Italian Renaissance, early Christianity, the Pythagorean period in Croton, 1960s California. All involved a temporary resurgence of Orphic ideals where people abandoned themselves to a mutant expression of their true feelings: to Chaos, to Eros, to the delights of the Garden of Eden. After each came a backlash by conservative forces, and people were burnt at the stake or thrown on pyres. It could be said that Ireland experienced its own bout of hysteria with the Celtic Revival and the uprising against Britain. We became drunk on the concept of blood sacrifice – willing to ride out into battle in the face of certain death for the honour of our country. Our own *jauhur*. What else could have inspired my great-granduncle to polish his boots, wax his moustache and kiss his pregnant wife goodbye before riding out to be killed in the Easter Rising? Nowadays the Irish language is our last relic of that delirium of the Celtic Revival, and it too was committing *sati*, with my brother and me fumblingly trying to pull it from the flames.

Chapter 14

THE TRAIN RIDE to Varanasi was spoiled only by the sight of so many families defecating on the clinker along the way. It seemed that railway lines were the public latrines of India. At one point, I saw a whole family, from granny to baby, relieving themselves on the same sleeper, and I wondered how many people must die each year in such circumstances. The Tiger was relieved to have escaped Rajasthan with the camera intact. The earth, which had been ploughed, eaten, shat out, thrown as pots and built into walls so often over so many centuries, had been ground to such fine dust that he was convinced it would work its way inside the casing and ruin the mechanism. We knew that in such a case we would have no option but to go home. This was a brand new form of camera, and it was unlikely that there was anyone on the subcontinent able to fix it.

The train finally spat us out at noon into the torpid heat of Varanasi Cantonment station – a medieval-aired place of diesel fumes and the smoke from a thousand tobacco-leafed *biddis* all lit at once. The passengers were like blood cells gushing out of a ruptured artery into the glut of more human viscera that clotted the platform. We cast ourselves into it, steering towards the entrance as best we could, towards the usual wall of bright beseeching faces waiting to pounce.

"To which place, mister?"

"*Namaste, sahib!*"

"What hotel? Welcome to Varanasi!"

I chose the least desperate, the only man without the vampire fangs of betel-nut chewing, and we threw our bags into his auto-rickshaw. He kick-started the beast like a stubborn mule, and we roared off towards the river.

The Vishnu Rest House rose up like a rock face above the Ganges, and from its roof the view was like from the turret of a lighthouse, with *saried* women bobbing like neon buoys in the water and men in white *dhotis* that fluttered like seagulls until they got wet. I had longed to see this river since my grandmother had first told me, when tucking me into bed at night, that everything on earth was a part of God, and that in India there was a river called the Ganges which was, in fact, a living god. I always knew that I would have to see such a thing with my own eyes. I used to dream of swimming in it. A river was so much more appealing than an old man in a dress.

It didn't disappoint. Admittedly the water itself smelt of sewage, but the mystic light shimmering through a diaphanous fog made it look otherworldly. The idea that it had come all the way from ice caves high up in the Himalayas through the parched northern plains and would eventually end up in the Bay of Bengal south of Calcutta seemed to make it not just a river, but the warp on which the fabric of India was woven. My mind, deadened by the train journey, could not perceive its true divinity straightaway, but I was prepared to accept it on faith. To 700 million Hindus, this was the Mother Goddess: distilled compassion in liquid form. Before it came to earth, it had spent millions of years nourishing the gardens of the heavens. Even a drop of it carried on the breeze could erase instantly all sins accumulated over a hundred lifetimes. Books written over 3,000 years ago claimed that it could heal the blind and the sick and make us all godlike.

Behind me, stretching out as far as I could see, was a decaying jumble of roofs and aerials crammed together like a complex circuit board. Everything for miles appeared in decay. Nothing was new or clean or well maintained. Power and phone wires webbed the sky. Verandas hung precariously out of walls, and rusted railings braced the windows.

My attention was drawn to the line where the river and the city met; wide sandstone steps called *ghats* acted as interlocutors. They were lined with hundreds, perhaps thousands, of men and women performing a complicated choreography of washing, bathing, chanting, sleeping, shaving, exercising and body building, all oblivious to each other. Brahmins squatted under large umbrellas, performing *puja*, looking like glacéed fruit in a large cocktail.

The Tiger took one look at the chaos and said, "We've got to film this."

I reminded him that we hadn't slept in thirty hours, nor eaten properly since noon the previous day, but he was already grabbing the camera and heading out the door.

Filming here was like shooting fish in a barrel. Every direction revealed a marvellous tableau. I felt voyeuristic at first, but no one seemed to mind the camera. The pilgrims were like zombies, their minds immersed in their ablutions or carrying out their *yoga*, their breathing and their bathing rituals with unselfconscious devotion. After weeks of being the centre of attention, it was disconcerting to find oneself ignored again.

At one point, the Tiger looked up from the viewfinder and said, "I'm going to need a PTC from you soon. A few sentences about what you're feeling, what you're seeing."

I dug out my pen and wandered off some distance to compose my thoughts.

Sometimes you reach a world that you can't understand – I wrote – *and maybe it's best not even to try. This is the Ganges river, a living god. Thousands of pilgrims flock here to die, and be released from the endless cycle of birth, death and rebirth . . .*

I was interrupted by a man with a stiff moustache and widely splaying jodhpurs who came bounding towards me brandishing a bandaged walking stick. He pounded me with the usual volley of questions and then said, "See this cane? It is my mother's. She is not needing it now. See her, over there. There she is . . . Wave! We have travelled 800 miles, you see? The last 100 we walked; now she will die. She is very happy. You must meet her."

I told him I was busy, but he just took my hand and pulled me across to where his mother lay like a large pupa wrapped in muslin sheeting. Around her were squares of bright *dhotis* and *saris* drying in the sun like LCD lights on the circuit board. She seemed to have slipped away a fair distance already and blinked at me more out of instinct than recognition. The sight of her frail skeleton made me wonder how she could ever have walked 100 miles, but although her body was wasted, her spirit still seemed strong. A wide smile began to spread across her face.

"She is very happy," her son said. "Lord Shiva is probably whispering in her ear right now, preparing her to leave, releasing her. You can hear the chains of reincarnation slipping from her body."

It was said that if you died in Varanasi your *karmic* slate was wiped clean and you never had to return to earth. This was why the place was so crowded with poor Hindus, who had the most to gain from not coming back.

"Do you see her teeth?" the man said, opening his mother's mouth like a vet and sticking four fingers up in front of him. "Four! Mama has four gold teeth! See?"

I stared into her mouth, but all I could see was a crevasse of dark, purple-stained gums.

"Yes, four of them!" he chimed. "My mother is a very lucky women. That is why I have accompanied her to Kashi, you see. If my brother Aja had come, he would have pulled them out and gone drinking with the profits. But I will make sure that Mama is cremated with all her teeth fixed in her jaw. She has loved us, and now this is what we can do for her."

He took two orange-juice glasses from a tiffin box at his mother's feet and filled them with water from a brass urn, handing one to me.

"*Om na ma Shiva,*" he said by way of a toast and raised his glass to mine. "This will help you on your journey. When you drink Ganges water, you are protected not just by Shiva but by all the gods. Varanasi is a ford between heaven and earth – a crossing point where gods and goddesses can descend to this world and mortals can leap directly to the afterlife."

I brought the glass to my lips. This was river water, the same slime that was flushing past us with a scum of dead skin and bandages floating on it.

"Lord Shiva," he said again, prompting me to drink up.

I could see the sewage pipes pumping out from the bank beneath me. The levels of faecal bacteria were a thousand times the WHO's standards for drinking water. It was not uncommon to see partially burnt bits of body from the funereal pyres floating by. Some bodies weren't even burnt first, but were thrown in with a rock tied to them. It was considered improper to burn the bodies of a *sadhu*, a child or a leper – these were just thrown straight in and allowed to ferment in the water.

I tried taking a sip, but the uterine odour was too overpowering.

"It is not the water that is dirty," the man assured me. "It is *so* pure. What is dirty is the rubbish inside the river – the smallpox and leprosy and such like. You need not have any worry; the water has a hundred different minerals from the Himalayas in it, and the dirt is no problem because of the two–way currents that processes it all so quickly."

I thought of the urine I had been drinking for months in my little hovel and how it had made my skin so clear, and also of the maharajas who had brought vessels of Ganges water to Europe with them until they realised that champagne tasted better. Seven hundred million people couldn't be wrong, I thought, and swallowed it back. It was one of India's many paradoxes that one of the most patently polluted places on earth was where people came to be purified.

The Tiger was filming a holy *baba* covered from head to toe in a coating of vermilion powder with wreaths of marigolds spread around him. I squatted down beside a child who was sitting in a basket on a dung heap, and waited to do my PTC. A second basket in front of the child was full of the most blazing saffron garlands with chains of ox-eye daisies arranged around it, forming an enormous eye which stared up from the shit.

We recorded the PTC and grabbed some more shots of scrawny acolytes and voluminous women, then broke off for lunch. We had filmed enough footage to make up for most of our losses in Rajasthan, and we splashed out on a big feed in a fancy restaurant.

There was a gang of Americans evangelists in the restaurant, celebrating a successful prayer meeting.

"I can't say what we do exactly," one of them said to me between sips of her milkshake. "It's different every day."

In fact I hadn't actually asked her what she did.

"We witness God; that's as vague and as precise as I can be."

I nodded glumly and turned back to my meal, but she continued, "Take, for example, last week. I was in this temple in Bodh Gaya, just admiring it, sightseeing really. I was being given a tour by one of the young monks – he was actually quite a honey! What with the buzz cut and those loose Buddhist robes that leave the arms bare. Anyway, we were talking and I was asking him about his beliefs, and he was asking about mine. He was being pretty defensive, you know? Like, 'Who is this Jesus anyway, and what do you mean he died for me?'

"Then suddenly out of the blue he says, 'How do I become a missionary like you, Prudence?' I couldn't believe it. It was too weird! But I felt the power of Jesus thrilling through me, and when I looked up I saw the monk's sincere eyes staring straight into mine. He wanted to be saved. I just said jokingly, 'Well, it helps to become a Christian and be introduced to Jesus first.' And he answered, 'How do I do that?'

"I mean, I was flabbergasted. It was then that the Holy Spirit clued me into what *He* had been working on all afternoon as the monk had been giving me the tour. 'Give him the invitation, Prudence!' came J.C.'s words, clear as a bell in my heart.

"'But Lord!' I said, 'Come on, can't You see I'm in a Buddhist temple, and he's a monk?'

"'Give him the invitation, Prudence!' came the voice again. And so, what was I to do? I asked that sweet young monk in front of all his colleagues, 'Do you want to live for Jesus?'

"'Yes!' came his reply, loud and proud. I asked him three times in all, just to be totally sure. Then I led him outside, away from all of his *stupas* and icons, and gave him a simple sinner's prayer. He asked me if I could say it for him, but I told him it was something he had to do on his own. I said the first few lines as an example, and I could hear him repeat every word! I saw how God was moving and took it as the greatest honour to escort that monk through the gates of Heaven at my side. We said 'Amen' together and I felt a cool breeze blow across my face."

Prudence looked hard at me to see if her message had been heard. *Really* heard. I had barely time to open my mouth before, with precise choreography, another of the group took up her baton and ran with it.

"I'm Jasper, Prude's pastor. Really, we're just mooching around here, enjoying the wonders of India. We actually advise our people not to visit monasteries."

He threw a mock frown at Prudence, and she laughed, and said, "I know – *busted*!"

Jasper continued in a Wisconsin whine, "I know people who've gone to a Buddhist monastery, and it's taken them days to recover. It's not something you should do for sightseeing – they're spiritually dodgy areas. Although, that said, I had a pretty profound experience in one myself. It was a few years ago now, mind. I was told about a real beauty up in

Dharamsala, and I snuck in with my camera, almost paranoid about what might happen to me!

"The place was full of scroll paintings and prayer wheels, but it was too dark to take photos. As I was leaving, I noticed a monk kneeling in a corner. I ignored him and went out to the car, but suddenly I had a strong sense that God was saying, 'I want you to go back inside and give that monk a Bible.'

"I thought to myself, that's just me, it ain't God, and I ignored the voice. But it came back even stronger. 'Jasper, give that *Buddhist* monk a Bible.'" He really stressed the word *Buddhist*. He was stern and regal this time, like Charlton Heston.

"So I fished out a large-print copy of the King James, and got my translator to go back inside with me and explain to the monk.

"'God is very pleased with you,' I told him. 'God is so glad that you want to know Him and are seeking His Word.'

"He just stared at me, but I could tell he was taking it all in, so I continued, 'It makes Him so happy that you want to know who He is!'

"He was beginning to cotton on now, and I could tell he was really humbled and a bit embarrassed, too, by my words.

"'That's why I want you to have this,' I said. 'It's the Holy Bible, and it will help you in your search.'

"He took that book from me and asked me if I would sign it for him. And, you know, I did, and I could feel the power and presence of the Holy Spirit flowing through me."

"Indeed!" I said, trying to hide my feelings.

He mistook it for sincerity, and his friends all smiled. They glanced stealthily between them, confident they had a *live one* here. But they made no sudden move. Like spiders, they bided their time, patiently luring me in.

Prudence had another story ready.

"You see, that's why it's so difficult to say what we do," she said. "No day is the same. I was taking a train with my team-mates to Bombay a while ago when I came across a boy from Toronto. His name was Garret, but he asked us to call him 'G'. He was doing a diploma in Mogul history near Madras.

"We told him about our work here and he scoffed at us . . . I have to say, I was a bit upset at first, but then I remembered 1 Corinthians 1:18: 'The cross is foolishness to the perishing one, but to the one who is being saved it is the glory of God.' And for the first time ever I really understood it, you know?"

She looked at me, waiting for acknowledgment.

"Anyway," she went on, "we said our goodbyes and, of course, I never expected to see him again.

"But sometime later the Lord led us to the beaches of Goa to preach His word, and who do we come across but 'G'! He had just had all his money and passport stolen and was in a terrible state. We took him in and fed him, and for the next four days we spent real quality time with him, and he began to understand our ways. Eventually his mom wired him some funds, and we said goodbye, but in parting, he said something that amazed me. He said that he had got to understand our faith only by watching us live our lives. Wasn't that something? He didn't commit his life to Jesus right there and then, but I trust that someday he will, and I am so thankful that I had the opportunity to be a part of 'G's' life."

I muttered something noncommittal, and immediately she pounced.

"Have you got God in your life?" she asked with terrifying sincerity.

I batted the question away with one of my own. I had been thinking for a while about *hijras* and Christianity. As far as I could remember, *they* were regarded relatively highly in the Old Testament. They come out well in it overall, being seen as guardians and protectors of the Lord's flock. I was keen to find out for sure from someone who'd know, but when I asked Penelope, she was reluctant to talk about it and just stared down sullenly into her plate of chips.

"Don't be afraid to speak of Jesus Christ, Mocha," she said, "to acknowledge his presence in your life."

"I'm not," I assured her. "I'm just interested in the *hijras*. Maybe it's unfair to spring it on you. I know some of those Old Testament references can be pretty obscure."

"I know every chapter and verse by heart," she said icily. "It's just that I don't want you getting the wrong impression about eunuchs – you can't always take the Bible literally."

Look who's talking, I thought to myself.

"It has to be interpreted by an expert," she continued. "It may seem to us now that eunuchs were praised and referred to as 'holy ones', but that doesn't mean we should replicate their example today. I don't want to encourage you to do anything rash for the Lord."

"I see," I said.

"Yes," she said, relieved that she was getting though to me. "I think it was all a misunderstanding – the early church fathers allowed themselves be influenced by Genesis 1:28, where the Creator is described as a union of maleness and femaleness, and also by Matthew 19:12, where Jesus praises 'eunuchs, who have made themselves eunuchs for the kingdom of heaven's sake'. But the early fathers went too far. They should not have castrated themselves. It was excessive. I know we all go through periods where we want to make manifest our love for the Lord, proclaim it from the rafters, but we have to ask ourselves: are we just doing it out of vanity? Do you know what I mean?"

I nodded meekly.

"If you were to castrate yourself now," she said sternly, "it would just be showing off – like something the Catholics would do. Saint Paul put it best when he convinced the gentiles to accept Christianity by asking them for 'circumcision of the heart'. That's what God wants from us, not actual foreskin hacking."

Chapter 15

THE TIGER AND I were down at the water in the pre-dawn of the next morning striking a deal with a rapacious boatman to bring us out on the river to film. The *ghats* were milling with life, with *sari*-clad women and men in loincloths, waist deep in the river, raising their arms to salute the golden orb emerging from the horizon with offerings of marigolds and tiny paper floats bearing candles.

Out on the water we rowed past edifices so worn and haggard that they looked as old as the city itself, though in fact they were built in the eighteenth and nineteenth centuries by maharajas from Rajasthan, who regarded it as a good investment in the afterlife to buy up some of Shiva's prime realty. It was a way of currying favour with the gods in light of the wantonness of their lives on earth.

As the sun blazed on to the dishwater-grey water, sending glimmers shooting into the lens, the Tiger purred with pleasure. Varanasi's earlier name was Kashi, meaning divine light, and the place still has an almost celestial incandescence. Rejected garlands of flowers from the funeral pyres floated past, and on the banks the washing-*wallahs* were wringing clothes into tight knots like wrestlers. Somewhere far off I could hear a *sitar* play a merry *raga*; it hung on the air like a whispered soliloquy. The pattern of notes was so complex and yet harmonious it reminded me of DNA – an infinitely tangled source of life. Suddenly the air was broken by a primeval drone, as six conch shells were blown together to mark the dawn of yet another day for the goddess of the river.

The first smoke was rising from the freshly stoked funeral pyres at the far end of the city, and we asked the boatman to row us down there. There were three different pyres burning – one ablaze while the others smouldered. At the river's edge, great cords of sandalwood were stacked ready to fuel the flames, while in the water a queue of corpses wrapped in bandages lay floating, waiting for cremation. The place was teeming with people chopping wood, raking the fires and tending to the bodies. The boatman brought us in so close to shore that we could feel the heat of the flames, but he told us not to film as is wasn't allowed.

I asked him if people really believed that the river was a god.

"It is not a matter of belief," he chimed. "It is a fact. Simply a fact! Even a donkey, or a Jew, or a Christian will find salvation if he dies in Varanasi. Just like that. No ifs and buts."

"What about Muslims, or *even* murderers?" I asked.

"No problem," he replied. "If they have bathed and drunk the water of the Ganga, then their soul is pure and their evil deeds are washed away. And if they have not, then they cannot die here. Shiva will not permit it."

I liked that idea, imagining an unrepentant Muslim who hadn't drunk the water trying to commit suicide in a hundred different ways, and each time Shiva foiling the plot somehow.

I asked him how Hindus viewed the hordes of tourists who stared at them as they prayed and washed themselves.

"Mostly," he said, "we welcome everyone. We like for the people to be interested. It's better than in the days of the Raj when you ignored us."

Cremation was the only element that had to be respected, he insisted. Anyone was welcome to watch – it was a public event – but not to take pictures. It was why mourners sometimes mobbed tourists seen with cameras. A Swiss man had been hospitalised the previous month when he had tried to film a cremation. A sign in the hotel warned that we would be liable for prosecution if caught.

The surroundings were so beautiful that I asked him would he mind if we filmed an interview with him – just a few questions about the river and the city.

"Would you like to communicate with my true self or my other self?" he replied.

"Your true self, I suppose," I said.

"This will not be possible."

"Why not?"

"How could your camera pick up my true self?"

"I know it looks small," I assured him, "but it's digital. It works in all types of light and conditions."

"Yes, that is what I mean."

"Huh?"

"Your camera is a digital, it is in the physical realm, but, you see, my true self is not."

The Tiger looked up impatiently.

"It's interdimensional," the boatman said.

"I see," I said

"And infinite also."

"You're talking about your soul, aren't you?" I said. "We don't want to film your soul."

"No, not my soul. Not your Christian thing starting at conception and going on in heaven or hell for ever and ever. I mean infinity, everyone and everything – all existence."

"Well, of course, we can't capture infinity on camera," I said patiently.

"But how else can you do justice to who I am? You plan to show only my fake shell?"

"Have you ever watched television?" I asked.

"Yes, Indian television I have seen very much, but I was hoping yours was more sophisticated."

I shook my head.

"In that case, it will have to be my fake self only for you."

"That's fine," I said.

"It is a shame, really," he said. "You should see my true self. It is really something – as big as a cloud, as big as the sky, in fact."

Back on land, we came across a shrouded corpse being carried on a bamboo palanquin, and we pulled out the camera and followed it through the city along with a procession of mourners banging drums and cymbals. I reminded the Tiger of what the boatman had said about filming the rituals, but he said it was different for television crews. We were not tourists; we were emissaries documenting a culture for others who couldn't get to see it. We had an obligation to capture life as it was lived. I shrugged, swung the tripod over my shoulder and hurried after him. The procession was chanting *Ram Nam Sat Hai* as it followed the corpse-bearers through the alleyways towards the river. A pregnant cow with painted horns, who also happened to be headed towards the river, was inadvertently leading them. We kept a few feet back out of respect, and the Tiger used his longest lens and telescoped in so that it felt like he was in the thick of it. As we approached the burning *ghat*, we paused, letting them go on alone.

I suggested going back to the hotel for an early lunch.

"That's life there!" the Tiger said. "Just look at it!"

I nodded and turned towards the hotel.

"We need to film it," he said. "It's what we're here to do."

I knew exactly what he meant, but part of me was thinking back to my father's funeral and how I would have reacted to seeing a camera crew loitering in the background.

"We're here to capture the essence of this place," he said, "and that's exactly what you're seeing."

I had been oddly affected by the sight of the corpse and the ritual of it being carried through the city to an open fire. It seemed so honest, so elemental. I was beginning to see how at odds people's attitudes to death were here with our own. The pilgrims I had seen on the banks of the river weren't just going through the motions. Prayer wasn't simply an empty ritual, a pious sign of devotion; their minds were actually being transported elsewhere through meditation. Possibly, they were ending up close to where I had been wandering myself in those months in the cabin. And they hadn't had to live in a hovel and drink urine to do it. Varanasi struck me as a city in which everyone regarded reality as being largely an illusion. It felt strangely reassuring. I wondered if the reason Indians were so often smiling and so ready to shake off every ordeal was that they didn't actually believe in it in the first place. They regarded the whole thing as a game. I wanted to know what enabled the woman with the four gold teeth to walk 100 miles and yet be so unquestionably happy at the end of it. Her expression contrasted so starkly with those in the nursing home my grandmother had died in. If the answer lay on the pyre – at the moment of the body's annihilation – then we had a duty to film it.

I waved down a young boy selling postcards and asked him if he knew a way we could film the pyres without being seen. We needed a raised area that overlooked the *ghats*. He ignored the question and offered a whole list of other things instead. *Yoga?* Drugs? Girls? Train tickets?

I shook my head to each and said, "I'll pay well."

"I know about everything," he boasted. "I am Beini of Benares. But the fires are forbidden."

I pulled out a ridiculous amount of rupees, and I could see his conscience falter. It was a month's wage I was offering.

"You pay first," he said, crestfallen.

He led us through alleys and backyards to an old gasometer jutting out over the river. It had a ladder bolted to its side which provided a perfect viewing stand. We could see right down on to the river, where the procession of mourners was now arriving. Beini and I kept watch in different directions while the Tiger set up the camera. Beneath us we saw a handful of men carry the body to the water's edge and splash water into its mouth, while the rest of the family bargained with a priest over the cost of firewood. The negotiations got quite heated. Eventually three of the attendants came over and carried the corpse on to the embers, packing it tightly with hay. The priest chanted an invocation and set the body alight with a torch of hay and started throwing earth and wood on to it. The attendants came forward, pouring ladles of clarified butter on, while a *sadhu* stood above them chanting.

We watched as the body was beaten down into the flames by one of the attendants, who then plunged a spear through its skull. This was to let the soul out, Beini explained. He said that if I listened hard, I could make out the sound of brains popping above the crackle of the fire. A foot which had burnt off was thrown back on. I thought of Mina and what she had told me about *sati*, about the women being tied to a log and laid on the fire. I shuddered.

Overall I was struck by how simple the sacrament was, how open compared to the sterile, euphemistic rituals at home. It left no doubt as to what was going on.

When only the skull and charred marrow of a few bones remained, an argument broke out between the mourners and the priest again.

"Scoundrels," Beini said. "They are like vultures. They pick out every extra rupee they can get. I think the family has no more money for wood, and now the priest will throw the bones into the water. If the body isn't completely turned into ashes, it cannot dissolve and become one with the river. The poor *wallah* will never find rest."

The Tiger was crouched over the camera, rejigging the focus depth, cajoling the lens into squinting just a bit further. At this distance, it had to rely on its digital zoom, and the tiny little one-chip mind was struggling to process all that it saw.

"You see those dogs down there?" Beini said. "They are so fat because they dig through the ashes to eat the bits poor families can't afford to burn."

"For Christ's sake," the Tiger said, appalled. He turned to me saying, "Run down there and give the guy some more cash."

I patted at my pockets, seeing if I had any rupees left, but I had given them all to Beini. The Tiger pulled out a roll of rupees and shoved them at me.

"Get him to finish burning the bloody corpse," he said.

I knew better than to argue when he was agitated, and I climbed down the tower and ran straight to the *ghat* as quickly as I could, beckoning the priest over and telling him I would pay whatever it took to finish the job, slipping the cash surreptitiously into his *dhoti*. He was a docile man who didn't really care what happened as long as someone was paying, and with a sour, alienated smile, he turned and went off to order another load of sandalwood. By the time I had got back up the tower, the wood was being heaped on to the fire.

The mourners became suspicious as soon as they saw what was happening and began questioning the priest. They had seen me talking to him and wanted to know what I wanted. There was a lot of gesticulation and loud voices until finally the priest seemed to get scared or lose patience and he cast desperately around him until he saw me on the tower and pointed straight up. When the mourners saw the camera, all hell broke loose. At first they shouted at us, but then one or two of the men raised their arms threateningly and made to come after us. It might have been to thank us, but we weren't going to wait around to find out. We threw the equipment into the bag, folded the tripod as quickly as we could and followed Beini down cobblestone alleyways into a warren of markets like something out of a passion play or *Indiana Jones*, with silk merchants sitting on bolts of sumptuous fabric and wild-eyed *sadhus* in threadbare robes selling temple spices to pilgrims who could have hailed from any era.

Beini was incredibly swift, managing almost by osmosis to pass through the crowd, but with all our equipment, we soon began to lag behind. The tripod in particular caught on every limb like an anchor seeking hold. I looked around and saw the mourners gaining ground. I could hear their shouts even above the usual cacophony: the strains of Hindi music blaring from squeaky tape recorders, the Islamic prayers blasting from ear-splitting megaphones and the touts trumpeting their chorus of *looking today, buy tomorrow . . . Very good price, local price, not tourist price . . . Hashish, kashmiri gold, good stuff, what you want.*

Boyhood memories of being chased by bullies and bootboys came flooding back. I didn't want to get beaten up, but most of all we couldn't risk losing the camera.

We passed from the paisley fabric section of the market to the padlock and chains section, where stall after stall sold what looked to be exactly the same model of Chinese lock with spools of heavy chain. The mourners were almost upon us, and from the intensity of their shouting, they were no less angry (or perhaps grateful) and were being joined by others along the way. I was finding it ever harder to fight through the mêlée of dogs, bicycles and goats, and part of me was considering just giving in. It was all too fraught – squeezing past three-foot-wide sacred cows in alleys of the same girth; pulling the tripod out of awnings that threatened to slice the top off my head. I thought of dropping the encumbrance and making a last dash for it, but without it there was no way we could go on filming. It would be the end of our work. It seemed we had no way out. Instant *karma* had got us. If we were lucky, we'd just be beaten up, but more likely we'd lose the camera and be deported for filming without a licence. I would be back in my hovel or in the German hypermarket stacking shelves.

Looking about, I realised there was no sign of Beini, and I was just about to give myself up, when something made me look up at the wall beside me. There was a door and above it a small pottery crucifix. I must have spotted it unconsciously from the corner of my eye. My mind probably recognised its familiarity and was instinctively drawn to it. I screamed at the Tiger to follow me, and we barrelled through the doorway, bolting it shut behind us.

Suddenly there was peace. We were in an enclosed courtyard with a bougainvillea bush in an urn at its centre. High walls surrounded the yard, and in the far corner was an open-air kitchen at which an elderly woman was washing rice. She looked up, speechless at the shock of our intrusion. I tried to greet her, but she spoke no English. Meanwhile, the mob had realised what had happened and were pounding on the door outside. What I presumed were insults were being shouted over the wall. The woman ran into the house, and we were left there gasping for breath and totally bewildered. I don't remember ever having been relieved to see a crucifix before. In fact, the sinewy figure writhing in anguish on perpendicular lines had always struck me as faintly outlandish: demeaning to the grandeur of mankind. Yet now I was suddenly struck by the power of the symbol as a declaration of fellowship and sanctuary. I realised what a relief it must have been to refugees and crusaders in the past to come upon one in foreign lands.

When the old woman reappeared, she was in the company of an even more elderly man in pyjamas.

"God bless you both," he said, in a tired wheeze. "You are in a bit of a scrape. Am I right?"

We explained about filming the cremation and what had happened, and he kept up a chorus of tut-tutting throughout. When we had finished, he turned and translated it all to his wife, who also tut-tutted, before finally turning back to us, "*Aachaa*, you are in a bit of a bind," he said. "We Christians believe in graves, but the Hindus love their fires, and they do not look kindly on disrespect."

He paused dramatically to listen to the angry chanting of the mob outside.

"That is not good. They are grief-stricken, you see? And upon their injury you have placed insult. They will not be easy to pacify. That said, you have been sent to my door by the grace of God, and I will not cast you away. You may have sanctuary here. Now come inside; I have something to show you."

We followed the man inside, where he proceeded to take down boxes of stuff – letters, photos, certificates of merit – and hand them round to us one by one. I looked at him questioningly, and he smiled shyly, shoving another photo at me. I realised that it was the entire, dreary detail of his life, documented on paper and carefully archived between plastic sleeves. With each item, there were myriad trivial details that he wanted to share with us. I felt like the whole thing had been a trap to lure us into his lair. He was delighted with himself and set to carefully rummaging through the boxes, picking out his favourites.

The torrent of this exhaustive detail after all the stress of the chase was just too much to handle, and I began to feel a splitting headache coming on. His wife shot a sympathetic glance as us but made no attempt to stop him. Instead she sneaked out to prepare tea and currant cake.

We began with the photos of his children. He spent about twenty minutes telling us what each of them was doing now. At this stage, my chest was beginning to tighten; I worried that I was in danger of suffocating in the minutiae of his past. The Tiger didn't seem at all bothered. He had tuned out completely and was busily digging compacted dirt out of the crevices of the camera with his Leatherman. When the old man started in on his college albums, I contemplated risking taking our chances with the mob outside. It was just then that I caught sight of a newspaper clipping of a scrawny birdlike figure standing beside a group of students. I recognised it instantly. It was Mohandas Gandhi.

"The Mahatma!" the old man said gleefully. "That was 1930! Such good times. That's me in the corner."

The Tiger looked up, suddenly interested, and we both craned over to see.

"He was recounting one of his stories," the old man said. "Probably the one about all of us spitting together and forming a puddle large enough to drown 300,000 Englishmen. This was his big thing: that since there were so many of us and so few of them, there was no need for violence. Unfortunately, he warned us, Britain would not be capable of understanding the concept of a peaceful war, and they would react with violence. This was just a few weeks before the Salt Tax march. He told us we were going to get beaten, but we weren't to raise a hand to protect ourselves.

"You knew Gandhi?" I asked.

"No, but I saw him many times. And he was right about the march; it *was* bloody. We were kicked and beaten, and we just lay there on the ground, with our broken bones and fractured skulls. It was like the horror movies they show on television now – covered in blood, you see? See this finger? It never set."

He wagged his little finger back and forth at an impossible angle.

"But that didn't stop us marching," he continued. "More of us came up from behind. And more behind them. Hour after hour, until eventually the police were too exhausted to lift their truncheons and they just allowed us through. We collected our salt – it was that simple. We wanted salt and we got it. It was ours, after all. The great white sheets that are the sea's gift to the soil. And we brought them home with us without paying even a *paise* to the King."

It was surprising to hear of Gandhi as a real person, not just the movie character with a bamboo staff and spectacles – Charlie Chaplin in a dishcloth.

"And you were on the march?" I asked.

He just waved his little finger again in reply.

"But how did you not react in defence? You must have wanted to – every instinct must have told you to?"

"Simple," he replied. "The Mahatma said patriotism was humanity. We were patriots because we were human, and humane. If so, there was no way we could consider consciously hurting an Englishman."

I thought back to my own family: three generations of patriots who, over the course of the twentieth century, had led rebellions, rallied troops, smuggled guns and shot people, possibly even killed them. I had been raised to revere their courage and sacrifice, yet hearing his account of waging war through not lifting a finger made me suddenly reassess it all. Somehow it seemed so much braver.

I mentioned this to the old man and he said, "Gandhi-ji wanted the British to do the same. He told them to let Hitler and Mussolini take possession of their island and all its beautiful buildings, but never to give him their minds, their souls."

It was no wonder Gandhi featured less in Indian life today; his ideas were too utopian, too evolved. I had been thinking about featuring him in the programmes, but when I read about his habit of sleeping naked with his grandnieces to test his resolve, and his campaigns to promote regular bowel movement and to stop people blowing out their nostrils on footpaths, I wondered how we could make him relevant to a modern audience.

I asked the old man what he made of Gandhi's odd proclivities – his eccentric ideas on the sanctity of latrines; his wish to get rid of railways, hospitals and lawyers, and return to the old ways.

"This was the shame," he said. "He was too far ahead. He knew about protecting the earth and about the limitations of machines before it ever dawned on the rest of us. He claimed that only when they invented a tractor that produced milk, *ghee* and dung could it replace a cow. This is what the UN people are now realising. He was reusing envelopes, promoting a healthy diet, asking doctors to prescribe fewer medicines long before anyone else."

The Tiger was growing impatient. He got up abruptly and went out to the courtyard, coming back a minute later to say that things seemed quieter now and that we'd better be off.

The old man shrugged and began collecting up his scattered documents. I thanked him profusely and made to stand up.

"It was nothing," he said, with a deflated expression. "I am only keeping Gandhi-ji's spirit alive. The spirit of Christ."

"But Gandhi was a Hindu," I said.

"Yes. So, too, was I until partition. When we started butchering the Muslims, boarding the trains and slaughtering everyone on board, I knew I could never call myself a Hindu again. I'm glad Gandhi was shot; that he was no longer around to see that."

Once we were sure we had all our equipment, the Tiger carefully opened the courtyard door and peeked out. It looked safe enough. People were still milling around the vegetable stalls, but no one took any notice of us. With a final goodbye we turned and closed the door behind us. Life seemed to have returned to normal. Predatory cripples were clamouring for *baksheesh*. Ambassador taxis hooted at imperious cows. A heady fragrance of jasmine rose from a spice stall, and children were scrubbing their teeth with twigs around a public latrine, scouring themselves with Lifebuoy.

Breathing a sigh of relief, we set off towards the hotel. But we had hardly gone fifty metres before two men came racing out at us from behind a fruit stall, and we had to turn and shoot back towards the crucifix. It took both of us pushing with all our weight against the door to slam it shut in their faces. Outside I could hear them calling for back-up.

This was more serious than we had thought. Who knew how long they were prepared to stand vigil? We had to get to Delhi that night. TnaG had sent new tape stock out to the Irish embassy, and if we didn't collect it soon, they might send it back. We had to find some means of escape and do it fast. I reckoned the police and every Hindu in the country would be on the side of the mourners, so it was no use going to them.

The old man looked delighted to see us back. He proceeded to pull out the boxes again and launched into the story of how his mother's village had come together to dig a new well. I sat back dejectedly, the constricted feeling returning to my lungs.

An hour later, I was approaching despair when I heard, out of the blue, the calls of *hijras*. They were mixed into the general sounds of the market, but it was unmistakably them – the familiar high-pitched caterwauling and clanging of bells as they sashayed through the market, scrounging money and causing havoc.

An idea came to me.

"Jemdanee!" I shouted, interrupting the old man in mid-flow.

"What?" said the Tiger.

"Jemdanee . . . you remember, I told you about her – the *hijra* leader!"

"You mean the castrati?"

"Yeah," I said excitedly. "She can get us out of here."

"How? Will her mellifluous nightingale voice carry us into the clouds?" he said sardonically.

"I'm serious," I said

"They're 500 miles away," he pointed out.

"Yeah, but there's a network. A family stretching right across the country. They all help each other."

"So what? You're not a eunuch, are you?" he said. "Or have you been keeping something from me? It would account for a lot."

"Seriously," I said. "They owe me a favour."

I tried shouting over the wall to the *hijras*, but there was no response. I thought I could let them know that I knew Jemdanee and ask them to help us, but they were making too much noise to hear. So, having asked the old man could I use his phone, I put a call through to Nizamuddin. It was Marat Khan who answered, and she was as dismissive as ever. I begged her to let me speak to Jemdanee.

"If you call again, we put a curse on you," she said and slammed the phone down. I debated whether to try again in the hope that someone else might answer. What I wanted was for Jemdanee to contact the local *hijras* here and get them to come for us, yet I didn't want to risk being cursed. I suppose the plan was a bit far-fetched, but I could think of nothing else. As it was, we had no option but to wait it out. We stayed there until nightfall, being drip-fed a man's life in forensic detail. At dusk, his wife served us dinner, and afterwards it was clear they were exhausted and needed to get to bed.

Around nine, we finally sneaked out. The market was largely abandoned, and we were able to make our way safely through the alleys, pausing at each intersection to check that no one was lying in wait. The place looked more ancient and evocative than ever with the candles flickering at the few open stalls where cauldrons of rice and *dhal* were being cooked over gas – their flames casting a golden glow on the surroundings and pumping smoke into the air. Now and then, drops of fat would catch fire, shooting up like will-o'-the-wisps into the night.

Back at the guesthouse, we ordered straight whiskies and went upstairs to pack. It wasn't safe here any longer. We took a taxi to the station and bought tickets on the last train to Delhi. The further we got from Varanasi, the better.

Overall, I was very glad I had experienced the place. It clarified many of the paradoxes I had come across and reminded me how impossible it was ever to understand India fully. I had read that things like the Ganges river and the word *OM* were manifestations of God in liquid and literary form, but I hadn't actually understood the concept properly until then. I had presumed it was meant in the same way as Catholics vaguely imagined that Jesus' heart was in a votive lamp. I hadn't realised that in Hinduism such things weren't seen simply as symbols, but were regarded as being actually what they claimed to be. The gods *were* in fact everywhere and everything. They were as fully manifested in this world as beyond it. The only thing that didn't exist was *this world* – the world we accept as our reality. *It* was the symbol. The entire physical dimension that we live and breathe in was only a dream, one of a whole series of dreams that we hypnotise ourselves with as a tool on the path back to our divine state as gods.

The ultimate truth in the eyes of Hindus, as far as I could understand it, was that we were god, and we had always been god, and we would always be. We were gods who pretended to live out silly, tawdry lives as humans now and again.

Chapter 16

THE RAILWAY STATION was overflowing with mail awaiting transport: balsa-wood boxes and bundles wrapped in hessian and twine with bright seals of red wax and labels scrawled in Indian ink, making them seem so much more exotic than normal mail. Just the fact that the timber chests were nailed shut and sealed with cord made their contents seem so much more mysterious.

On the train, all I wanted to do was rest and sort through the jumbled thoughts racing around my mind, but the smell of burning body still clung to my clothes, and in the overheated carriage it sweetened to the intensity of cured pork. An engineer sharing the compartment with us was determined to make small talk. The Tiger hid himself behind a copy of the *Times of India* and refused to be drawn, but I felt I should at least allow him to fire off the usual volley of name? native place? and so on.

When he was finished, I made as if to go to sleep, and dutifully he took up his newspaper, but a few minutes later, he was pulling at my sleeve.

"The wicket was so obviously crooked," he said.

"Sorry?"

"The wicket," he said, opening the paper towards me. "Look here. 'The enmity felt by our cricketers regarding the perfidious behaviour of the opening batsman in the first innings in this year's test match has debased British loyalty. Not since the Indian Mutiny has such an inequity been . . .'"

"I'm sorry," I said forcefully. "I don't follow cricket, and I'm really very tired."

He quietened after that, retreating into his paper, but when I got my diary out, he became animated again and, pulling out an exercise book of his own, he began writing as if mimicking me. He kept looking over his shoulder at me as though trying to cog. Out of instinct, I put my arm around the page, like in school, and he proceeded to peer over it. Finally, I closed the diary and looked up at him. He was beaming merrily.

"Would you like to know what I am writing?" he asked like a child with a secret.

"Sure," I replied, noncommittal.

"A letter to my daughter. It is her first day of school today."

"Ah," I said, melting somewhat. "Did you wave her off in her uniform and satchel?"

"No," he said sadly. He looked as if he might cry. "I am far from home. My family is back in Alwar; I won't her see for a week."

"Alwar is beautiful," I said, to buck him up.

"You know Alwar! But it is only so small. Nobody knows Alwar. You visited? Did you see the fort? Did you like it? So splendorous, the ramparts, yes?"

"Actually, we didn't get quite that far in the end. We were looking for a man . . . Bhartrihari – a sort of holy man."

"Bhartrihari!" he cried. "You were looking for Bhartrihari-ji?"

"Yes, you know him?" I asked.

"In Alwar, everyone knows Bhartrihari – or *knew*, I should say. Bhartrihari is no longer with us."

"What happened?" I asked.

"He has left."

"How? I mean, did he do the whole thing, with the concrete tomb and all?"

"Lord Bhartrihari leaves in only one way," the engineer said stiffly, as if it were self-evident, "as befitting the master of immortal *yoga*. His disciples placed him in the tomb, and we all now await his resurrection. Roy, my friend who was his *chela*, tells me he remembers that on the last occasion it took 144 days. I know your Jesus did it in three, but he was just showing off. It is not good for the system to do it so quickly – the non-physical strands of DNA can become tangled. If he hadn't ascended so soon afterwards, he would have ended up riddled with arthritis or schizophrenia."

"But last time was 108 years ago, wasn't it?" I asked.

"Just under, I think."

"So how can your friend remember? He's not immortal, too, is he?"

"No, of course not!" the engineer said, laughing. "Roy isn't immortal – none of the *chelas* are. They die and reincarnate each time. That is their *karma* – to be with Bhartrihari at his *yoga* demonstration each century. They have attended twenty-two so far."

"You mean, every 108 years they do the same thing?"

"Precisely – they are born, grow up, help bury him and then wait around until he reappears."

"Every 108 years!"

"Precisely," said the engineer. "They are like a search and rescue team. It is not so easy to re-enter orbit, you know. In fact, it's bloody tricky. They cannot be exactly sure where he will materialise."

"But that's well over 2,000 years!" I said. "So you're telling me that Bhartrihari was doing it before Jesus' resurrection?"

"Who else do you think taught the Jew?"

"Did Roy know Jesus?" I asked incredulously.

"I don't know. I never asked, but I doubt it – he doesn't remember very much about his past lives. None of the *chelas* do. Bhartrihari tells them each time."

I was about to ask him why they trusted Bhartrihari. How did they know that he wasn't lying? How can anyone know that Bhartrihari is immortal if no one lives as long as he does? But then I remembered Lans, and interrupted myself mid-flow. "Will Roy be seeing Bhartrihari again?" I asked urgently.

"Of course," he replied. "And again and again and again."

"Well, would you mind giving him a message to pass on to Bhartrihari?"

I told the engineer about Lans and his worry that the immortal *yogis* were leaving the planet and that we weren't ready to live without them yet.

"Tell your friend not to worry. It is not so much that Bhartrihari will leave as that we will all become Bhartrihari."

I was totally lost now.

"Are you saying we're all becoming immortal *yogis*?" I asked.

He paused for a long time, thinking about what he was going to say. He seemed to be mulling over different wordings, different ideas. He was quiet for so long that the Tiger looked up from his paper to see what had become of us. A blind hawker came shuffling down the aisle, rattling her tray of mirrors, key rings and bric-a-brac at each row. I bought a little torch, more out of guilt than need, and just at that moment the tannoy burst into life, announcing with indecipherable urgency the name of the next station. The engineer spoke up again.

"You know, Bhartrihari leaves messages for his followers before the entombment? Maybe your friend would like to hear the latest one."

"Yeah," I said, "maybe."

"I can get Roy to send one to you, too, if you like."

"Don't bother" I said.

"I insist."

"No, really." I said, "I don't get the whole Bhartrihari thing. I can't see what's so special about him. It's like you're worshipping his death."

"Huh!" the engineer snapped. "Talk of pot and kettle."

"What?"

"Pot and kettle," he repeated. "It is your Christianity that is hooked on death worship, not our Hinduism. Without Jesus dying you cannot be saved – isn't this right? Your communion ritual is actually akin to necrophilia."

"Now listen here . . . ," I said, my hackles rising in spite of myself.

"No, you listen: in Hinduism, the earth and heavens are teeming with life – just look at the Gopuram of the Madurai Meenaksi Temple. There isn't space for a finger to be inserted, it's so full of colour and life of every kind. But go to Notre Dame or the Dom in Cologne – such marvellous engineering achievements, but their only purpose is to make you feel small. Even big gargoyles to frighten you. What a waste of skill! We in India are riddled with corruption and nepotism, but we are white as the driven snow compared to your churches."

The train was pulling into the station, and he put away his copy book and got up and walked to the door.

Chapter 17

THERE WAS NO sign of the new tape stock at the embassy in Delhi. Peadar promised to look into it and told us to check back with him in an hour. We went off to find a coffee shop which he had told us was just beyond the diplomatic enclave and, on the way, we took the opportunity of snooping around the colonial bungalows and art-deco boxes in the area, admiring the lush gardens of mangos and jacarandas and being stared at by the Punjabi security guards patrolling them. I was conscious of the sense of absence of the British officials and their wives, who had built these houses and planted the gardens and who were now replaced by rich industrialists and the few members of parliament wily enough to have amassed a fortune.

We came to Birla House, the home of one of the few native industrialists the British had allowed to share in the country's profits, the majority of it being siphoned straight back home. It was here on G. H. Birla's veranda that Gandhi had been shot dead after a prayer meeting. There was a plaque outside with a quote from Tagore likening him to Buddha.

Since meeting the old man in Varanasi, I had been thinking more and more that we should try to do something on Gandhi in the programmes, but the Tiger was adamant that there was no point; he was no longer relevant. "Do you think the dancers at the MTV rave were thinking about him while dancing their tits off for 50 Non-Stop Bangle-jiving hours?" he said.

That wasn't the point. It was inevitable India would move on. Einstein even predicated it: that future generations would find it hard to believe that such a person as Gandhi ever existed; that he would be either mythologised or ridiculed. Einstein said Gandhi represented a new and more evolved concept of human relations, and I was beginning to see what he was getting at. Gandhi's idea of the peaceful struggle was like a leap of consciousness that had changed everything. Without it, the 1960s could never have happened. Both Martin Luther King and Nelson Mandela admitted that without him they would not have existed.

I tried explaining this to the Tiger, and to be fair he did give it some more thought, but he just couldn't see how digging latrines or doing mud packs for lepers had any relevance now.

"Do you think the half million soldiers on the Kashmiri border are thinking of Gandhi? Or the nuclear experts aligning missiles at sites in Pakistan from their underground silos? Or what about the ministers who agree to spend the billions on nuclear arms while half the country can't read?

"If you want, we can do a short piece in Birla House about the murder," he added by way of compromise.

But I didn't want that. I didn't want Gandhi seen as just another executed icon like Kennedy or Lennon or King. Television was perhaps the wrong medium for him anyway, for a man who Tagore compared to Buddha. What needed to be said was too evanescent for words, never mind pithy television sound bites. Certainly not in an awkward, jerky jalopy of a language that didn't *do* pithy.

If there was one thing I would have liked to get across, it was the faith that Gandhi had in mankind. For me that made all the other odd stuff excusable. He saw the god – the flame of divinity – inside each of us, which we blatantly deny is there a thousands time a day.

Back at the embassy, Peadar had bad news: he reassured us that the tapes had turned up safely, but not in Delhi. They were in the Irish embassy in Cairo. Somehow they had found their way into the diplomatic bag, but he assured us that he would get them back by morning. By way of consolation, he offered to take us out on the town that night.

We had agreed to meet Peadar at the Rodeo Bar, and when we arrived we found him deep in conversation with some ex-pat businessmen and diplomatic colleagues. The bar aspired to southwest-hicksville-chic, with Indian waiters dressed as cowboys and mock saddles as bar stools. The customers, trendy young Delhites with money and attitude, were like no Indians I had seen before. Some of the women were straight out of *Scooby Doo*, each with a tight jumper, pants and a scarf draped over the shoulder. Peadar introduced us, and we spent a weary hour listening to ex-pat shoptalk until I caught the Tiger's eye and signalled that we ought to leave. We were just saying goodbye when Reg, the gay campaigner from the burger bar, came in.

"Isn't this the naffest place you've ever seen?" he said. "Makes you feel like spanking your inner moppet. If I see another long-maned thoroughbred in a chiffon *sari*, I swear I'm gonna hurl. I mean, what do they think this is, a cross between *Happy Days* and the Bhagavad Gita?"

"It's no worse than anywhere else," Peadar said snappily. "Anyway, I had to meet some trade clients here."

"Well, shame on you," Reg said. "You're giving these boys a totally wrong impression of Delhi life. Believe me, boys, this isn't just a one-Starbuck town."

"There's Starbucks here?" the Tiger said.

"No! It's just an expression. I mean it's not all suck-ville. Things are brighter. I'll take you out one night and show you all the stars, and the bucks, too!"

"Bollix," said an English businessman who had been downing straight shots. "This is about as bright as it gets: a buncha guys and a buncha girls drinking Malibus and Limca, drooling over each other, but doing nothing about it."

"Not true, Sabrina," Reg said petulantly. "You should get out more. Nothing suckaroos quite as bad as this place."

"Bollix," the Englishman repeated. "I've been around all the bars in this city, and there ain't no more action. The girls are all waiting for Mummy to find them a nice boy. None of them ever dare do anything themselves. Some of the really naughty ones will arrange a date to go and hold hands at the movies or share an ice cream at Nirula's, but it always goes wrong. They end up running back to Mummy, waiting for her to rustle up some eligible engineers, accountants, entrepreneurs, whatever. They'll choose whoever seems to be the most modern outside and traditional inside. It's the same every time."

"What planet are you living on?" Reg exclaimed. "There's a whole studilicious scene out there. I mean it. You should come out with me some time. I can get you pelvic every night."

"I'm not interested in your gay saunas or gambling dens – you can keep your sordid vices to yourself."

Reg shot a glance of mock outrage at us and said to him, "Look, man, why don't you just take five in decaf land, okay?"

The man grumbled, swallowing another shot. Reg turned to us.

"Anyway, I wasn't talking about that," he said petulantly. "I'm talking dance clubs, chill-out zones, the whole sextacular vibe. I swear . . . !"

"To be honest, nothing would surprise me any more," the man interrupted in a more conciliatory tone when he had taken two in decaf land. Reg didn't even bother turning round to him, but the man went on, "These people are adapting at the speed of light. Only a few years ago, I started selling them Old Spice and Lux around the villages. They couldn't get enough. Now it's all Calvin Klein crap – I'm dropping plane loads of it into Indira Gandhi every week. It used to be just the wives of diamond dealers and foreign exchange junkies, but now it's everyone. Mom has a spanking red Maruti supermini, her kiddies live on pizza and Coke. They've even started going to the beach! I sell them the full enchilada: deckchairs, barbecue, the lot. They end up looking like Malibu fuckin' Barbie. And then they buy designer luggage to carry it all in! I'm telling you, these people will trump us all. Although I admit we still have to tweak some stuff, like those garish tank tops the boys wear. And then when they get to the beach, they are so horrified by nakedness they spend all their time in the video kiosk watching Kevin Costner movies."

At one point, Reg leant over to me, saying, "So what do you make of Tara's transformation?"

"What?" I said.

"Her transformation? Her new campaign."

"*Her*!" I cried. "What do you mean *her*?"

"Did you not hear?"

"Oh, God!" I said.

It could be only one thing – that the deed was done – and I didn't want to know.

"Oh, yeah," Reg said.

"Yeah, what?" I said.

"Tara says she's a woman now."

"Oh, I know that," I said, relieved. "I thought you were going to tell me she'd had the operation. But what's this about the campaign?"

"Have you not been in touch?"

"How could I?" I roared. "Jemdanee won't let me."

"Jemdanee!" Reg cried dismissively. "Tara's not with her any more. She blew that joint long ago."

"Huh?" I managed. "What? Tara's gone?"

I found I was feeling proprietorial, like a mother being told her son had remarried or moved country.

"You didn't know?" he said.

"Know what?" I cried

"Really?" he said.

I glowered.

"I'm staying out of this," he said, sensing things were more fraught than he could know. "Why don't you swing by the burger joint tomorrow? She comes most days after lunch."

I had difficulty in grasping what Reg was saying. I had come to terms with the fact that Tara was with the *hijras* now. It made some sort of sense. In a way, it was like being institutionalised – like what we used to do with people who didn't fit in back in Ireland. Yet, now it seemed everything had changed again.

When I got to the burger bar next day, I found it closed up and empty. I rapped on the window a few times, but there was no reply. Then I heard laughter coming from inside the kitchen, and I tried the door handle and found it unlocked. I walked through the restaurant to the bead curtain at the back and stuck my head through. Reg was bent over the fryer, kissing a boy in thick glasses and a buzz cut. They looked up when they heard the beads rustling, both pouting at me in annoyance.

"You're early," Reg said.

"Why aren't you open?" I replied.

"Slept in," he replied provocatively.

His friend gave me a knowing wink and slipped his hand around Reg's waist.

"Is this him?" the friend said, widening his marsupial eyes at me as though I were headlights.

"Mocha, meet Donald. Donald, Mocha," Reg said lazily. "Donald is on study leave from Syracuse. Looking at . . . what is it you're looking at again?"

But Donald wasn't taking any notice. He was busy drinking me in, ranging his eyes up and down.

"So you're the famous Mocha," he said finally with a Capote lisp. His tone was triumphal, as though he had set a trap for me and I had walked straight into it. He was twisting his neck from side to side and tutting like the maid in *Tom and Jerry*. For extra emphasis, his spine was bent back with his arms braced at his hips. It was quite a performance. "Mocha, the saviour of mountain boys; isn't that right?"

He spoke in a drawl, an alluring, dramatic drawl.

"I've also heard the term *slave trader* used in reference to you," he went on. "Which is it to be?"

"Who is this person?" I asked Reg.

"Donald! I'm Donald," Donald said cattily. "Senior lecturer in socio-anthropology at Syracuse U – check the website if you like."

He looked about twenty-two.

"Yes, but *who* are you?" I repeated.

"Reggie has been really good to me," he said in a more conciliatory manner, before raising his eyebrows knowingly and dipping a finger into the chip basket to bring a chip decadently to his lips.

"Right," I said.

"Donald is on a research internship," Reg explained. "He's looking into the popularity of cross-dressing in literary discourse and . . ."

"No, no, not just the popularity," Donald interrupted with irritation. "The fact that it represents an under-theorised recognition of the necessary critique of binary thinking, whether particularised as male and female, black-white, yes-no, Republican-Democrat, self-other, etcetera, etcetera. The fact that the 'third' is that which questions binary thinking and introduces crisis – a crisis which is symptomatised by *both* the over-estimation *and* the underestimation of cross-dressing. But what is crucial here – and I can hardly underscore this strongly enough – is that the 'third term' is *not a term*. Much less is it a *sex*, certainly not an instantiated 'blurred' sex as signified by a term like 'androgyne' or 'hermaphrodite', although these words have culturally specific significance at certain historical moments. The 'third' is a mode of articulation, a way of describing a space of possibility. 'Three' puts in question the idea of 'one': of identity, self-sufficiency, self-knowledge."

There was no doubt he was an academic.

"Chicks with dicks, she-males, klingers, ladyboys, tranny-saurus rexes," Reg summarised.

"Sorry?" I said.

"That's what he's studying. The whole Red Riding Hood phenomenon. The innocent girlie witnessing the primal. All that shit."

"Yes, yes," said Donald enthusiastically. "Freud's Wolf-Man in a dress, cross-dressing actors, the inexplicable, the taboo . . . like parental coitus. All this is grist to my mill."

Reg looked at him proudly.

"When I told him about the *hijra* thing, he almost wet himself. Hot-footed out as quick as he could," Reg said with delight. "The college is paying for the whole kit and caboodle!"

"Where's Tara?" I asked.

"He'll be along soon," Reg assured me. "He always is."

Reg pulled open the chest freezer and took out two burgers, flipping them on to the pan. I smiled, remembering Salim-bi's car, named after these sacred "dung cakes", as he called them.

"Be prepared," Reg said seriously to me. "You'll notice some changes in Tara."

He grabbed a bottle and sprayed oil on the burgers and sent them skating like pucks across the stainless steel.

"You found a real live one with that boy Tara," Donald said to me. "I underestimated him at first, that's for sure."

Reg poured me a coffee, and I went back out to the empty restaurant and sat down anxiously to wait. I didn't have all that much time. The Tiger had agreed to film some GVs and wild-track on his own for a few hours, but we had arranged to meet up again for the magic hour: that time of day when the world turns golden just before the sun sets and when most shots that make it to the final cut in any programme are taken.

After a few minutes, Donald came out of the kitchen and slipped into one of the genuine Burger King seats opposite me. He slid my mug across to his side, cradling it between his palms and sipping from it coyly.

"You look sad there all on your lonesome," he said.

I smiled wanly.

"I'm just thinking," I said.

"Yeah, well, I wanna say – wanna tell you like – that I think what you did for Tara was precious and noble," he said. "I mean it. Precious and noble. I can't imagine what it must have been like for him up there with all those hairy mountain tribes. He must have been so sad, so confused."

I didn't know what to say; clearly Tara was spinning stories about himself.

"Believe me, I feel for him," Donald went on. "I know a little bit of what he's talking about. I had the same myself."

Surely he didn't have leprosy? I thought. Or didn't have to contend with the intransigence of a tribal community, but I said nothing – he had the look of someone who wanted to *share.*

"Up until eleven, I was called Clare. Can you believe that?" he said.

It would certainly account for the youthfulness of his skin.

"The youngest sister of a family of three," Donald said. "'Mommy, Mommy, Clare uses the bathroom funny,' my cousins used to say, but I never took any notice. Amazing how we block things out, isn't it?"

"Uh-huh," I said.

"It was only when I began hearing girlfriends talk about their breasts sprouting and menstrual periods and stuff that I knew something was wrong."

I tried giving Donald my complete attention, but as he was talking, a gang of *hijras* came in. Chatting and joking, they congregated around a table, folding their *saris* to fit into the tractor seats and shouting up orders at a young man in a serving apron. Donald took one look at them, shrugged and went on with his story.

"I suppose before that I may have just been blocking it out," he said. "That's what my therapist says. Whenever I daydreamed about the future, I never imagined myself as a happy mom in an apron with kiddies all around. I saw myself with a moustache and a red sports car. A real hunk, you know? Isn't that wild?!"

I nodded. I was trying to listen and at the same time keep an eye on the *hijras.* They were intriguing. It turned out Reg's place was a regular hangout for them. There was always quite a gathering, with various groups stopping in to pass on tips to each other about recent births or upcoming marriages. It wasn't because they liked Western food particularly that they came, but simply because many of the other restaurants refused to serve them; or if the owner acquiesced – out of an out-dated Gandhian sense of fealty – the customers would stare and make sneering comments. Things were different in Reg's. Most of his customers were backpackers staying in Paharganj, or NRIs (non-resident Indians) who had acquired a taste for junk food abroad. In the eyes of the locals, we were all as untouchable as each other and might as well eat out of the same odious trough. I noticed a few *hijras* from the Nizamuddin community in the group, but none of them took any notice of me.

"Where I grew up, pictures of naked people were hard to find," Donald was saying, raising his voice over the chatter. "Men or women – and certainly not anything in between. How was I to know what we were supposed to look like?"

It reminded me of something Tara had told me about how the other boys in the leper station would sneak into the doctor's surgery to look at the anatomical wall chart showing the most common areas of leprosy infection on men and women. The woman in the picture was naked, and he could never understand what they found so titillating about it. To him it was of no more interest than the height chart next to it.

A loud laugh came from the *hijras*, and Donald swivelled around in his seat to look. One of them, a large lady who looked like Elizabeth Taylor in later years, waved at him, and he went over to bid her *namaste*. Most of them clearly knew who he was, and those who didn't weren't at all shy like they had been with me in Nizamuddin. They chatted warmly. I was surprised overall by how unintimidating the various *hijras* I had met were. Madame Singh Guli's guest at the drinks party had given me to understand that they were aggressive and frightening, but I never found that. When Donald came back, I pointed out this discrepancy to him, and he said that sometimes they could indeed be pretty vicious. He had seen some shocking scenes, but it was only as a form of defence when they were attacked. Intimidation was their last resort in a society that quite literally wanted nothing to do with them.

"And believe me, I know how they feel," Donald said. "The world doesn't want to know about people like us, people on the margins. They prefer to label us freaks. Even my own mom didn't want to know. At one point I said to her: "Mom," I said, "I get hard down there." And she just brushed me off. She did! She ignored me. I guess she was scared. A few months later, a teacher twigged it and insisted I go and see a doctor. But he was no help. All he did was pull out a load of photographs of nude women, saying, "Aren't they so pretty and nice? Don't you want to be like them? Don't you want to be normal, too?"

"What the fuck is normal anyway? Huh?"

Fortunately, this was a rhetorical question, as I was probably unqualified to answer.

"Take me, for example," he went on. "I'm completely normal, but in my own unique way: genetically male but with an undeveloped uterus lining and testicular tissue. Who says that's not normal?"

I nodded diligently without tearing my eyes away from the *hijras*. It amazed me how like women they were – women all over the world: gossiping, touching up their make-up, giggling like schoolgirls over shared secrets and pulling at their hair. The only thing that marked them out was the way some of them rubbed nervously at a patch of stubborn facial hair, but even they, when they ordered from the waiter, did so as women, with eyebrows arched suggestively and eyes twinkling. They were definitely more feminine than masculine – or neuter, for that matter. But, that said, their femininity was more akin to a worldly Western sort than a submissive Asian.

The moment Tara walked in, all the *hijras* looked up like zebras at the sniff of a hyena. He certainly cut an imposing figure in his traditional *sari* draped loosely over a T-shirt and jeans in the 1970s disco style he had developed in Almora. His fringe seemed to have grown long, and it hung down provocatively over his eyes. On his head was a peaked cap with sequins stitched into it. It was set at the same jaunty angle I had seen him study when we first arrived in the city just a few weeks before.

I could see the *hijras* inclining over to welcome him, but he walked straight past them when he spotted me. I understood what Reg had meant about a change. He was growing more confident by the week, grown-up. He bent down over me, enveloping me in a hug.

"Mocha, honey!" he said. "How are you?"

His appearance, his maturity, his general demeanor had changed completely since I first met him. His ability to shape-shift was uncanny.

I was taken aback, and in the minute it took me to recover, he swivelled the seat around and sat into it saddle-ways, bending over to lean his elbows on the table and stare through wisps of hair straight at me.

"How are you, my man?" he repeated. "Wow, did I miss you!"

I was still trying to get over his new fluent Americanisms, trying to think of some appropriate reply, when he allowed the chair to swivel back again and he shouted into the kitchen, "Hey, Reggie," he called. "Isn't that so? Haven't I been missing this Irish honey?"

Reg came out wiping his hands.

"Sure is, hon. Sure is," he said. "But you haven't been pining. You've been good about that. Nothing I hate more than a piner."

"Tara has been keeping busy, all right," said Donald proudly.

"Well, someone has to," Tara shot back coolly.

"You've left Nizamuddin?" I said.

"Let's just say we are parting company. I still am so very close to all the girls there, but I am seeing things differently now. Playing different games, yes? Juggling different balls."

"Right," I said.

"Tara is a bit of a hero in town," Donald said. "Tell him what you do."

Tara looked abashed.

"Oh, go on!" Reg chided.

"Oh, it's nothing really," Tara said humbly. He was already reverting a bit to his old speech patterns. It seemed that the influence of Reg's Americanisms went only so deep. Tara was still experimenting with personas.

"Tell him!" Donald said. "I'm so proud of you."

"Just a bit of this and that," Tara said. "It was Reg and Donald who told me about it, about the clinic in the hospital here. They do gender stuff. Taking the young babies with diddly problems and changing them, making them more *normal*, they say."

"What is normal anyway?" Donald said again. "That's the question, right?"

Tara ignored him and continued.

"I think they are really scareapalooza of the *hijras*," he said. "They don't want any more the third gender in India. Everyone will be man or woman and perfect. This is what they are wishing. It is horrible. So we protest at the hospital. We make signs, and all the *hijras* come with posters, and they shout slogans and mantras at the nurses and the people. We kick their lard-ass butts."

"It's barbaric," Donald said. "That's what it is. They're amputating malformed clitorises and remoulding penises. Tearing out the sensitivity, destroying any chance of orgasm in later life. It's no different from female circumcision in Africa, except that here it's done by doctors, not witch-doctors. Officially sanctioned."

"I managed to access some funds in the States for the campaign about a year ago," Reg added. "But until now no one was willing to come out on record about it. There's been nothing in the papers. Total cover-up job. That is until now, until these pickets. This'll get people talking. With the *hijras* on board, we can make some serious noise."

I couldn't help thinking that Tara might, in fact, have left one manipulative group only to be co-opted by another, but I was careful not to say too much.

"Why?" I asked Tara. "Why do all this?"

He smiled brightly in reply, but said nothing. I wasn't sure how free he was to talk in front of Reg and Donald, so I switched tack and summoned the nerve to ask the question that was most on my mind.

"Did you have the operation?" I asked.

"Don't be worrying," Tara laughed. "I am learning soon after, that you were right: not just the marbles they were taking, but diddly, too. I was real dunderhead. Duhh, like Homder Shimsham."

"Homer Simpson?" I said.

"I was so wrong!" he stressed. "They cut all of diddly right off – not just marbles, but diddly itself! I saw it. It was . . . ohh-awful."

He sighed pitifully, seemingly lost for words, then continued in a plaintive tone, "Mine is so itsy-witsy, I don't want to be losing any."

"You don't have to," I assured him.

"After seeing Gilia, I am so scared, Mocha-ji."

"Gilia?" I said.

"You know Gilia!"

I shook my head.

"Yes, you know!" he insisted. "You met her in the house. Very young she is and caring for Marat Khan."

"I thought *you* were caring for Marat Khan," I said.

"Many people caring."

"I don't remember her," I said. "There were so many of them."

"Very beautiful, and hair down to her waist."

"Really, I don't, Tara."

"Of course, you do," he said. "She was sweeping."

"Oh . . ." I said, it beginning to click. "With the scarf."

"Yes! With the lime scarf. He was still very much male boy then."

"Well, what about him?"

"It was his – well, her time. Johnny-Scissorhand time. Only one is doing each time and it was Gilia . . . It was so terrible, Mocha-ji! We stayed up all the night until maybe four. We had to wait until the rooster was crowing, you see? It was so long and lonely and cold. Then everything was a great rushing and all of us helping with the undressing and washing with the soap and the yellowy paste of turmeric and other things, I think. And Jemdanee ask her what she wants to eat and someone go fetch it, and Jemdanee, she ask very serious to Gilia now if she want to become woman, like."

"And did she agree?" I asked.

"'Yes!' she say. Jemdanee asks us all to hear the answer. 'Yes!' she say, very loud and clear."

"But what if she had said no?" I asked.

"She say yes," Tara repeated, misunderstanding me.

"Yes, but what if . . . ?"

"Too late to say cheers big ears, no can do. Time to get with the programme. Scissorhands is coming from far away to do the cutting. This was because she was very good at cutting and also maybe because if she was bad we would not have to see her every day and be thinking of poor Gilia. It is all happening very quickly. I think maybe we are all tired of waiting, you see? The woman told Gilia to fill her mouth with hair so we would not hear her screaming. If she had to scream, she must say the name Mata Bahuchara – this is our goddess. Most beloved goddess. And she tied a piece of string around Gilia's diddly and with a slash ever so quick she sliced it off on to the floor . . . It was totally chainsaw – blood everywhere, all over everywhere. But the cutting woman said not to stop the bleeding. She wanted all maleness to flow out. She said it was up to the goddesses now – they would fight to see who would keep her. We help by slapping Gilia in the face many times to keep her alive."

Donald's face was squirming.

He said, "You don't even know what chainsaw is, do you?"

"But you said this," Tara said defensively. "It's exactly what you said to Reg."

Donald sighed. "I said Texas Chainsaw Massacre; it was a joke. Tell Mocha what they did with the penis."

"The cutting woman, she wrap and bring it outside," Tara said. "Then with piece of wire hot from the fire she stick in the wound to make a hole for pee. Already poor Gilia was big and swollen like a gourd. So big as your bottom. You think the skin will burst and all her guts will fall out, and still the swelling just gets bigger and bigger. Remember when Buffy finds coach feeding steroids to the swim team and they swell up like sea monsters? Like that!"

"Forget Buffy," I snapped. "What about the hot oil."

I had been haunted by the image of the hot oil poured on the wound since Jemdanee mentioned it. It sounded like something out of a Mediterranean cookery book, as if for preserving olives or sealing a bottle of Burgundy.

"Yes, yes," Tara confirmed. "We use the oil and smoke from frankin-cense, too."

"What about medicine?" I said. "Painkillers?"

"No, no," he said. "Only afterwards. Not allowed for ceremony. Swelling, it was so big his legs not coming together. It was all boggy down there like a swamp, and he couldn't pee. Jemdanee said to him, "Pee! You must pee." But he cannot. She tells him the woman has made a hole for him, but it was all so fat and swollen together he was sure the pee would never come out and he would burst. He rolled around on the ground try-ing to push it out the hole, but it wouldn't come and he was crying so loud. Every time his *sari* brushed against it, his face looked like he was having fingernails pulled out by rats."

"How is he now?" I asked.

"Oh very fine, Mocha," Tara said brightening instantly, all traces of the previous anguish vanished. "Thank you very, very for asking. Now, she is most fine."

"I see."

"But it made me be stopping and thinking," he said. "Do I really want the snip-snip? I ask myself, and then I am thinking, no, not so much really. So I exit stage left."

"You left the *hijra?*"

"Yes, sir," he said.

"But I thought you couldn't leave."

"Well, I did," he said, raising his eyes innocently. "Vamooshed."

"Where are you staying? What are you doing?"

He puckered his lip coquettishly and shook his head.

"Huh?" I said.

He repeated the action, adding haughtily, "No! Reg says you do not want to know where I am staying, what I am doing. He say, better to keep lips sealed as Poppins' hymen."

I didn't press him. He was right. In truth, I didn't really want to know. It was easy enough to guess. Even among the various diplomatic staff, there was enough demand for good-looking young Indian boys who kept themselves clean and could speak good English. Probably one such encounter a month would pay all his living costs. I would have thought his leprosy and gender ambiguity might have mitigated against him, but there's no accounting for taste. Anyway, most of the leprosy had cleared up now, and you certainly couldn't tell unless you knew what to look for. At least, he was no longer contagious. Either he or Marat Khan had evidently been good about keeping up the treatment since I'd last seen him.

Donald was turning around, looking out the window. There was a crowd outside. Some commotion.

"They've brought Niishraah out, have they?" he said knowingly.

"Niishraah?" I said, my ears pricking up. I tried to keep my voice steady. "You mean, from Nizamuddin? The princess?"

"Normally she stays at home," Donald said, "but sometimes . . ."

"What?" Reg said to me, interrupting Donald mid-flow. He had noticed my face turn puce and my flustered attempts to turn round and have a proper look. The swivel seating would turn only so far, and I was having trouble wrangling out of it.

I pushed my hair nonchalantly out of my eyes, concentrating on making eye contact with him, and said, "Nothing."

"I think Mocha-ji has the hotties for Niishraah," Tara chimed.

"Ooooh!" Donald jeered.

I denied it vehemently, but all I was thinking of was her eyes, wide with secrets.

"Have you had a hug from her?" Reg asked.

"No," I said. "Of course not."

"You've never had a hug? Oh man! You've gotta have one."

"Oh, yeah," Donald agreed.

"A hug?" I said.

"What do you think all those people are doing?" Reg asked, pointing out the window.

"What do you mean?" I said.

"They're queuing up. It's what Niishraah does. Didn't you know?"

When I had finally untangled myself from the seat, I turned and went straight outside. At the centre of a crowd of people was Niishraah, with her tiny arms wrapped around an enormous man in a tight tunic. Her hands were grappling with his waist, trying to pull herself in closer to him. She was murmuring something up into his ear, and like a powerful tug boat, her frail body was managing with surprising ease to set his massive whale-form gently swaying back and forth. I realised there was something not quite right about the scene, and then it struck me that while he was swaying, she remained absolutely motionless. Somehow his enormous momentum had no apparent effect on her, as though she were in a different dimension and not affected by the forces of his one. It went against all the laws of physics – especially Newton's second and third motion laws.

The crowd was simply staring on entranced, their eyes wide and trusting.

"We wither without love," a woman beside me mused, more or less to herself, but in my general direction. I found myself nodding.

When the man finally stepped away, Niishraah noticed me and beckoned me forward. There were a few grumbles from the others, but I paid them no heed. She kissed my forehead and wrapped her arms around my shoulders.

"I am the vine that roots you to your love," she said by way of greeting, but then she stepped back, letting me go, unfurling her arms and saying, "It is a bit wrong . . . first, you must spread your legs – yes, like this, the width of your shoulders."

I did as she bid.

"Good," she said. "Now the knees – bend them."

She came forward and hugged me again.

"Very good," she said, "but don't forget the pelvis," swinging hers forcibly into mine.

Her body was warm, like radiation through an iceberg.

"It is like hand into glove," she said, beginning a purring noise that rippled right through me.

The warmth increased.

"You, too," she said. "Make noise now."

I sighed dreamily and found myself purring easily in harmony with her. She smelt of roses, and her bosom was so soft. I could feel her heart pounding into me, brimming with love. I knew it was nourishing my bloodstream, curving its way around the tangled helix strands of my DNA. I felt like crying but didn't let myself. Then she whispered into my ear, "Cry!" and suddenly the tears began to flow. My belly rose up and down frantically, convexing into the cavity of her belly, and she clung tighter. When the gasping had eased, she loosened her grip and we came apart. She lent outwards and looked at me with a silent smile. Then suddenly her mouth flashed wider still, and she kissed the tears from both my cheeks.

"Good," she said, "very good," and with that she moved on to the next person in line.

I was floored – hurled back into Sri Gupta's wire world. I steered my way somehow back inside the restaurant. Reg and the rest were waiting there, smiling up at me.

"Sweet, eh?" Donald said. "Sweet as a nut."

"It's why she never goes out with the others much, why she stays at home," Tara said. "It's always hard to get through the market with everybody wanting her."

Tara looked around, suddenly agitated, and said he needed to go to the lavatory, but then he just sat there waiting, looking back furtively occasionally at the *hijra* table and staring at them all until one of them got up and walked through the restaurant past us. Immediately, Tara followed her, and they made their way to the entrance of the kitchen where some exchange took place between them. Tara then slipped through the beads out of sight.

Seemingly to distract my attention, Donald went straight back into his "what is normal" argument.

"Are you normal?" he asked. "Am I? Just 'cause I can menstruate through my penis, does that make me a monster? This tangled web of reproductive ducts and vesicles is what makes me who I am, and Jesus knows, I'm proud of it. I'm the true American patchwork quilt. The baked Alaska of gender. I'm certainly not queer – maybe Reg is, but me, no. The only way I could even have a homosexual relationship would be to have sex with someone like myself! Not likely."

Tara came back out of the kitchen almost straightaway, staggering fractionally, but with a jaunty swagger and his head cocked at an irregular angle. His eyes bulged like a calf's while suckling. He was almost a caricature of someone who'd just had a hit of speed or a toot of cocaine, or at least a toke on a very strong bong.

I suspected that it was this latter that he had done. He sat down and reached across to me.

"My good ole buddy," he said in chirpy Americanese again. "My homeboy."

"Sorry?" I replied.

"Oh come on, just having laughs. Don't be blaah. Be yippee!"

Where was he getting all this?

"You're still reading the Buffy books?" I asked.

He shook his head. "No, I'm finished all. Now I read Armistead Maupin. Reg has all the books. Michael Tolliver is such a hero!"

"Who?"

"You know? Michael! Mouse from *Tales of the City*."

By introducing Tara to the world, I had somehow spawned a monster.

"So, are you coming out partying with us?" Reg asked me, emerging from the kitchen looking as sharp and edgy as Tara had. It was clear that drugs of some nature were being taken.

"With who?" I said.

"Us!" Reg said.

"Yeah," Tara whined. "*Please,* let's go partying. There's so much of cool places I want to show you."

"*Pardy-ing?!*" I said, mimicking his mid-Atlantic twang.

"Cut the boy some slack," Reg said. "He's just real vibed about seeing you."

"*Pardy-ing!*" I said again. The word just sounded so odd. I realised I was echoing my father.

"Oh, come on," Reg said. "What's with the trauma? Just get over it, why don't you."

A purdahed woman with three children and a mouth of gold teeth came in. Reg waved at them and sent one of his staff down to serve them.

"Are we going out *again* tonight?" Donald asked wearily.

"There'll be some gag-alicious boys, I'm sure of it."

"You promise?" Donald said.

"Is Gandhi a Chinaman?" Tara replied.

"No, he isn't actually," I said testily.

"I *know*," Tara scoffed like an indignant adolescent. "That's the whole point."

"No, it isn't," I said. "If you're trying to mimic the 'is the pope a Catholic', 'does a bear shit in the woods' structure, the statement has to be self-evident."

Tara frowned and I felt bad. It was clear he wanted to impress me. He had probably been polishing the phrases for days. I ought to have been more encouraging. Overall, Buffy was probably not the most inappropriate star to set one's compass by. In fact, her life as the only vampire slayer on earth was oddly relevant. A ditzy blonde condemned to an uncertain existence on the margins of society, alienated from everyone around her, wandering through graveyards and dark alleys in the dead of night. Other than her few friends in the Scooby gang, her only contact was with leprous-skinned, half-dead demons. Neither Buffy nor Tara had chosen a life in exile, but both accepted it with grace and always tried to make the best of it; to seek out joy and friendship and always to look fabulous, no matter how rough things were. Buffy would have given anything to be just a regular girl, wiggling her pompoms at high school play-offs or waving meekly as she was crowned Miss Something-or-other. Tara would have hoped for something similar if he had known about it.

At least Buffy's wasn't the self-indulgent, morally repugnant world of *Baywatch* or *The Bold and the Beautiful*, which was what was aired on

Indian television. Her character was compassionate, intrepid and resourceful, and the same could be said for Mouse in the Armistead Maupin books. Tara's life had been tough from the start, and he needed to know of others whose lives were equally fraught – for whom every day was a struggle against the loneliness of isolation. A publicly gay man in San Francisco, Mouse managed to live a positive life in a culture decimated by Aids. Most of his friends were HIV positive, but they strove to overcome it and clung bravely to the hope of a brighter future, diligently placing their belief in their own cocktail of multi-drug therapy.

As Buffy herself says, "I wish every day wasn't a struggle, but life isn't about wishes; it is about choices."

Tara asked me again would I come out dancing with them that night, and I said I'd definitely consider it. I realised that it was a side of India that we hadn't yet covered in the programmes. It might be interesting to explore. My only reluctance was having to introduce the Tiger to this lot. I shuddered to think what he might say. I promised Tara that I'd talk it over with him and ring Reg's place later that night, then I ran off to be in time to help the Tiger to film the golden hour.

Chapter 18

A S IT TURNED out, I needn't have worried about the Tiger. He made a few disparaging remarks all right, but overall he found the idea of my little leper boy bringing us out clubbing to be so bizarre that he was keen to get it all down on film.

"I'm kind of curious, actually," he jeered. "He'll be the first castrato I've ever met."

"Shut up," I said.

"Is he's any good at singing? Maybe we should tell the Vatican – I'm sure they'd love to have a new, young trainee contralto twittering his vocal cords under the frescoes of the Sistine Chapel. All the *prima donnas* and the *primo uomos* would go crazy for him."

"Plonker," I said.

"What?" he said, innocently.

"Nothing."

"Can't you take a joke?" he said.

The main problem was that our new tapes hadn't arrived yet and were now not expected to reach Delhi until later that evening. The Tiger was beginning to panic, but Peadar reassured him that nothing ever gets lost between embassies, just chronically mislaid. They were bound to turn up soon, he promised, and he agreed to stay behind at the office until the last delivery arrived, then bring them straight into town to us so that we could film in the evening. I rang Reg and we all agreed to meet up in Nirula's on Connaught Place after nine. It was a spot I had wanted to check out for a while. It was said to be the first outpost of yuppie culture in Delhi, boasting that it had introduced Cajun chicken wings and the all-you-can-eat buffet bar to the subcontinent.

Although the Tiger and I arrived early, the place was already hopping with couples coyly courting over pineapple pizza and well-off students sipping ice-cream sodas and gossiping in Hinglish: high-pitched Hindi-English pop talk with a mid-Atlantic twang.

"The *Chichti* crowd are a so totally fab bunch – so up for it, yaah?" I heard one girl say. "They hate stuff like, 'Oh! She's so nice, and he's so nice. Fantastic!' *Kitne Door, Kitne Paas* – yaah!"

"You know, we're failing completely to *get* this place," the Tiger said having taken in the scene. "We're not even scratching the surface."

A girl in raunchy low-cut jeans led us to a banquette, handing us huge plastic-bound menus containing an encyclopaedic array of American junk food.

"This place?" I said, glancing about.

"Exactly!" he said.

He was waving his arms around him, exasperatedly.

"My name is Chandana, and I will be your hostess tonight," the girl in the low-cut jeans said.

"We came here to document all this," the Tiger said to me.

"Nirula's?" I said.

"No, not Nirula's, the whole damn thing! This!"

I nodded knowledgably.

"But we're not getting it," he went on. "I'm getting some great market scenes and old weather-beaten faces, but the real story of India is here."

Sometimes my brother's mind worked so quickly he left me stranded far behind.

"Where?" I said.

"Look around you!"

I looked around, uncertainly.

"Over there, for example," he said, pointing to a pathologically shy couple fumbling over a basket of chicken nuggets and curly fries. The boy wore a lurid polyester shirt with tight black jeans, while she was in a drab *sari* masked by a woollen jumper.

"Yeah," I said, unconvincingly.

"Now look at the tables opposite," he said.

I noticed boys at one table, girls at another, all eyes trained on the courting couple. It was as though they weren't so much on a date as lab rats taking part in an experiment, an anthropological study of the new phenomenon of public courting.

"Look at him, the poor fool," the Tiger said. "His head is practically shrunk into the basket with shame. And see the way she's calling out for free refills of coffee as though her life depended on it. She wants everyone to know she's no longer a tea-drinking Indian, but a sophisticated coffee drinker. It's hilarious. These people are like pioneers of Western culture. That English bloke was right: soon everyone will be wearing DKNY and drinking Starbucks. Have you read any of the agony aunt pages in the papers?"

I had noticed these – advice columns teaching teenagers how to look and behave. Teens were a whole new strata of society, and they were desperate for guidance – from NRIs (non-resident Indians) especially, who were considered oracles by the young. The best columns of all were written by *Bhangramuffins* (Brit-Asian wide-boys) or some of the Silicon Valley programmers who still kept in contact with home.

"Do we know that bloke sitting at the next table?" I asked the Tiger in a whisper, pointing at a fair-skinned Indian boy with a ludicrously plummeting fringe. I was sure I recognised him from somewhere.

"He does look familiar," the Tiger said. "It's not the receptionist from that hostel with the beds on the roof?"

"No, definitely not," I said, shuddering.

I tried to avoid the boy's glance, thinking that he might look over and recognise me and come over. It felt a bit disconcerting, and I was just about to approach him when it struck me that in fact I didn't know him at all. He was the face of a chocolate bar and a mobile phone company that I had been seeing on billboards for months

There was a girl with him talking non-stop in that sing-song *Hinglish*.

"Like how in college we used to take *firki* of some nut who thought she was God's own gift," she said. "Some silly Ms High Heels who was a real drama maharani, you know? A real Meena Kumari in the making."

Her English was pure jolly hockey sticks, and she had the

fair-skinned, almost-European look that was a symbol of status more powerful than any designer label. It was practically a prerequisite for any job in television.

"These are the people we need to be filming," the Tiger said. "Everyone knows about palaces and leprosy, but they don't know about that girl over there in her Gucci power suit."

On a television screen above us, a boy with gleaming teeth and khaki chinos was bouncing up and down on a pink plastic sofa. He was reading out pop gossip over a dance-track backbeat.

"Nikhil is sooooo hot. I could lick him," one of Chocolate-face's friends was saying. She had a diamanté stud in her nose, and her blouse was semi-transparent.

"Knowing you, you wouldn't be just licking him," the boy next to her said.

"Ugh, Deepak, you *bazaari*, puhleez! Don't always be gross. Your mind is like the sewer."

"That's not what you say when . . ."

"Deepak!" she screamed.

I thought about where we were, on the inner ring of the three rings that make up Connaught Place, and remembered Sri Gupta, the ear-wire man, who must have been still sitting somewhere right below us on his stool outside the water closet with his blades and whetstone arranged around him. Two such juxtaposing worlds existing on the same spot at the same time reminded me of some of Frau Doktor Lieberman's most far-out dimensional anomalies.

"I'm going to ask them can we film them later," the Tiger said, getting up and walking over.

It turned out that Chocolate-face had spotted our camera equipment and thought we were some important foreign crew. The Tiger's stylish clothes had made an impression on him. His disaster-chic outfits were still as starched and immaculate as when he arrived, yet now, with a newly authentic ruffled-around-the-edges look that made him look still more distinguished. He had become bronzed and toned from hauling the tripod around the Rajasthan desert, which just added to the whole director-on-location look.

"Hey-yo! You guys get in from where?" Chocolate-face asked, in a pseudo-1960s way that reminded me of Austin Powers. "You shooting a movie, yaah?"

The Tiger told him what we were up to, and they got into conversation about the camera. Chocolate-face couldn't believe something so tiny could make television, and the Tiger told him about the new digital format and how for the first time ever cameras could be intimate, allowing for a more humble style of filming. The old analogies between film crews and armies on the march didn't apply any more. They swapped notes on lenses and filters and stuff, but before the Tiger could ask Chocolate-face about doing some filming with him and his friends, the others all turned up – Reg and Tara and Donald. Peadar turned up, too, but without the tapes. They were still in stasis somewhere between Egypt and India. The Tiger was furious. We were losing valuable time. He was curt with Peadar, but I managed to calm him down after a while. There was no point in taking it out on anyone. Things worked differently in the diplomatic world, and we just had to accept it. My feelings about Irish diplomats were still raw since my experiences when I was dying of rabies a few years earlier in Ecuador. In some ways, Irish diplomats were similar to the *hijras* in the role they played in our society up until recently: they offered a haven for eloquent, cultured young men, many of whom were gay, to cultivate their interests in music, dance, languages and sexual preferences out of sight of general society.

Tara and Reg recognised Chocolate-face immediately. It turned out that he was on a television show they both adored. Tara was on him like a shot, batting his eyebrows and telling him how much he loved his work – both his ads and his TV work. Chocolate-face responded all too eagerly. It was amazing to see Tara's skill at playing people. His perky Himalayan features and newly wrought western confidence set him apart from the crowd, and he could coax a response from a stone.

"*Mar sin, seo é do choillteán bheag, an ea?*" the Tiger muttered to me, looking over at Tara disparagingly. "*Do chastrato óg.*"

"*Éist,*" I said, trying to hush him up.

"Why? Does he speak Irish?" the Tiger said derisively, but in a lower voice.

Fortunately, Tara was too busy chatting up Chocolate-face to notice.

"He's no poster boy, is he?" the Tiger went on. "I'd say he'd be safe enough in the Vatican cloisters – the bishops won't be rummaging up his cassock."

"*Éist!*" I said again.

"Seriously, though," he said. "He doesn't look like any leper I've ever seen. Hs face is a bit scabby, but otherwise . . . Reminds me of that bloke from *Miami Vice*. Are you sure he's not infectious?"

I didn't have a chance to answer as Tara came sauntering over to the Tiger with his hand extended.

"So, you're the famous brother!" he said exultantly, shaking the Tiger's hand warmly. "It is great to finally meet you. Mocha-ji has been telling me so much about you. All good things, don't be worrying! How are you? I heard all about the problem with the tapes and I am so sorry. It is my great wish that they are coming to you so very soon."

"Thanks, Tara," the Tiger said awkwardly. "I'm sure Peadar is doing his best."

"Oh, yes!" Tara agreed heartily. "The embassy people are always so good, I find."

Reg suggested we head straight to the club as no one was really hungry, but Chocolate-face insisted we join him instead at a party he was going to out in Chanakyapuri. Tara and Donald jumped at the invitation, and so we all ended up out on Connaught Place waving down a fleet of taxis. I tried at first to hail an auto-rickshaw, but the girl with the diamond nose frowned, saying, "Only the poor take *chuck-chucks*", and got me to wave it on.

Three black and yellow Ambassadors were promptly summoned. They docked awkwardly beside us and took us out through the Delhi dusk to Chanakyapuri, to an imposing bungalow with a marble patio, where Chocolate-face led us through the garden and past some bearded guards to a private club in a mews out the back. There was a gang of cool, young Delhites posing outside, all dressed in white pants and shades. They seemed to know Chocolate well, and there was much awkward high-fiving and rapper handshakes. Inside, the place was hopping although it was still early. It was basically a disco bar in someone's shed that had been kitted out with a long bar of agate tiles, backlit to show up the colourful strata. Behind it was a wall-to-wall video screen on to which rave scenes were being beamed from a Bombay nightclub via satellite. I'm not sure if it was happening live or not, but suddenly we were transported to a thrumming, pulsating dance party where Bombay software engineers and Bollywood rupee zillionaires were thrusting and grinding to an incessant techno beat. I had heard that India was a leader in rocket programming and satellite aeronautics, but never imagined that their technology was being used for this. The girls' midriffs on display were a world away from the quick flashes of bare belly revealed by a well-draped *sari*. These bare bands of gym-toned dusky skin were being consciously flaunted, set off by low-slung hipsters and cropped T-shirts. The Bombay club seemed to be on three levels, with a large veranda extending out to a beach at the back.

A bank of smaller screens overhead was playing everything from Sky Sports to a James Bond movie, to what seemed to be MTV USA showing another dance party by a pool in Florida with everyone in bikinis and speedos, either dancing or cavorting semi-naked in the water with inflatable dolphins and bananas. It made the Bombay party look frigid.

At the back of the little bar was a tiny dance floor on which a handful of couples pretended to dance to a slow song, but actually were smooching. It appeared that although showing skin was fine in modern India, kissing in public was not yet acceptable.

My attention was caught by a skimpy pair of sequinned shorts at the MTV party in Florida. Their owner was writhing her groin into the camera lens. The camera pulled back to reveal a surgically enhanced body with peroxide hair. She was staring down into the camera, smiling absurdly and wantonly tossing her curls. I wondered could she ever conceive of the fact that she was being beamed live into a bar in downtown Delhi. Her prom-queen body was finally attracting the attention it deserved, far away from the no-doubt-appreciative, high school student faculty, and local softball team, whose realm it had been limited to up until now. As she turned, she revealed well-toned buttocks with a tattoo on her upper thigh which must have attracted the attention of the cameraman, as he quickly zoomed in to it, so that it filled the screen. It took me a second to grasp what it was, and then suddenly it clicked. I was left floored by its significance, by the momentousness of what had just occurred. The sight that had come radiating out of the screen into this dingy club was nothing less than an incidence of transcendence, with an attendant resonance that was barely graspable. The tattoo was of a tiny ω – the symbol for *Om*. Suddenly we were in the presence of God beamed live from the USA. For if the mere mention of the word *Om* evokes the manifestation of God in the physical realm, its written representation is more potent still. It is said that seeing the symbol cannot but be a transcendental experience – a profound moment of *darshan* (connection with the divine through a human entity), which would have blessed even the smooching couples on the dance floor, although they weren't looking at it and weren't even aware of its existence.

It was an odd night all told. I was amazed at Chocolate's keenness to befriend us and couldn't decide if it was because of our cachet as cool European film-makers or if, in fact, he fancied Tara. Whatever the case, Tara was certainly showing signs that he could take care of himself in the big bad world, attracting whatever support or attention he needed. I began to notice his uncanny ability to turn situations deftly to his advantage, and the rather unworthy suspicion occurred to me that perhaps he had been playing me all along. Had that tentative visit to my shack and the subsequent public flaunting of his sexuality been a well-planned ploy to get him out of there? Had he been able to guess the consequences, and known that I would feel obliged to become embroiled?

I dismissed the idea, thinking that I was just being over-callous and paranoid. Overall, the evening was a real eye-opener, and although we didn't get anything on camera because of not having tapes, I was glad we had come. I knew that sexual liberation was nothing new to India – the country had after all produced the original sex manual a thousand years ago – but it was interesting to see that it was blossoming to such an extent again after so long in hibernation. I had read how film stars were not allowed to kiss on screen and that couples were harangued or hauled off by the police for making out in public. I had thought that all that still applied.

Chapter 19

FIRST THING NEXT morning, I was on to the embassy, but the tapes still hadn't arrived. Now things were getting serious. We had only a few weeks left, and we couldn't afford to lose any more time. The Tiger said that we'd have to look for an alternative, as the chances of finding the right tape stock in Delhi were next to none. Sony had supplied the tapes to us free because we were the first people in Britain or Ireland ever to try using them for television. The format had been designed for obsessive home-video nuts, but proved to be so good that television stations realised they could broadcast footage filmed on it. The images were recorded digitally, which meant that when you got back home, you could simply stick them into a computer, manipulating them in any way you wanted, changing the tones and resolution to bring them up to practically cinema quality. The whole thing ended up costing the camera industry a fortune, as people in the profession traded in their high-end equipment to switch to these cheapo DV models at a fraction of the cost.

I suggested we give Chocolate a ring in case he knew someone in the industry who could hire us a professional camera for a few days. It would be expensive, but presumably the insurance would pay up when we got home. The Tiger agreed it was worth a shot, but when I rang Chocolate's number, I got his mother who said he had flown down to Bangalore that morning. She gave me the number of one of his friends, Deepak, whom I rang, but he wasn't very forthcoming. Eventually, he admitted that a cousin of his dabbled in television and might be able to help. We arranged to meet up later at a *Kwality* restaurant in a Gotham-city-like ghetto of drab apartment blocks on the outskirts of town.

When we got there, Deepak was waiting with his cousin Kristin. It turned out that Kristin's father actually ran a television station, which sounded like a perfect stroke of luck. If anyone could help us, he could. They told us the station was just near by, and we asked could we go there straightaway.

Deepak led us into a tiny litter-strewn lane, and I was surprised when he opened a heavy fire door that led into the shaft of a stinking elevator whose light was broken. There was a woman sleeping rough on the ground and two men crouching over her. I asked what we were doing there, and he said the station was right above us. The Tiger and I looked at each other in concern. I gripped tighter on the camera bag, and he brandished the tripod defensively. The lift brought us to the eighth floor, where the door opened straight on to Kristin's parents' living room. His mother was sitting on a couch watching a television veiled by an embroidered doily. She was munching Bombay mix.

"Where's the station?" I asked.

Kristin pointed to the corner. Bolted to the window ledge was a satellite dish connected to a basic amplifier and modulator. There was a VCR player and a small television stacked above it, while scattered on the floor were some reels of cables and connectors.

"Dad is a dish-*wallah*," Deepak explained. "He rebroadcasts satellite television and wires it to the people in the area. This is the control room for all these blocks of flats."

Like a broker on Wall Street, he gestured expansively out the window. "He has hundreds of subscribers."

I wondered if this was what Gandhi had meant when he talked of cottage industries. Ever since CNN turned its satellite a few degrees to face the subcontinent, a seismic shift had been set in motion. The days of mind-numbing saccharine soaps and Gandhi eulogies were over for good, as satellite hackers hard-wired the country's living rooms into the global jet stream of news, sports, soaps and MTV.

"What do you broadcast?" the Tiger asked, looking around him in wonder.

"We don't broadcast, we *rebroadcast*," Kristin said.

"What?" the Tiger asked.

"At first, just the fighting in the desert. We hacked into the signal from CNN during the Gulf War, but it was hard; you needed a 12-foot dish to catch it. Father joined with some local restaurant owners to put up a dish, and they all used it. Our Muslim neighbours were willing to pay any price for news of their Middle Eastern brothers. Soon we had cables snaking right through all the buildings, over trees and across roads. The government didn't like it, but they pretended it wasn't happening; they needed to know what was going on as much as everyone else."

"So, you just show CNN?" the Tiger said.

"No, that was in the first years, before Star TV came and we all turned our dishes. It has the best programmes – *Santa Barbara, Baywatch, The Bold and the Beautiful*. All the people come wanting these programmes."

I had heard about Star TV from the Christian missionaries in Varanasi. They regarded it as a sort of malevolent crusade sweeping the country, introducing hundreds of millions of people to the adulterous, car-chasing perdition of drugs and liposuction that constituted American life, according to cheap television programmes. The missionaries wanted to get their view of a pious, sanitised America across, but it was hard to argue with actual television images. The likes of *Kojak* repeats and rap videos were having cultural repercussions far beyond what anyone ever intended. They were speeding up the process of unpicking the stranglehold of asceticism and deeply rooted taboos that had held the nation together. This was good in some ways for the missionaries, but they would have preferred if the programmes hadn't also sullied their illusion of a pristine, church-centred Utopia back home.

In the end, no one in leadership was very happy with satellite television, but there was little they could do about it other than shoot the sputnik out of the sky. It was left to the few moderate Western voices in the country (mainly consisting of the BBC Asia Service and responsible backpackers) to offer an alternative version of life in the West. Backpackers in particular, while trekking in the most remote regions, provided some evidence that all Westerners were not as vapid or egocentric as the duplicitous bimbos in soaps and music videos. But in their own way, backpackers, too, provided a false picture of us. Being amongst the most idealistic and adventurous in society, backpackers possibly offered too favourable a portrayal of who we really are.

"Where's Father?" Kristin asked his mother, in English for our benefit.

She pointed upwards, not once taking her eyes off the screen. She was the ideal advertisement for the allure of her husband's wares.

Kristin flung open the window, craning his neck out and shouting up to his father. They had a farcical conversation back and forth along the side of the building about whether or not he knew someone with a professional camera. The father shouted down things like, "Ask Mama if Uncle Padu's Super 8 is still working, *na?*"

He said this in Hindi, but with the words *Padu* and *Super 8* in it, it was obvious enough what he was talking about.

Finally Kristin pulled his head in, shaking it regretfully.

"No, I'm afraid. He says to try the Lajpat-Rai market. It's in Chandni Chowk in Old Delhi. Maybe there they have black-market camera?"

We went back down to the street where Kristin approached some friends who were tinkering with the engines of a pair of battered Baja scooters. After a moment, he jumped on the back of one and got Deepak to take the other, and they told us to jump on behind. We drove into town, right into the rickshaw and buffalo-cart maelstrom of Old Delhi to a *Blade Runner*-like congestion of ghetto hawkers selling dirt-cheap satellite dishes and signal amplifiers. Kristin turned to us.

"You can pick up anything you need here," he said. "Everything for television."

The Tiger glanced around, shaking his head dubiously. It certainly didn't look very promising. This was not where we wanted to be. Bushy-haired old men were stooped over trays of transistors and moderators, selling various reconditioned, outdated tat: tarnished buckets of cables, connectors and assorted knickknacks. It was a classic case of a well-meaning Indian not wanting to let you down, stringing you along as long as possible, delaying the moment of disappointment. I thought of my spectacles beaten into shape on an anvil, my sandals stapled with catgut.

We thanked the boys for their help and went back to the hotel. Peadar was there waiting for us. He had good news.

"We've found your tapes," he said ominously.

"Great," the Tiger said. "Are they here?"

"Yes," he said hesitantly. "In India."

"Let's go and get them," the Tiger said.

"You don't understand," Peadar said. "They're in customs."

"So? We'll go and collect them."

"No," Peadar said. "You see, they were labelled as tapes from TnaG, and the Indian government can't find any listing for that channel. They think it's suspicious."

"Well, we'll just explain that it's not," the Tiger said breezily.

"It's not that simple," Peadar said. "The government is under pressure from America right now to clamp down on stuff, to keep an eye out for anything suspicious. The FBI has been installing surveillance devices – X-ray machines, sniffing machines – in the ports and post centres. The post office sorters in Delhi are so spellbound by their sniffing machine they're getting no work done; they keep bringing in stronger spices to see can they fool it. Anyway, your tapes have certainly caught their attention. You have to admit they do look a bit suspicious."

They were about the size of a snuffbox with a little spool of metallic black tape visible through a clear plastic window. They certainly looked high-tech, the sort of thing you'd imagine handed over in a rolled-up newspaper in a Berlin café during the Cold War. An espionage tool designed by Q for James Bond.

"So what happens now?" the Tiger asked.

"That's the question," Peadar said, clearly biding his time.

"Well?" the Tiger asked.

"They've asked me to . . ."

"Wait there," the Tiger interrupted. "I thought you said they were going in the diplomatic bag? Surely that doesn't go through customs?"

"Clearly we don't put everything in the bag – it's just a term," Donald explained. "The rest goes with a special secure post. It's not normally checked, but I suppose the tapes must have made them suspicious."

"What can we do now?" I asked.

"Well, by rights you hand over the rest of the tapes to us, and we pass them on to the government."

"Are you out of your mind?" cried the Tiger.

"We could say that you had already sent them home, if you like. Haven't you filmed enough by now anyway?"

"No way!" the Tiger bellowed. "We've barely scratched the surface."

"I'll check back with the ambassador," Peadar said. "Maybe there's something . . ."

The receptionist came shimmying through the lobby towards me to say that there had been another call from Madame Singh Guli. She had been leaving messages in the hotel for the last few days, having heard through the diplomatic grapevine that the "young Irish film-makers" were back in town and taking it as a personal insult that we hadn't got in contact.

"Have you not been on to her yet?" Peadar said, chidingly. "Tut-tut! She's been driving the ambassador up the wall at every function he's at. She's desperate to get you to one of her soirées."

My status had risen considerably now that I was part of a film crew documenting her country, and she believed that she had fair claim on me, considering the help she had given earlier. I knew she wouldn't let up until I had made contact with her, and so reluctantly I put a call through to the big house.

A servant answered, and when I said my name the line went dead as he unplugged the apparatus to carry it to wherever the great lady was in the cavernous expanse. I imagined him echoing off down a long corridor.

Finally the line came live again, and Madame was full on, "Ahh, Mooo-ka, so glad you found the time! I have been soooo worried, soooo worried when you didn't come to call. I want to be of help, Mooo-ka, yaaah? I want to assist your great work in documenting our subcontinent. And I know that so, too, do you wish to help. This is wonderful because there is a little filming job that I think you will be wanting to do as a favour. But let's not talk here and now. I will send the car tonight after sundowners and we can dine. We can talk of all the things then."

Madame Singh Guli, allowing no space for refusal, handed the receiver back to her servant who first held it up to his ear and blew into it, checking for something or other, and then cleared his throat loudly before terminating the call. I could hear his breathless grunting and could almost feel the contempt for his mistress vibrating down the line. It seemed to me that just as it was expected in India that the rich would patronise their servants, the servants in turn were supposed to disparage their masters. I found the whole culture of vassalage in India odd. Nobody of any status did any active work; rather they ordered it to be done. It was easy for Madame Singh Guli to invite me to dinner, as someone else would cook and buy the food and mix the drinks and even drive to collect us. The house would always be spotless. There would always be a man ready to bring in tea at the right time. And if he wasn't there, many millions more were ready to take his place. It wasn't just the rich who had servants; everyone except the lowest of the low had some form of hired help. Even the backpackers and New Agers in Almora had local boys whom they would send off to get *samosas* or Limca sodas when they got the munchies. It never occurred to them that the child might be hungrier and thirstier than themselves. Although I had had someone to bring wood and milk to my little hovel over the winter, I always insisted on fetching all my own water and doing my laundry, more out of an ingrained sense of guilt than any common decency.

If there was any way I could have refused Madame Singh Guli's offer, I would have. This was no time to be off partying. I thought that the Tiger would hit the roof when he heard, but actually, when I told him about who she was, he was kind of interested. He thought she sounded like something out of Forester novel.

We both moped in our rooms for the rest of the day, the Tiger labelling tapes and me reading the papers. It was pointless going to see anything or meet anyone as it would be too frustrating not being able to film it. In the late afternoon, there was another call to the hotel to say that Madame Singh Guli's car would be arriving an hour early. We barely had time to have a shower and change before it pulled up outside.

Being back in the city now and as immaculately polished as a hearse, the Rolls Royce was unrecognisable from the bovine tank that had conveyed Madame Singh Guli in such a stately fashion into Baldoti leper station four months earlier. Its entwined Rs, sprouting superciliously from the bonnet, looked more ridiculous now than regal. In fact, the car looked so bizarre, idling ominously on the pavement under the wary eye of its audaciously moustached chauffeur, that the Tiger commented, "I reckon what Britain and India most have in common is a sense of the eccentric. It's why they gelled so well. Who knows, maybe it was why stars in the 1960s took on Indian *gurus* and psychedelic Rollers as icons. It was all *far out*."

The car ferried us to an international hotel where the chauffeur informed us that our hostess was awaiting us. The lobby was empty except for two temple priests, whose foreheads were smeared with horizontal stripes of paste and whose faces were batik-creased with laughter. Each carried a steel *tiffin* box of *idlis*, and dangling from the *dhoti* of one was a titanium mobile phone. I approached him, thinking that Madame might have sent him for us, but he had no idea who I was. Soon a receptionist appeared, and, overcompensating for not having been at her post, she arranged for two porters and a maid to lead us to Madame. We followed them downstairs past the laundry rooms to a gym, and just as they were about to show us into the sauna, I stopped them.

"No!" I said, urgently. "We're here to see Madame Singh Guli. She is expecting us."

"Yes, yes!" insisted one of the porters eagerly. "In here! She will see you."

Before he had a chance to open the door, there was a call from behind us. "Mooo-ka, darling! Over here!"

On the far side of the room, Madame Singh Guli was spread astride a computerised exercise bike, with stacks of blinding white towels balanced in front of her. Her neon leotard was stretched like sandwich wrap over the rising dough of her arms and belly. The bike was one of a bank of machines stretching across the room, each being pounded by sweating Indians, quite a few of whom were talking to visitors who stood patiently in front of them. The others were talking into bakelite phones or staring disconsolately at fading photos of Hindi film stars that had been cut from magazines and crudely pasted over the inoperative television screens. A smell of incense lingered heavily in the air, but couldn't quite mask the pheromones.

"I'm so glad you could come," she said after we had positioned ourselves in front of her as indicated. She continued pumping breathlessly away on the bike. "My husband is hosting sundowners today, so I thought . . . phew . . . I thought, we could meet here first and . . . get started on business, then go straight to dinner . . . huuaaaah!"

She let out an exhausted sigh.

"We have so much to get through," she added, before slugging greedily at her water bottle and pouring a generous stream down her forehead.

It was hard to accept that I was standing talking to a wealthy, cultured, middle-aged Indian women as she went through her exercise regime. Somewhere along the lines of cultural assimilation stretching East-West, there must have been a crossed wire that left the impression that since fitness was esteemed and flaunted in the West, the act of getting fit should also be flaunted – even to the point of inviting others to watch. How had Indian women got from practising *sati* and wearing veils to this? I marvelled at the rungs of the ladder that Madame must have climbed to get from her mother's closeted life in the back kitchen to the pyrrhic victory of being able to sweat it out in public in a hotel gym.

Madame clearly saw nothing odd about the situation. I could see that she was lost in delight at the sight of the Tiger, who admittedly did look very fetching in his crushed linen jacket, the Armani initials clearly evident on the lining. She was flashing her eyes at him as though she were half her age. I was glad that one of us made an impression, as she had clearly been underwhelmed by my appearance on our previous encounters. She practically purred when the Tiger grudgingly told stories of his time working on films with Julia Roberts and Brad Pitt. She took no notice when he tried to explain that as location manager and trainee assistant director he hadn't actually got to spend time in their Winnebagos with them, but she quizzed him on every minor detail nonetheless and wanted his opinions on all the great auteurs of European cinema and, most importantly, on what he thought of "our own humble Bollywood fare".

There were three other women in the gym, one a Westerner, whose skin had the pallid malignant quality of Caucasians abroad – like dermatological snapshots of fungal oddities in medical journals. She was the only one who attracted leery looks from the men. A high caste Brahmin, peddalling so fast that his sacred thread was chaffing against his underarm, sneaked furtive glances at her. Amidst the surrounding swarthiness, she was an expanse of bare tundra.

In time, Madame got around to telling us what she wanted. She was making a publicity video for her current pet charity, the Society for the Emancipation of *Daalit* Women, and she wanted the Tiger to film it. It was vital to get an outsider's perspective, she said. It would take only a day or two, and she was willing to fly us down to Bihar for it. There could be no cash payment as her finances were being investigated by a government committee at the time, but she would make sure that anything we needed during our stay in Bihar was catered for.

We explained about the tapes and she pooh-poohed the problem, saying it was inconsequential. The only issue was whether or not we would be willing to help her. The Tiger bristled and, through gritted teeth, pointed out that it was far from inconsequential. He began to explain about the new digital format, but she flicked her fingers dismissively and shouted for someone to fetch her a phone.

There were two old-fashioned phones sitting on a stool right beside her; all she had to do was reach out and lift the receiver, but evidently this was too much. A young boy in tennis whites promptly appeared from nowhere to dial her house and hand her the receiver. Once she had informed her staff that we would be arriving shortly, she lowered her tone and muttered something else in Hindi to her secretary, and then handed the receiver back to the boy.

"Shower time," she declared, dismounting and heading towards the changing rooms. "We will have no more talk. I am truly pooped."

As I left the gym, I could hear the drone of the machines spinning behind me, and I thought of Gandhi's spinning wheel – his symbol of honest labour and integrity which was still at the heart of India's flag.

We were whisked to Madame Singh Guli's drawing room for drinks and through to the dining room for dinner before I knew what hit me. The meal proved to be suitably excessive and ostentatious. Madame ate heartily, and I could imagine the generous ladles of *ghee*, rendered butter, in every dish returning the fat that she had just rendered off herself. Yet, nobody would ever notice; one of the wonders of a well-draped *sari* is that it hides so much. Over drinks in the Swarovski crystal room afterwards, she continued flirting with the Tiger.

"So, how do you become famous Irish film director?" she asked.

"I'm not famous," he said.

"And so modest, too!" she cried. "This is why Julie Roberts and the starlets are loving you so much, I am sure. Tell me all about yourself."

"I got into it, I suppose, because I liked movies," he said.

"We all like movies," she said, "but we don't become big-shot film director."

"I used to watch a lot of black and white movies when I was young," he explained. "That was really it. When I got older, I had to ask myself what I wanted to do in life, and I thought, why not make movies?"

"Such confidence!" she swooned. "He is thinking he likes movies, and so he becomes big-shot director. Simple as that! You must come see the children at my orphanage. You can tell them about following your dream. Inspire them! Isn't this right, Mocha? You must be so proud of your big brother? Is he your inspiration, your *guru*?"

"Sure," I managed.

"By the way, you were asking my cousin about the *hijras* on your last visit, I hear," she said to me. "You should have come directly to me, you know. Straight to me, that is what I am here for. I am here to help. All that *cha-cha-cha* about the *hijras* and their status in the royal courts is hogwash, *na*? So, too, the singing and dancing guff. Believe me, I should know! SHESO – my Society for Hijra Educational and Social Opportunities – went belly up last year. I was hoodwinked! Hoodwinked!

"You see, although many of them are still beggars, *fakirs* you could say, who have given themselves to God, there is now a *hijra* mafia. Sajda, Delhi's 'eunuch queen' – I spit on her grave – was gunned down in court after testifying in a murder trial. It was all over the *Hindustan Times* – exposing their whole damnable high-rolling criminal underworld and casting my charity right on to the rocks. You can only imagine! Who would give money to criminals? *Na*?"

I tried to make some reply, but it turned out to be another rhetorical question, and she ploughed on right over me.

"It seems that Sajda and her filthy castrates – Krishna forgive my vile mouth – had a network of police and politicians who helped them carve out an empire. It was extortion and debt collecting but without force. There was no need. Instead they embarrassed people with lewdness or oaths or showing genitals. Even, they took out contracts on each other like Chinese underworld scum. Can you imagine?! I held a gala lunch for SHESO and no one turned up! It was mortifying. As if I, too, were a criminal . . .!"

I could see the Tiger growing ever more weary of her incessant chatter, and, fearing he might lose his patience, I interrupted Madame to say that it had been a long day and we should perhaps be getting back to the hotel.

"But we haven't arranged about the *Daalit* women yet," she protested. "When can you film them?"

"*Muna chuireann tú stad léi táim chun í a bhualadh – sracfaidh mé na seoda grána sin óna muineál,*" the Tiger said to me, explaining in Irish exactly what he would do to her if I didn't shut her up.

"I told you," I said to her as firmly as I could. "We have no tapes."

"And I told you not to worry," she said sternly.

"And how exactly do you expect us not to worry?" the Tiger said through gritted teeth. "I'm trying to make a series about India, and your government has confiscated my tapes!"

"You worry so much," she said gaily. "In India there are always ways . . ."

"What?" the Tiger spat.

"Ways!" she repeated calmly. "There are always ways. Now where was I? Oh, yes, Sajda. She used to travel to Paris business class on shopping trips and even had a chauffeur-driven limousine with armed guards. Always she came plastered in gold and gaudy jewellery – even Swarovski, can you imagine? A *hijra* in Swarovski! It was sick. A sick fetish. *The Times* said she should sell some of her diamonds if things were so bad for the poor *hijras*. Oh, I was mortified!

"So you see, my boys, this is the point I've been wanting to make: don't you, too, be hoodwinked. It's my duty as an Indian to protect the visitor. You must be careful with the eunuch, that's all I'm saying. That's all I'm saying."

I nodded determinedly. I didn't let on that I had had any further dealings with them. It was none of her business. The Tiger was looking around him impatiently. There was only one thing on his mind.

"You will promise, won't you, sweetie, to do this little film for the *Daalit* people," she said to him, patting him encouragingly on the knee. "A quick trip down to Bihar, and it will all be done lickety-spit, yes?"

"I told you . . ." he began again in an angry voice.

"Forget all this worrying!" she interrupted, and, clicking her fingers, she whistled for Rafik, her attendant.

There was an ominous silence as Rafik failed to respond.

"Oh, Rafik!!" she bellowed. "Rafik-Rafik-Rafik . . . !"

Like a moorhen anxious for its chicks, she kept up the call until finally Rafik appeared, scurrying into the room, buttoning up his vest and slicking back his hair as he came.

"Ma'am?" he said.

"Has that silly tape mess been sorted out?" she asked.

He bent down low to her ear and whispered something. She nodded and then dismissed him.

"It is all fine," she said to us. "Just a big cock-up. Now the tapes are in your hotel in the morning."

"Really?" the Tiger said.

"Yes, yes," she said dismissively. "They are there, so you will do this thing for me, yes?"

"But . . . ? What about customs?" the Tiger said.

"Poppycock," she said. "Customs poppycock. In India things are differently. You *gora* never understand."

The Tiger and I looked at each other in puzzlement. We had no idea if she was telling the truth or not. As usual, we were out of our depth.

"If the tapes are in fact there, Madame Singh Guli," the Tiger began with as much emollience as he could muster, "we would, of course, like to help you in any way we can. That said, I think Mocha and I would be concerned that we might not be properly attuned to the local cultural sensitivities to do them service. The subtleties of Asian societies can be so indecipherable to an outsider."

She frowned, but he went on nonetheless, with increasing *gravitas*.

"In all my experience working with the great Hollywood directors, they have always told me that the truth is best told by someone from within the culture itself. I could never live with myself, Madame Singh Guli, if I had inadvertently misinterpreted the *Daalit* women. Their heritage is too precious to risk such misrepresentation, wouldn't you agree?"

She made muttering noises, but before she could continue, the Tiger said, "And so, my professional opinion is that the optimal situation would be to have a local director on this particular . . ."

He was interrupted at that moment by the arrival into the room of Clari, Madame's eldest daughter, who wished to be introduced to her mother's guests. The Tiger and I jumped eagerly to our feet, keen to move the topic on, singing the praises of the great meal her mother had served us and telling her at length about the work we were doing in India. She had been educated in California, where the family had moved during the 1970s when her father was one of the leading lights of the Green Revolution, a modernisation drive that had increased India's agricultural output through fertilisers and new techniques. He had set up a company in Bakersfield, shipping billions of dollars of agrochemicals and farm machinery back to peasant farmers at home.

"If you're looking for real India, you're in the wrong place," Clari said when I told her about the last few days in Delhi. "This city is just a museum now. The future is in the south: Bombay, Bangalore. There's no ocean or river here. You can't have a great city without these. Water fuels people; it sparks creativity. This place is dry and wizened. A viper's nest of Ali Baba and the Forty Thieves."

Her judgement seemed unnecessarily harsh, especially considering the fact that as an NRI she had been afforded the rare opportunity of a foreign education. It was up to people like her to defend the country, I felt, to see its potential. There was barely a trace of her Indian roots visible in her appearance. Her hair was dyed a mousy colour, and she was wearing a shoulder-padded jacket and garishly dangling earrings. She reminded me of a mafia wife or even Sajda, the eunuch-queen. It struck me that these newly affluent Delhites had certain things in common with the old maharaja/maharani class. Not only had they made their money from the sweat of peasants, but they also shared the maharajas' heightened sense of vanity. In a country more commonly associated with asceticism than narcissism, there was a profound interest in physical appearance, which was epitomised by the sight of Madame Singh Guli on her bike. It reminded me of the Maharaja of Patiala in his iced pool with his women being pruned and shaped around him. The *hijras* weren't the only ones being plucked, trussed and stuffed with their own giblets, sitting pretty on styrofoam trays.

"Now, Moo-ka, you naughty boy," Madame scolded brightly, switching topic and subtly accepting the Tiger's refusal to go to Bihar. "Why did you never tell me who you and your brother really were? You scallywag! If it had not been for your ambassador, I would never have learnt of your family's lineage. 'A distinguished line of freedom fighters and revolutionaries,' was what the ambassador said. 'Cohorts of the great Éamon de Valera and Michael Collins.' You little minx!

"When I saw you in the leper colony, I thought you were another bloody do–gooder – nothing more. But this is wonderful news! Wonderful! We must hold a gala dinner. I insist! *All* my friends will want to meet an intimate of the great Irish president. The Gandhiites will be thrilled, of course. I can just see their pinched little faces lighting up! They revere him, don't you know? Without de Valera and that cunning fox Collins, we would never have got our freedom. Gandhi-ji himself said he owed them the deepest debt. They were his inspiration, you see? Why else do you think we would make our flag green, white and orange? We owe you everything. We may have been the Jewel in the Crown, but you were always the Emerald."

I tried explaining that I was seven when President de Valera died, and that although my family had been close to him and to Collins, too, things had got so bitter during the Civil War that they had never spoken again. But Madame didn't want mere details getting in the way of the dinner party she was already planning in her mind. As far as she was concerned, we were members of a Republican aristocracy, and she was determined to flaunt us to her friends. The tricolour would be its theme, she said. The chef would make a special Irish stew curry. She'd serve shamrock-shaped *chapattis*. Her mind was racing forward on full throttle until the Tiger finally pulled her up short, explaining that the whole idea was out of the question. If, indeed, the tapes did in fact turn up, we would have no choice but to leave Delhi as soon as possible to film the remainder of the series. We still had to capture a sense of life in the Himalayas in whatever time was left to us.

"Poppycock!" she said. "What do you want to go there for? A wilderness of tribesmen high on cannabis. And so cold! India is the dusty plains. Here is where you must stay. Forget the filthy mountains – they just make you nauseous."

She had convinced herself that we were some kind of ersatz royalty – the first of any kind of European aristocracy to dine with her since the British had so suddenly and unreasonably pulled out fifty years before. She was desperate to cling on to us. I worried whether our preconceived assumptions about India might be as misguided as hers were about Ireland.

We left an hour later, promising that we would give further thought to her idea of the dinner, and that at the very least we would attend one of her soirées before leaving the city for good. In the Rolls Royce on the way back, the Tiger said that he had consented to this final pledge only on condition that she managed to get us the tapes.

Sure enough, next day the tapes were waiting for us in the lobby when we came down for breakfast. There was no proper explanation given, and we were both too excited to question it further. We were just told that there had been a miscommunication and that it was all settled now. The Tiger tore open the box, checking that they hadn't been tampered with in any way, and he told me to set about immediately preparing for our trip to the mountains, booking a train as far as the railhead at Kathgodam and ringing Khim Singh in the *chai* shop to let him know we were on our way. We were both keen to set off as soon as possible, but I managed to convince the Tiger that we ought to keep our promise to Madame and pop in at the drinks party that evening.

Madame had made sure that all her Gandhi fans were in attendance, and they honed in on us as soon as we walked through the door, plying us with questions about our family's revolutionary past and the possible links between our grandparents and Gandhi or Nehru.

I did my best to play along with it at first, telling whatever stories I remembered my grandmother telling me about de Valera when I was young, but the Tiger was having none of it. He thought the whole thing was ludicrous. He could see no real link between the Irish and Indian independence movements. It meant I had to work twice as hard telling them what they wanted to hear.

"Our grandmother fasted for weeks on end," I said. "Up to a month at one stage in the 1920s – just like Gandhi a decade later."

"No, it wasn't anything like Gandhi," the Tiger rejoined. "She was in prison and was fasting for her political rights. Gandhi did it when he was free. And he wasn't doing it for his own rights; he wanted to shame the government into treating his country with dignity. One is the action of a cornered vixen turning on the hounds – a frantic, desperate act, as illogical as a bee sting. Gandhi's peaceful fasts while out in the world were symbolic and liberating – a recognition that all the wonders of life were worth nothing if his cause was not met."

I was surprised by the Tiger's defence of Gandhi. If he felt like this, why hadn't he allowed me to feature him in the programmes?

"Because he's not relevant now," he said when I asked.

The Gandhiites were appalled by this.

"As far as I can see, no one with any real power is keeping alive his legacy today," the Tiger said.

"What about Sugata Mitra?" one of them said.

"Who?" we both asked.

"Sugata Mitra, the computer-in-the-slum guy – he's like a twenty-first century Gandhi."

I had never heard of him.

"He's come up with a way of teaching computers to half a billion kids," one of them explained. "He built a PC, with a joystick and touch pad, into a wall in a slum and then just left the kids to play. Within minutes they knew how to control the cursor. To them it was a magic television where you could move things inside the screen. They noticed that when the cursor changed shape you could go somewhere else by clicking. Within minutes they were surfing the net, and after a day or two they were cutting and pasting things, dragging and dropping files, creating folders. They taught each other and even made up a whole language for things like *save* and *disk* and *file*.

"Mr Mitra claims if you gave him a few million dollars, he could get 500 million children computer literate in five years. That's 12 per cent of the planet! Guess what the most popular programme was?"

I shrugged.

"Microsoft Paint! These children never had paint or paper before – suddenly they could make art. They went through every button until they worked out how to draw and paint pictures, making thousands of drawings, and even managing to download an MP3 player so that they could play music, too. '*Yeh daal roti dega kya?* (Will it give us food?)' the older people asked – it was about the only thing it didn't do."

We decided to stay on in Delhi for a day to see could we track Sugata down, but when we told Reg, he poured cold water over the idea.

"It's pie in the sky," he said. "Rural India has no electricity; how will they run the machines? Even in the villages that do, half of the people are illiterate – what good is it? And what about phone lines? What they need is blackboards first."

"Solar power," I said. "Cellular phones. Computer-based literacy programmes?"

"I'm just saying," he said. "It's not as easy as it seems."

We never managed to track down Sugata Mitra; it seemed he was away at a conference. Reluctantly, we abandoned the idea and headed north, back to my home from home in the Himalayas.

Chapter 20

THE TRAIN HAD brought us as far as it could into the Himalayas, but at Kathgodam the terrain became too steep and we transferred to a taxi. I had chosen a little Maruti minivan because the driver undercut the Ambassadors by half, but already the engine was struggling against the incline, and it was looking unlikely it would make it up. If there had been any strands of tread left on the tyres, they could have come to some temporary arrangement with the tarmac, but they were as smooth and fragile as balloons. We had already suffered a blow-out, and, of course, the driver didn't keep a spare. He had to flag down a passing car and somehow wheedle theirs from them.

After about an hour of slipping and skidding, we agreed to cut our losses, and we paid the driver off and continued on foot. The climb was steep, but the air so pure and the mountains so spectacular that we hardly felt it as we tramped along the river canyon. The sun was just beginning to set when we reached the famous lookout point at Brighton's End Corner just ahead of Almora. The sight of the Himalayan peaks of Nanda Devi and Durga Kott rising in the distance, pristine under a fresh coat of snow, now turning pink and orange in the dying sun, was a fine consolation for the walk. It was good to be back in the life-enhancing hills again, with their orchards of peaches, plums and apples, and their tiny terraced fields of rice and tea. The biting chill in the wind blowing down from the snow peaks was energising. I had warned the Tiger in advance, and we had dug out our woollen jumpers. Suddenly the world seemed brighter. Mountains lend a sense of perspective, and already I could feel the pure air banishing the confusion of the previous weeks on the plains.

The Tiger was enchanted by Almora: its cobbled streets, colour-faded façades and tight-packed bazaar. On a step outside the Kailash restaurant sat the fax man who had sent my irregular letters home throughout the winter. He stood up grandly when he spotted me and gave me a hero's welcome. He was wearing the same homespun trousers and heavy grey shawl he had worn all winter. They were tattered and soiled now, but his hair was as immaculately oiled as always, and he was preening his moustache in the reflection of a pewter soup terrine, like a dancer about to go on stage. I admired for the hundredth time the antimacassar he used as a dust cloth on his fax machine because I knew how fond he was of it, and it gave him the opportunity to explain once again to the Tiger what the Hindu symbols that were crocheted into it meant.

We sat down in the cobbled gutter, and a *chai-wallah* brought us two cups of steaming tea. The cobbler tottered over, pulling from his pocket two tiny dolls made of strips of Dupont tyre and handing one to each of us. They had been made by an acolyte of Swami Vivekananda, he said, and were blessed. Immediately I felt at home again and wondered how I'd ever left this place, or survived so long in the dust below.

My brother was fascinated by the fractal nature of the bazaar – a sequence of dark gaping mouths with heavy counters upholstered in oil-cloth spanning their width and framed by pale blue shutters hanging on either side. Behind each counter stood a bright, attentive face, smiling and ready to serve. Although it looked as if they all stocked the same wares, in fact each specialised in something slightly different: the best Basmati, the freshest almonds, the finest-ground cumin, the most generous credit. A few of the owners raised their hands in *namaste* to me. Others, remembering that I had had dealings with the leper station, considered me unclean and were less forthcoming.

Sitting straight across from us was a reminder of why I had fled from Almora: Tara's grandfather, one of the best tailors in town, was poised cross-legged on a blanket on the pavement, feeding a seam of over-patched trouser into his Singer. Cataracts had, fortunately for me, left him almost blind, and I doubted he could see me. I noticed the evening sun catch the silver lining on a heavy woollen overcoat lying beside him awaiting mending, turning it the pink of the snowcaps. I shifted into the shadows so as to be less visible. I knew I would have to confront Tara's family sooner or later, but not just yet.

We took a ride with a passing pony cart the last few miles up to Khim Singh's *chai* shop where I had first taken the phone call from the Tiger all those weeks before. There was no sign of Khim anywhere, and so we continued on down the hill through the trees to my old homestead. I was keen to show my brother my little hovel, my own personal version of Thoreau's cabin on Walden Pond, and we carried the tripod and camera bag with us in case the light was suitable for filming when we got down there. Halfway down the hill, I was stopped by a wiry-bearded man who came running at me from behind a mighty larch. It was Nadav, an Israeli who had been living there for months. He snuggled his lip in to my ear, murmuring something, and latching his arms around my shoulders protectively.

"Nadav," I said. "How's it going?"

He didn't reply, just stayed holding me, rocking me gently back and forth, and mumbling incoherently into my ear. The low drone made my inner ear quiver, sending shivers down my spine. The Tiger watched on uneasily.

"You've got to go and see Bingo," Nadav said determinedly after he had exhausted his murmurings.

"Okay," I said. "I've just arrived with my brother; maybe . . ."

"You've got to go and see him," he said again, letting go of me. "Promise?"

"Sure," I said and, mollified, he continued on past me up towards Khim's.

The Tiger wanted to know what that was all about but I waved him off.

"Maybe later," I said, with a horrified chill in my voice. This was no time for explanations. The sight that hove into view through the trees had knocked the air right out of me. I was standing there, just staring at the view of my little house through the trees. The implications of what I was seeing were still only beginning to register on my mind, sending shock waves through me. My little stone cabin, cowering beneath pine trees in a cleft in the valley, was exactly as I had left it. Physically it hadn't changed, I was sure of that, but only now did I see it for what it was. The filthy, squalid pit it truly was. By right it was suitable only for animals, if even them. How had I not seen this before? This sacred capsule that had provided a launch pad for my journeys into realms of imagination and tranquillity, to the very borders of sanity, had somehow shape-shifted in the time I was away, leaving no trace of the nurturing cocoon that had given me the freedom to explore the limits of consciousness; no remnant of the angelic voices or the cosmic light shows that had lit my path.

I had referred to my house as a hovel only in a jocular, self-deprecating way. It was meant affectionately. I never considered it an accurate term. I had described it to the Tiger as a simple sanctuary in the hills, as cosy as Bilbo Baggins' Bag End. A cross between a nest and a nexus. I had told him he might find it a bit Spartan, but that was what I liked about it: it provided protection from the rain and the prowling mountain leopards, and that was all I needed.

Now, seeing the damp-sodden walls smothered in cobwebs, the *ghee*-smeared dirt floor and fetid eiderdown, I realised for the first time quite how low I had sunk. The Tiger was genuinely horrified, and was finding it hard to disguise the fact. He was looking around him at the soot-stained bed, the congealed spittoon and the urine containers lined up on either side of the fire pit – fortunately empty but still reeking of excreta. What could I say to him? How could I explain it? My confidence was truly shattered.

And things had been going so well for me until then. I had even dared imagine that perhaps I could make a career in television. My PTCs were becoming more fluent and my demeanour more confident. Secretly I had some ideas about introducing more alternative ideas into the programmes. Seeing as how I was being handed this soapbox, it was my duty to run with it – to get out into the public domain the pioneering concepts that careered through my head and that the world really needed to know. One of the first issues I wanted to address was the disillusioned seekers like me who come here to the mountains from the developed world looking for answers. I wanted to highlight the importance of their work, breaking down borders, questioning the status quo and exploring the outer limits of thought. I thought that my little hermitage could provide an interesting angle on it. Viewers would be intrigued to see the place – my cocoon of transmutation. It had never dawned on me that it was such a pit.

Something you'd see in the judicial review of a patient taken into care. Or a charity appeal on television.

In my defence, it should be said that the place was a lot worse before I moved in. I had gone to considerable lengths to clean it up. Khim Singh had been using it as a barn, and the two of us had spent days clearing out manure and routing an extended family of swallows nesting in the eaves. I had whitewashed the walls and got a local man to knock up a stove out of an old galvanised bucket, and Khim had agreed to hire a carpenter to make a door and some furniture for me, but he ran out of wood before he got to the table, so I ended up eating my meals off the floor.

"And this was what you wanted to put on TV," the Tiger was saying, more in sadness than in anger. He was looking around forlornly, pausing now and then, as he searched for words. "You know this isn't a hermitage; you know that, don't you?"

"Mm–uh," I said, miserably.

"It's a bloody humanitarian crisis," he said.

"Mm–uh."

"Look, if you have some sort of self-flagellation fetish that's fine, but believe me, no one at home wants to see this – an over-educated waster going to seed."

It was a bad moment. A sad moment for both of us, especially for me as I had just been working up the courage to tell him that I wanted to share my piss–drinking regime with the viewers. I wanted people at home to know that French dentists recommended urine gargling and that the chief surgeon of Chicago State Hospital believed that drinking a glass of urine a day would dramatically reduce the prevalence of heart disease. This was important information that needed to get out there.

As best I could, I recovered my dignity and steered the Tiger back up the hillside to the guesthouse which I had booked for him. It was clear that I could no longer stay in my cabin, and I got the guesthouse owner to pre-pare a second room for me. The rooms were like something out of a Sussex cottage of a century ago, with high spring beds, bedpans and embroidered cushions. The place had belonged to a Bohemian British couple who had haunted the margins of Bloomsbury before retiring to die in the Himalayas, where they had built this sprawling, porticoed bunga-low in a grove of cedars looking out on to Nanda Devi.

One of the things that had attracted me to Almora was the quirky hill-station feel of the place. For anyone brought up on Benny Hill and naughty English seaside postcards, the place had an unmistakably comic feel to it. The British had built these quasi-Wordsworthian idylls as sentimental reminders of home, and still today they seemed to be lampooning the idyll depicted in Ealing comedies. I had to admire the audacity of their creators. The British had chosen the most picturesque hill tops, shaved them of trees and built mock-Tudor villages on them, complete with teashops, miniature theatres, Gothic churches, croquet pitches and lines of quaint rose-dappled cottages with twitching net-curtains and names like Blackberry Bend and Dingly Dell – all clinging on to a series of perilous ledges 10,000 feet in the air.

The hubris of creating these snow-globe villages in the one region that had always been the abode of the gods and where Lord Shiva rode his bull with Ganga, the river goddess, coiling through his hair, was what got me most. You had to admire their tenacity. Monkeys and barking deer used to invade the gardens frequently, leopards and black bears would maul the servants, and a sudden mudslide or earthquake could wipe out the tennis courts or the ballroom just before a great fête or jubilee ball. Nevertheless, each year, when the heat became unbearable on the plains, the entire bureaucracy of the Raj would trek hundreds of miles up into the mountains on ponies and donkeys to Simla or one of her sister towns, so that for half the year one fifth of mankind was ruled from villages connected to the outside world by little more than a pony track. It was so eccentric that only the British could have pulled it off.

I was woken early next morning by an espalier pear tree rattling against the tiny lead-paned window, and I heard the low whine of the conch shell ringing out across the hills. I recognised the call immediately as that of Nadav's friend Bingo, who had been blowing the day into existence in this manner since he had first come to the mountains a year before. A *sadhu* had initiated him, promising him that if he played for the mountains every morning, they in turn would see him right. Reluctantly, I steeled myself to get up and go after him, to fulfil my promise to Nadav. The piercing morning cold was still a shock to me after my time on the plains. I had spent the night burrowed under two blankets, a quilted eiderdown and a moth-eaten baize comforter that I had found stuffed behind an old walnut chest of drawers. There was still six hours of chill until noon, the point at which on most days the sun managed to wrest back control from the glaciers and high snowfields which wielded control of the thermometer at night with merciless abandon.

As I clambered across the hillside towards the rock on which Bingo usually blew the conch, the sky was lit up with streaks of blue, and the grey snowcaps were turning gold in the rising sun. I reached the rock just as he was wiping his lips and wrapping the shell back in its chamois. He took one look at me and spat.

"You left us, you fuck-wit; you went and left!"

He scrambled down to the far side of the rock, which jutted out over the valley like a pulpit, and I had to run around it to catch up with him.

"I'm sorry, Bingo," I said. "I'm sorry."

His face crumpled like a Pierrot clown.

Bingo was Israeli, too, like Nadav. It seemed that no matter where I went in the world, I bumped into Israelis straight out of the army, and they were always in either one of two states: boisterous and belligerent if they were *en masse*, or else lost and despairing if they were on their own – broken shards set adrift from their companions. I had come across them in Africa and South America, and so was not surprised to find Bingo and Nadav living in a hut a mile or two from me when I arrived in Almora. Classic examples, young ex-conscripts whom the war had eviscerated. Despite Nadav's earlier hug, we weren't so much friends as acquaintances – the only non-Indians who went to Khim's on any regular basis. On my weekly trip to the lepers in Baldoti and the market in Almora, I would invariably meet one or other of them in the *chai* shop, smoking *charas* and fulminating at anyone who'd listen. They rarely made much sense; the *chillums* which they sucked on day and night left their brains an addled mess. The worst was when they got their hands on Khim's rotgut whisky, which turned them dark and brooding. They would pick at the old scars, rehashing the same stories about razing vineyards and orange groves with bulldozers along the lines of combat. They had been involved in much actual fighting and bloodshed, but it was the memories of their destruction of those farms and the faces on the farmers watching that seemed to haunt them the most.

"I hear you're not getting out much?" I said to Bingo when I caught up with him, but he kept his eyes low.

"Bingo!" I said. "Come on, talk to me. What's going on?"

Although I wasn't particularly close to Bingo or Nadav, I found myself feeling oddly protective towards them. One of the paradoxes of my hermitic existence was that the fewer people I met, the stronger my connection to them was. There was an odd intensity to life in the Himalayas which may well have been down to, as Lans Okalsom claimed, the electromagnetic frequency of the rock.

Bingo began shuffling back up the track again.

"What's up?" I said.

"You left me, you fuck," he said. "You really did."

"I didn't leave *you*, Bingo. I just left."

He exhaled mournfully.

I had made sure to let them both know that I was going before I left for Delhi, but they didn't really take much in. I felt like a parent having patiently explained to his children that he was going out for the evening, only to find them inconsolable on his return. They had been infantilised by the army and found it hard to deal with stuff. Everything was a crisis.

"You'll never guess what I did!" I called brightly. "Where I ended up bringing Tara!"

He looked up suddenly; I knew this would get his attention. Bingo rented a cabin from the family of Sangev – Tara's boyfriend – and had taken a particular interest in their blossoming love.

"What?" he asked, plumes of breath rising out of him like a dragon.

"I'll tell you all about it," I said. "Come on! We'll go back to your place – it's freezing here."

"No, tell me now," he said.

"First, a cup of tea," I insisted. "It's 6.30 in the morning – I'm freezing."

"Okay," he agreed, "but in your place."

"I'm not staying there any more," I said. "And anyway your place is just around the bend."

Bingo stopped, put his hands in his pockets like a cussed child, and said, "No!"

I took no notice of him and continued up along the track towards his cabin, which was just a few metres ahead. I walked on like you do with a toddler, goading him to follow and not looking back.

At the cabin, I pushed open the door, and the smell hit me like a blow in the face.

"Jesus, Bingo," I called back. "What the hell!"

The room was pitch black except for the embers of the previous night's fire still smouldering in the hearth. I pulled back the blanket that was nailed across the window just a fraction, letting the grey morning light seep in to reveal the earthen floor covered in what looked like hundreds of dead wasps. I took a step back, gagging on the smell, and as my mind processed the scene it occurred to me that these couldn't possibly be wasps. Suddenly I recognised the smell: the sick stench of skunk. These tiny tubular forms were *charas*. Tiny lumps of *charas*, carefully wrapped in cellophane. Green *charas* – the best quality, hand-processed cannabis resin.

I looked at Bingo, but he didn't say a thing. His only concern was that I might step on the lumps, and he was pushing me on to a cushion on the floor by the fire defensively. A much larger slab of *charas* wrapped in tin-foil was lying on a log beside the bellows.

"Bingo?" I said. "What's up?"

"I've got to get out of here," he replied.

"No, we have to talk," I said.

"No, I mean out of Almora – leave India. I'm losing my mind here. I've gotta go."

"Maybe it *is* time to move on," I agreed.

"Right," he said. "But where? I mean, really, where can I go? I'm not going back. Never. I can't. If I saw Ben Gurion Airport again, I don't know what . . . I don't. I'm dead."

"But what about your family? Your friends?"

"I'm not going," he said more urgently. "I'd choke. It's poisonous. The air, the thoughts, the words. I'm thinking London. My uncle sells cars in Golders Green – a big place right by Hampstead Heath. I can stay with him a while. I just need a bit of cash first . . ."

I knew what was coming next; I'd heard it too often before. The temptation was too great not to think about it at least; you head home from your holiday with some wonderful memories, and you bring just a little something extra with you.

"Just one run," Bingo was saying. "I get into Heathrow around Easter. They'll be too busy to search properly. They'll just wave us through. Another Jew home for Passover."

"Oh, man!" was all I could say.

It was hard to argue with his reasoning. If he could conceal just half a kilo of these little maggots, he was sure to make ten grand in London. He was just the latest in a long line of people with the same idea – and a reasonable percentage got through. What's more, he thought he could get his hands on some Hasidic garb – the full thing: Homburg hat, black gartel and all. If he were in those, odds were he'd be waved straight through.

It was so tempting, so easy. The only difficulty was the preparation. The *charas* had to be cut and compressed into cherry-pip size lumps, and each lump then wrapped and sealed with flame and then resealed a second time just to make sure. Finally, each of the hundred little balls had to be aired to get rid of the smell of burnt cellophane and then stuffed, one by one, up his bum. There would be a lot of digging and prodding with fingers involved. It could take hours, and it was never easy, especially if you didn't have anyone helping you, and Nadav had made it clear that he was not going to take any part in it. Of course, he wanted to help his friend: the notion of *achva* – brotherhood or sticking together through thick and thin – was what the army was built on, after all. But Nadav knew that if Bingo got arrested or if the packages burst and he overdosed, he could never face Bingo's parents or his old battalion buddies again knowing that he had helped. At this stage, they were almost brothers, and it was up to at least one of them to come back home sane and free. The very idea of Zionism was depending on them: the notion that the struggle for a homeland was worth the sacrifice of each generation's young. The hope was always that, in time, they would get over the ordeal, and fortunately some did.

The only advice Nadav had given Bingo was to chop the *charas* into balls. Initially Bingo had wanted to wrap a large lump in a condom and simply stick that up instead. The lumps worried him. He feared he mightn't be able to keep them all in on the long flight home; some might go missing in his intestine.

"What other choice have I got?" Bingo said to me, looking around the shrapnel-scattered room. "You tell me."

That same feeling of despair washed over me as had so often before on meeting Israelis abroad: despair at how their obsession with *Lebensraum* robbed them of so much. I thought of Niishraah. Of how wonderful it would be to have her up here, hugging Bingo and Nadav, or even getting her to Israel so that she could give the country one of her most powerful, magical hugs that took away all the hurt and replaced it with love.

"Hey, don't worry!" he said. "It's simple – a piece of cake. I just stroll through the airport and flip the gear straight to the brothers for 10 K. Then I cut lose. I won't go risking any back end on the deal – I'm not a total schmuck! I'll start over – a new leaf. Hang out with my uncle, sell a few Volvos, brush up on my Cockney slang. Find me a nice goyish girl; maybe a Sloan Ranger, who knows? I'll be fine."

I tried reasoning with him, but even as I laid out the arguments, I knew that I wasn't convincing. How could I know where his mind was at? He humoured me as I went through my spiel, then he took the chamois-wrapped conch and handed it to me.

"Mocha," he said solemnly, "you have to promise me you'll blow this when I'm gone."

"Well . . ." I said, reluctantly stretching out my hand to accept it, but then pausing. "Maybe you should bring it with you instead. Golders Green needs the cleansing sound of a conch more than this place. The Himalayas will do just fine without you, Bingo. But you're going to need all the help you can get. Keep on blowing it in London – just hope it steers you right. Think of it as a song-line stretching back here, keeping you in touch."

We hugged and I let him get back to his work. I just hoped he wouldn't end up blowing the conch behind bars.

Chapter 21

A GENUINE PRE-WAR British fry was being served to the Tiger on heavily veined Wedgwood when I got back to the guesthouse. I sat down at a Hampton Court place mat and had just poured myself a cup of Earl Grey when Khim Singh walked in. He wanted to know what we were going to film and how he could help. I said I hoped that he wasn't offended that I had moved out of his cabin.

"No problem," he chimed. "Always some other loony *gora* is coming along looking for a dirty cave. I'll have it rented in a jiffy."

The Tiger sniffed derisively and got out a pen and paper to plan the next few days, but before he got a word down, Khim Singh cut him short, laying his hand firmly on the paper.

"No," he said. "Before business, first we share *chillum*."

He pulled out a tube of baked clay from his frayed tweed jacket and a jam jar full of mint-green wads of a chewing-gum-like substance. The same stuff that was on Bingo's floor. It looked slightly powdery, like the underbelly of a moth, and had been squished together into the texture of glazier's putty.

"We're not smoking," I insisted. "We've got work to do."

"Yes," Khim Singh agreed. "Work now, but first we smoke."

He waved the pipe at me, and the stink of stale embers rose through the room.

"It is tradition," he argued. "First smoking, then business."

"I don't care, Khim Singh," I said.

"But it's Amma Kana's own homemade *charas*. You know Auntie Kana, yes? She makes very best. All day she is standing in the heat rubbing plants, and her hands so covered in pollen she can't even scratch nose. For her, we smoke a little, *na*?"

I held my ground. I had been caught out badly by Khim before when I had first arrived in the mountains and Wolf, the German man who built the leper station, had sent me off to his farm to find accommodation for myself. Khim had shown me the cowshed that he would convert into a cabin for me, and I had eagerly accepted it. I can't blame the *charas* for that decision as it was only afterwards that he offered me the pipe. Before agreeing a price he had insisted we smoke together as a sign of friendship, and he had handed the lit *chillum* to me ceremoniously. I felt honoured and had diligently filled my lungs with smoke. Immediately my focus narrowed to two settings – micro zoom and ultra wide – and for the rest of the day I kept jumping indiscriminately between the two. There was no controlling it. Hopping, without warning, from the inner workings of his nostril to an overview of the Himalayan range. It left me in no condition to bargain, and I agreed immediately to whatever price he quoted just to get the hell out of there.

I had arranged to meet up afterwards with Wolf again, for a tour around the leper station, and although I managed to keep it together for the first bit, when he got the nurse to show me how the dosages of medicine were calculated, I suddenly jackknifed into paranoia, thinking that he would know I was stoned and would presume I was a drug fiend who would end up killing all his precious lepers if left in charge. I wanted to come clean and confess all to him, but I didn't know how he'd take it, and so instead I took deep breaths and managed somehow to keep it together for another while, even while the matron gave me a demonstration of how to clean out the pus from a septic wound and cut away the dead skin.

The worst part was when my mind suddenly flash zoomed through the flaky leprous skin as she was cutting it away, and I ended up deep in the putrid crimson pool beyond. I had to choke back the vomit.

"Don't let the pus worry you," Wolf had said when I had let out a low moan. "Leprosy isn't all that contagious, as long as the patient is taking his medicine."

I had not been able to stop myself asking, "How do you know if he is or not?"

"That's up to you to find out," he said. "That'll be your job if you choose to stay on."

After that, I vowed never to smoke again, but it took real resolve. The locals were proud of their produce – particularly the powdery green first-pickings which were hand-rubbed by the women, who milked only the finest, most THC-crystal-drenched buds – and were easily offended if you didn't partake.

It was days later that Wolf left and I somehow found myself as un-official part-time medical supervisor of Baldoti leper station. He had got into his Maruti jeep and driven off to his next leper station, waving back to his lepers and mouthing his mantra at me: "Remember, three steps, Mocha – drug ministration, wound sterilisation, patient rehabilitation."

I nodded dumbly at him. Poor man, his confidence was so misplaced. Fortunately he never got to see the cow byre I had agreed to rent, but even the look of me on that short tour through the station should have set the alarm bells ringing. In fact, that day on the tour was the first time I ever saw Tara. I remember he was as shy and reticent as the other lepers, but he had a disconcerting stare – or at least that's how I remember it. He kept winking at us, following our group as we toured the compound. If this had been an orphanage, or a dog sanctuary, and I was a parent looking to adopt, I would say that he was the little puppy who most wanted to be taken home.

The Tiger was a bit disappointed by his first impressions of Almora and couldn't see all that much worth filming. I had thought we could do a feature on the leper station and also take some shots of the mock Home Counties cottages, which he agreed to, but we needed something more. We needed something really momentous to end the series on. Khim, who had by now reluctantly put away the *chillum*, suggested "the long hairs" and their parties up at the temple.

He was referring to the community of seekers and *yoga* junkies who hung out further up the mountain, up near Kasar Devi. Most of them came following the likes of Swami Vivekananda, the great sage who had visited in the nineteenth century, or Timothy Leary, the counter-cultural icon who lived here in the 1960s; or Gandhi, who believed that the energy of the place was the most powerful he had ever come across. These Western seekers all claimed to be in search of spirituality, but invariably they got hooked on *charas* and spent their days getting wasted with wandering holy men who came by on their way through the Himalayas on pilgrimage. There was always some new *guru, swami, baba, sadhu* or *yogi* coming through, and the dropouts would give them food and shelter in the hope of a gift of *charas* in return. Of course, they had plenty of their own *charas*, but hash from a holy man was considered *prasad*, holy food, and gave a much purer high.

Most evenings you could hear their chants of *Jai Shiva Shambo . . . Hara Hara Mahadev!* echoing down the valley like a Scouts Jamboree. These were invocations which the *sadhus* insisted they invoke before each toke on the *chillum*. *Bom Shankar* was another. Their chanting continued as regular as birdsong the whole time I was in the mountains; but as the full moon approached, it became louder and more sustained as holy men came down from their caves and hermitages to celebrate the moon festival and were joined by hippies up from Goa.

I stayed well away from this group most of the time, and had found out only by accident about the parties, one night when I heard my name being called across the mountainside just as I was about to go to sleep. I recognised the voice straightaway as that of Witlauf, a Swiss girl who lived higher up the mountain. At first, I tried ignoring her, but I knew exactly what she wanted. She needed help. In all likelihood, her two young children, Suria and Durga, were cowering under their bed at that moment, hiding from their father. I had told Witlauf earlier that she should call on me if things ever got really bad.

Although people in the area generally knew that I wanted to be left alone, I had come upon Witlauf one morning, about a week after I had rented the shack, standing outside my door in tears, with her two children in tow. She was very apologetic but said that there was nowhere else she could turn. I had made them tea and let them play in the yard for a few hours until her partner Hosto, the children's father, went back up to his cave again and left them in peace. She had met him at university six years earlier and had fallen in love with him, a sensitive soul whose compassion for animals and commitment to environmental causes was beyond anything she had witnessed before. He was like a fragile angel, and they had fallen madly in love. But as soon as they had arrived in India two years earlier, things had begun to change. His sensitivity had been so assaulted by the horrors he saw around him – the diesel-spewing buses, the tiger aphrodisiacs, the Bopal disaster, the open sewers and deforested hills – that his compassion had warped into a bitter outrage. The level of daily abuse here had blown his immune system, turned him septic. Ever since, he had been half a man – a wounded troll, lashing out when his anguish became too much to bear.

Witlauf had brought him and the children out to the desert to clear his mind and clear his lungs of the fumes, but the dead wasteland of Rajasthan had just plunged him deeper into despair. She tried steering him east, to the lush plains of the Punjab made fertile by the Green Revolution, but this again only increased the suffering as he saw how the fertiliser was turning the soil to dust and killing the water. No matter where they went, all he saw was bleakness. His bouts of rage were becoming so frequent and so venomous that he couldn't be held responsible for his own actions. They considered seeking psychiatric help until, eventually, they made it up here to the mountains, the timeless, tranquil Himalayas, where they had been happy for a spell. They began organising vegetable plots for the locals and teaching them how to compost. Hosto had carved Punch and Judy puppets and built a little collapsible theatre booth, and Witlauf wrote environmental parables to teach the locals about sustainability and the evils of the petrochemical industry. For a while they led an almost idyllic existence, growing all their own food and overseeing the development of an ecological paradise around them. Everything had seemed perfect until the day a panther made an ill-judged attacked on a nearby village, making it as far as the porch of one of the houses where a baby was sleeping on a rope cot, before being scared off. The locals had immediately vowed revenge and arranged a party to hunt it down. Seeing them with their pikes and sickles heading up into the mountains after the endangered, no doubt hungry, animal had been too much for Hosto, and he had got drunk and knocked his wife out cold that night. When she came around, she found her mouth bubbling with blood and two of her front teeth at her feet beside her. They both realised that it couldn't continue, and he had agreed to leave the family for their own safety and to retreat to a cave further up in the hills. But every now and then, his paternal instinct would get the better of him, and he'd make his way down to see the children, bringing with him hand-carved toys he had made out of pine cones or dolls he'd woven from reeds. For a few days things would go well and they would be an idylli-cally happy family again, but something always set him off. He'd see a farmer tapping a pine tree for resin, or beating an ox, or ploughing too deep, or too shallow, or over-irrigating, and the fuse would blow, and he'd lash out at whoever was nearest – normally his wife. Without really know-ing what he was doing, he would thrash her – suddenly finding himself with clumps of her hair between his fingers and his knee in her belly.

I had agreed that Witlauf could seek shelter at my place whenever she needed to. As long as I didn't have to talk to her or the children, it didn't bother me so much. In fact, it was nice to hear Suria singing and chortling to himself among the trees. They were the most aptly named children: Suria means sun in Sanskrit, and he radiated light and warmth, while his four-year-old sister Durga (meaning, the goddess of chaos) was already displaying her father's psychotic temperament and had a marked fondness for arson. She was for ever sneaking into my room and knocking over can-dles or flicking matches on to the rattan mat, calling for help only minutes before the flames reached my bed. Durga was the only four-year-old I've known with latent suicidal tendencies. She used to smash a glass and then teasingly run a sliver over her major arteries, and whenever her father was most riled, she'd goad him further by crushing a flower or an insect under foot or leaving the tap on, flagrantly wasting water. She played him as a sleep-walking matador would a bull.

That night, as I was in bed listening to Witlauf calling out my name, I knew that I had to go to her. She had never called out like that before, no matter how bad it got. It was the last thing I wanted to do – I had made a strict rule of not getting caught up in other people's drama, *dharma*, what-ever. It was hard enough not to get bogged down in my own. But after a while my sense of duty got the better of me, and I threw on a jumper and some cords over my thermal long johns and headed across the hill with my torch. It was very cold. I never got over the intensity of the wind that blew down from those ice citadels on the roof of the world. The furrows of the rice terraces were lit up like zebra skins in the full moon, and as I approached I could see Hosto running through the trees in the opposite direction. He was a coward at heart, and as soon as he was confronted by an outsider, he invariably fled. Inside their house, I found Witlauf sitting on the edge of the bed, badly shaken. Her face was tear-stained and bruised. The children were, as usual, underneath the bed.

"He's gone," Witlauf whimpered, and they came crawling out.

The three of them looked so tragic sitting there that immediately I said that they could all come back to my place, that I'd make them cocoa, but she said that she'd prefer to go up to Kasar Devi. There was a party on for the full moon, and all her friends would be there. He'd never dare hurt her in their presence, especially if the revered *sadhus* were there. He was always so meek and pious with them, although this probably wasn't necessary: Indian holy men would have regarded a few slaps to one's wife as quite acceptable. They drew the line only at outright battery.

She hoped the party would take the children's minds off the ordeal. The only problem was that Kasar Devi was about two miles away, and Witlauf was scared to walk there through the forest at night. It was a dark, intimidating place at the best of times, full of knobbly, prehistoric-looking rhododendron trees choked in vines, and fronds and roots that seemed to rise up out of nowhere. If a panther came upon her, sensing her shaky, weakened state, he might easily realise his advantage and attack – and in such an occurrence there was no way she could protect both children. She asked me would I mind coming with her: a gang of four would be safe from anything except wolves, and it was unlikely that they would have descended this far from the snowline so early in the season. And so we set out with only my torch for protection and a blanket around each of us to ward off the cold.

It was that night I found out about the full-moon parties. They were pretty far out, like bacchanalian scenes in pre-Raphaelite paintings. About a hundred people, mostly Westerners, but a fair smattering of locals and holy men, too, all gathered around a series of fires, smoking and listening to the elder *sadhus*. It seemed that at any one time almost everyone was in the process of loading, lighting or cleaning a *chillum*, or if not that, then smoking one. The smoking involved a complicated ritual of first chanting an invocation, then raising the *chillum* to the heavens, then to one's third eye and then bowing one's head low. Only then could one bring the *chillum* to one's mouth and inhale deeply. It was a matter of personal taste how long one kept the smoke in before exhaling the vast grey-blue cloud and passing the *chillum* to one's neighbour. For hygiene's sake, everyone had their own rag through which they smoked the pipe. There were so many pipes going around that it was never more than a matter of minutes before the next one came along. Considering how stoned everyone was, I thought it was amazing that they managed to remain upright.

Suria and Durga went off to play with the other Western children while I followed Witlauf over to the fire to where four naked, ash-smeared *sadhus* were talking in an animated sing-song of chuckling and chortling, seemingly oblivious of the cold. A handful of devotees were listening to them, hanging on their every word. Of the four, one seemed in charge; his hair was more matted and his feet more dung covered. He had ill-fitting false teeth, a sculpted nose and a handsome bearing. When he saw Witlauf approach, he raised his hand and touched her forehead beatifically, and she reddened, her tear-stained eyes lighting with joy. She sat down close to him and he went on talking with a slight American accent about the evils of slouching. He was staring upwards as though preaching to the stars, and although it was hard to make out what he was talking about, from what I understood he was saying that slouching was mortally dangerous because one's *chakras* were opened by *charas*, which sent the *kundalini* energy soaring up one's spine. If the path was blocked, it could just as easily coil back on itself to create a cancer. The spine was like a flag pole along which the veil of awareness rose, he said, and if the pole wasn't grounded in the earth it would topple and the flag wouldn't raise to full consciousness.

He talked in a wonderfully slurred and resonant way, littering his language with profanity.

"You know why you come here?" he asked, before rushing on in answer. "You come to have the shit kicked out of you! You are all basically *dharma* bum-fucks – *karmic* crashes that your own society spits out and sends to us. No offence, I, too, am a *karmic* crash. But the difference is, I know it. You must smoke *and* meditate. Don't forget that, you crazy fuck-ups! Don't just smoke; meditate . . ."

Then he drifted off for a full minute before coming back and concluding, ". . . in this way you will achieve unity with cosmicness. The shit – the sensory tumult – will be stilled, and you will be whole again."

We nodded sagely. Witlauf sucked deeply on the *chillum*. The *sadhu* caught sight of two hippies kissing on the far side of the fire and was off again.

"As for your egos and filthy sex-obsessed minds – they will kill you. Stone dead. Why do you men shoot your *kundalini* out your dicks? Tell me that! You must breathe. Breathe in deeply and allow it all in, and when it's in, hold it in – don't go shooting it into the next hole you see. You are animals. Be Shiva, control the *lingam*."

"Yes, *baba*," they intoned in unison.

Then he took a lozenge of green hash from a mahogany snuffbox and placed it ceremoniously on his tongue. He smiled a blissful, love-drenched smile at us all, and gobbled back the hash as though he were an iguana with a fly. When he had recovered from the bout of ecstasy that this brought on, he began a long, rambling and largely incoherent monologue, "It's about gendering; metamorphosing the known . . . not just love, but light enlightening love. No Renny without Stimpy. There must be balance – the seesaw of uncertainty . . . sea of sand grains . . . It's seeing beyond the sea and stumbles engrained within us. The convoy and caravans of duality, dichotomy, and pointless time-space *dharma*. Not continuums. I blow continuums! Infinity. Definitely. Beyond is lighthood, Buddahood, maybe neo-Nirvana. Play well, my disillusioned loonies. Play well."

With that, his head cranked down on to his chest, and he seemed to conk out.

"Wow," Witlauf said dreamily.

"Yeah," I said dubiously.

"D'you understand?" she asked with a gentle thrill.

I shrugged.

"Don't worry," she said. "It's in his energy."

Durga was curled up asleep in her lap now, the deep-etched frown that had soured her face when I had seen her peeking out from under the bed was finally easing. Suria had wandered off somewhere. I looked around to check on him and noticed him huddled up with his friends around one of the smaller fires. They were all watching something intently on the far side of the fire. I was happy to see him bright and somewhat buoyant again, and I got up to go over, but as I approached, he and his friends ran away giggling. It took me a moment to realise what they had been staring at. On the far side of the flames was a girl in her mid-twenties lying naked on the ground. Bent over her were three men kissing her and stroking her thighs with a feather. The men were Westerners, although they were so covered in hair that it was hard to be sure. They were almost naked, wearing only *lungis* – a type of Hindu jockstrap – and were totally absorbed in their various tasks of pleasuring the girl. They wore frowns of deep concentration, almost meditation, and looked completely stoned. The girl was evidently bored by the whole thing. She reminded me of a medieval fertility carving I had seen on a castle in Ireland.

I went back to Witlauf and told her.

"Oh, that's Muriel," she said nonchalantly. "She's from Lyon. She calls herself a portal, an orifice of Shiva's temple. She spends most of her time fasting, but at ceremonies like this, she allows the men wash away their sins through her. 'The eternal meat of comeback flushes through my sewers,' as she says!"

I was slightly shocked. I didn't know whether to admire her selflessness and courage, or to save her from herself. I left Witlauf again and went back to have another look. The men had grown so bored or stoned that they were getting up to leave. One of them wrapped a pashmina around Muriel's shoulders and led her over to the fire, where she hunched up and rocked herself back and forth. A girl beside her began humming a Waterboys tune, and the men went back to the main fire.

Muriel looked so lonely and lost that I felt impelled to sit with her. I squatted down beside the fire, but she was so engrossed in the humming that she didn't notice me. Someone passed her a *chillum*, which she pulled on once or twice, and then she fell back in a paroxysm of fumes. I declined the pipe, and instead, noticing that Muriel was shivering and seemed about to drop off into unconsciousness, I put my arm around her and made some lame attempt at conversation. I don't think she heard me or even that she was aware I was there. We sat there rocking slowly back and forth.

Another girl with only slightly more clothes on, who was watching us from the far side of the fire, came over and said, "You're bastards, all of you. You live in the gutter. Sewer obsessed – septic sludge. Poor Muriel is your drain. Poor Muriel. All she wants is your feathers – this is her *karma*."

The girl then fell into a fit of giggles, awakening Muriel, and she joined in, giggling so hard that she shook the pashmina right off her. I pulled the soft fabric back over her shoulders and asked her as meekly as possible why she did what she did. She just laughed at me.

"She wants to make you pure again," said the other girl. "Pure like H_2O. There is no difference between this and waiting in line at the meat counter. It's all *samsara* – an illusion filling the eternal void . . ."

The girl faded off as Muriel blanked out again, reeling over on to the ground. I checked that she was still breathing, and then, covering her with an old Nepali rug she had been sitting on, I left her.

Someone somewhere beside me was saying, "We are in the shit. The shit is everywhere. Only the truly great ones, you see, are out of it. Beyond shit. We must all try. The shit is the shit – just creates more shit, that's all."

Chapter 22

KHIM WAS RIGHT that the full-moon party would look great on camera, but there wasn't to be another one for a few weeks, and the Tiger couldn't stay any longer. We were running out of money. I suggested we do some interviews with the people who attended – Witlauf or Muriel or Hosto – but the Tiger dismissed the idea.

"This isn't radio," he said. "You can't have talking heads without images."

Khim suggested we ask Muriel to do a demonstration of her *karmic* sewer practice for us, but luckily the Tiger vetoed this, too. I was keen to capture some sense of what the Kasar Devi crowd was up to, but I couldn't think of a viable way to do it. In the days after that first full-moon party, Witlauf had made me see some of the value in what they were doing. She had called in to see me the morning after the party with a kilo of almonds as a gift, and we got talking about the night before.

"It was your first time?" she asked.

I nodded.

"Don't judge them," she said. "They're not all drop-outs, but pioneers. I admit some are extreme – their ideas will just fizzle out – but others are coming up with something really new. We're the guinea pigs. It's about breaking free. Have you ever dropped acid?"

I shook my head.

"If you had, you would understand where the Green Movement

comes from. Not from the farmers; they had no idea of the bigger picture, the macrocosm of which their little field was a part. Only shamans knew these things. That is what Aldous Huxley and those others tapped into. Then Timmy Leary and his friends found the same. They knew that places like these in the mountain – the Rockies, the Andes, here – could focus the drugs, make them stronger. It's the same now with the *sadhus*. They are so high they can see all the things, but unfortunately they are too stoned to explain them to the rest of us.

"This is the big problem Hosto is having," Witlauf continued. "He came because of Swami Vivekananda. You know him?"

I shook my head.

"He was here in Kasar Devi in the 1890s. He said all wisdom was in three words: *tat tvam asi*."

"*Tat tvam asi*," I repeated.

"It's Sanskrit. It means . . . Actually, I can't tell you – it is too power-ful. It was what messed up Hosto at first. It blew his mind; suddenly he clicked on to everything of who he was and what was happening; now, he can't face going back. He knows every day things are changing. All we can do is wait. There is nothing else. Things are getting better, but so slowly. We must wait for this lot to sort it out."

She was pointing down at Suria and Durga, who were playing on a terrace below us.

"They have the answers. Look at Suria and you almost see the answers inside him, just waiting to get out, waiting for him to grow up and put them in place. Hosto senses this, too, but he's too impatient. He feels the pain of every tree that dies. The toxins are killing him. Do you know he's up on charges for beating a man unconscious? A woodcutter who was sell-ing firewood. Hosto said that the tree was still alive when he chopped it down, and he started beating the woodcutter with the logs. He is on life support now in Delhi – how is that going to help the environment?"

I thought back to Swami Vivekananda a hundred years before and to Timothy Leary forty years ago and how they must have both sat smok-ing around the same full-moon fires. The only changes were that today's generation wore thermal fleeces, bobble-knit hats and Nepalese hemp pants instead of the *kurtas* of Vivekananda's time or the harlequin pants and Merry-Prankster tunics of Leary's. It looked less like an Elizabethan pageant now but was still fairly far-out. The most significant difference was that in the forty years since Leary, many of his ideas had become accepted. He and the other 1960s icons had stumbled upon a new way of looking at the world, in part by going back to the teachings of the Eastern mystics like Vivekananda and others. They captured it so that we could all get a glimpse. They more or less rammed a spanner into the cogs of modernity that had been grinding since the Industrial Revolution. Flower Power was like a Reformation: a handful of freaks setting the world on a different tack.

Perhaps that was what the guys up at Kasar Devi were doing now. In another forty years, Muriel's idea of flushing the eternal meat of come-back through her drains might catch on. She was just the latest in a long line of dreamers daring to think outside the box, like the Romantic poets before her and the transcendentalists and existentialists and Beatniks. Even Tom Paine, founding father of the American Republic, champion of reason and author of *The Rights of Man*, had advocated vegetarianism, "promiscuous intercourse" and nursery schools. It is in the nature of pioneers to explore absurd notions on the path towards common sense. Women as cisterns, as passive receptors of effluvia, may well be an answer to something or other.

I had been less certain about the merit of my own pioneering thinking since suffering the shock of the sight of my cabin. Nonetheless, I was still aware of the great opportunity afforded me by the soap box of the camera. I felt obliged to make the most of it, thinking back to previous times when I would have done anything for such a chance – like when I was involved with the anti-logging campaign in Canada, or the anti-war protest in Ecuador. I thought of the evangelists, Penelope and Jasper, and the lengths to which they would have gone for a chance to get their message broadcast over the airwaves.

It was only when the Tiger had mentioned that all TnaG's programmes would be subtitled in English that I realised the full potential of these programmes. I had presumed that the audience figures would be negligible, consisting mostly of tufty-eared West of Ireland turf-cutters, thick-stockinged farmers' wives, patriotic schoolteachers, embittered Christian Brothers, disaffected civil servants, IRA bigots and spinster librarians. If the programmes were really being subtitled, the potential audience suddenly increased dramatically: first off, there were the four million people in Ireland and then the hordes of others in Irish bars around the world who got Irish television beamed to them on satellite. I would be appearing in bars from New York to Shanghai – like the MTV prom queen with the tattoo on her bum.

It was an unsought opportunity, but now that I had it, it was up to me to run with it. I referred earlier to the fact that people like me would invariably have ended up in the priesthood in earlier times; this is because of an innate need to proselytise. Already I could feel around the fringes of my mind the stirrings of messianic delusion beginning to creep back in.

Part of me was determined not to give in to it, but how could I be certain that those blissful thoughts I had had during the long months alone in my cabin weren't in fact enlightened revelations that appeared ludicrous now only because I had allowed myself be dragged back into the mire of conventional thought? Part of me truly believed that those angelic voices were real and might possibly have come to me, like Lans Okalsom had, because they knew that I would be making a television series. Perhaps I was the only full-seeing person in a black and white world. The others believed that the millions of beautiful shades of black, white and grey were all there was. Would they thank me for showing them the truth? For freeing them from darkness?

Maybe urine therapy wasn't an appropriate topic, but what about those angels? Wouldn't it be great to get the message out there that they were just waiting to whisk us away if we had the courage to take the first scary steps down the path towards the abyss? I knew that if the Tiger caught me trying to proselytise, he would batter me. I would have to be subtle about it. It wouldn't be the first time seditious ideas had been slipped on to the airways. They had managed to get them on radio during the French Resistance and in animation in Communist Hungary and in movies during the McCarthy years. Even in Ireland, when our language and customs were outlawed, we had managed to keep the flame alive through coded folksongs and stories. Surely I could do something similar? I had an advantage in that my Irish was far better than the Tiger's; if I talked fast, he might not notice. All I had to do was decide what the hell it was I needed to say.

The fact that trailblazers frequently seemed ludicrous at first was brought home to me by something I found out only after the Tiger had gone home. It had to do with education and, in fact, was loosely connected to Tom Paine's ideas on nursery schools.

I stayed on for a few more weeks after the Tiger flew back to Ireland to get my bearings and prepare myself for conventional life back home. One day, Witlauf invited me to Suria's eighth birthday party, and although I didn't want to go, she said he had asked for me specifically and would be upset if I wasn't there. I felt I owed it to her to go as she had been teaching me how to knit over the previous weeks. I knew she had her own reasons for wanting me there, too. Her father had flown in from Switzerland, hoping to convince her to bring the children back to *civilisation,* or at least to let him bring them back and be reared by their granny. It was a tug-of-war, and I think she wanted to show me off as proof that her friends weren't all stoners. My role was as the model citizen, laughable as that might seem.

The party turned out to be great fun. Witlauf's dad knew magic tricks, and we all dressed up as farm animals and put on a show. Things went brilliantly until Suria and Durga tickled me so much that I roared laughing and woke up Hosto, who had come down from his cave for the party. He stormed out of the house to where we were sitting around a little fire, picked up the water that was being boiled for tea and poured it over the flames.

"Are you all fucking mad?" he roared. "Do you want to burn down the last bit of forest in the Himalayas just so you can have a cup of tea? Is that more important to you?"

He was like a child kicking over the sandcastle so others couldn't play.

"You are all wasters, and you're the worst," he said to Witlauf, who was rushing around washing dishes, doling out muesli biscuits and boiling rice for lunch.

The rest of us looked quietly away.

"You do nothing," he went on. "You sit around with your breasts hanging out, wanting everyone to fuck you, but no one would go near you – you ugly dog. Why don't you ever do anything? You are so bad. You ruin everything. Why must you ruin everything!"

He slapped her soundly across the cheek.

Suria was really upset. He went first to Witlauf and caressed her stinging cheek, then went over to his sister and began laying into her with fists and feet. Hosto had already gone back to bed by this stage. I could see in Suria's eyes that he couldn't quite believe what he was doing; somehow it felt good to be lashing out at someone. He had been the most peaceful, loving child as long as I'd known him, and I'd never seen him so much as pinch Durga before.

Witlauf had gone out to the well to dry her eyes and compose herself, so I felt obliged to step in and pull the children apart. Their grandfather was just looking on in horror. I pulled Suria to me and gave him a hug and asked him to come for a walk with me. We headed down to the pool at the spring where I used to fetch my water and bathe once a week when I was still living in the cabin. It was a heavenly spot, teeming with butterflies and dragonflies, and monkeys swinging through the trees. The glacial water came pouring straight out of the rock, splashing into the pool beneath us and creating so much ozone that the air practically danced with vibrancy and our skin bristled with well-being. I asked Suria about his grandad and what he thought about leaving the mountains and going back to Zurich.

He paused for a long time before flicking off his sandals and plunging his feet into the water, saying, "I'm not going anywhere. My lessons are here."

I told him that there were plenty of schools in Switzerland. But he just sighed, saying I didn't understand.

I asked him to explain but he wouldn't, until eventually he said, "It's not about schools. I don't want facts; I want tools to help me understand."

I said nothing. He was only eight, and I thought he was probably parroting something he had heard elsewhere. We dropped the subject and instead began a long drawn-out story in which each of us in turn made up a line about the *yeti* who was said to live somewhere in the region. As usual, his parts of the story were far fresher and bolder than mine. We played for about half an hour with the damselflies skimming over our heads and the monkeys lounging on branches far above us.

Suddenly the peace was shattered by a ferocious screaming – the monkeys were panicking and had begun shaking the branches madly. Then, just as quickly, they fell quiet again. We saw them poised anxiously, staring straight ahead, baring their teeth. I was about to throw something to get them to go away, when all of a sudden they raced off through the trees en masse.

Something had scared the life out of them. I stood up, looking around me, but could see nothing. A dark storm cloud was rolling in off the snow peaks, but that couldn't have provoked such a reaction.

"Panther," Suria said placidly.

I looked at him hard. In my heart, I knew he was right. Somewhere above us was a leopard lurking. We hadn't heard it crashing through the trees, and so it was almost certainly still above us, waiting and watching – possibly preparing to pounce. The lowest branches were about twenty feet from us – an easy drop for a big cat, I surmised. The foliage was so dense that there was no way we could see through, even if the animal had been directly over our heads. I realised that I didn't even know what colour to look for. Fawn? Black? White? Tan with black spots? I had never given it much thought. Khim had warned me about the *kukuriya bagh*, the man-eaters, as he called them, when I first rented the cabin, and I had diligent-ly taken his advice and carried a big stick and pepper spray with me for the first few months, but gradually I had grown lax.

I concluded that it would most likely be black, unless it was a snow leopard, and that it would come from above, unless it had already dropped silently into the long grass and was stealing up from behind right at that moment as we craned our necks upwards into the branches. One thing was certain: it knew precisely where we were. Suria and I knew that we couldn't just stay where we were. We had to make a run for it. And without saying a word, we gripped each other's hands and looked each other square in the eye, readying ourselves for flight. I squeezed his fingers and felt the sudden maturity in his grip. He had cast off childhood in that second and become a man focused on survival. He was ready to do whatever it took. An image of child soldiers came to mind; how they could switch so easily from playing to killing – the survival instinct always there, ready to kick in when needed. We rose as one, jumping high and pulling each other forward, running through the trees, hand in hand, laughing in a type of mad hysteria. I knew that once we were out of the trees, we would be fine. It would never risk crossing an open rice terrace in daylight. It was frightening but exhilarating also. As we ran, I realised that I had never felt so alive. At the house, we both collapsed, panting for breath and still laughing – electrocuted by the thrill of being back on the food chain.

"You wouldn't get that in Zurich!" I said when I had recovered my breath. "Or in Geneva, or Dublin or anywhere."

Suria stopped laughing. He said that it didn't matter because he was never going back. He said that he was staying right here, but he wouldn't say why. He just shook his head and said he couldn't say.

"Come on!" I said. "We've almost been eaten together. We've survived – we're heroes! You can trust me."

He sighed, "Sure you won't tell?"

"Cross my heart, hope to die."

He looked doubtful.

"I promised, didn't I?" I said.

He murmured something about a woman called Marylyn who taught them at school. He said he didn't want to go anywhere she wasn't.

"She must be some teacher," I said, smiling.

I understood completely. I had had a crush on my own teacher when I was five. I even got my mum to invite her to a lunch at my house. She was under orders not to butt in on us while we were eating, just to prepare the food and leave. I still remember the anticipation of sitting at the window waiting for Miss Philippe, in my best ladybird tie and plaid shirt. I remember the moment she pulled up in her little Mini.

I didn't ask Suria any more about it, but when I mentioned her to Witlauf later, she seemed surprised that I knew and told me to keep it to myself. That made me curious. I asked Suria could he bring me to meet Marylyn some day, but he was hesitant.

Two weeks went by and I kept on reminding him, but he said that he kept forgetting to ask. Khim told me that there was no one called Marylyn at the local school, which made me wonder. It was just three days before I went home to Ireland for good that Suria brought me a note from Marylyn saying that she would meet me in the *chai* shop next day. And sure enough there she was: a middle-aged woman with long, straight, grey hair and beautiful cheekbones as pale and shapely as pine nuts. I was sure I hadn't seen her among the Kasar Devi crowd before. She wore a surfing hat high on a tall forehead and was at least six feet tall, dressed in slender black combats with a tight T-shirt. You wouldn't say she was scrawny, but there wasn't an ounce of extra fat on her body. Her eyes were as green and bright as an acetylene flame, and they burned with intensity. I wondered how I had never seen her in all the months I had been here.

"Well, I sure have heard a lot about you and your television work," she said as she shook my hand. "All good – don't you worry! It's just that I don't get out all that much, but I hear most of what goes on."

I ordered her *chai* and she settled down on a stool, curling her legs around the transom, her movements suggestive of a *yoga* adept.

"I'm just your classic hobo Yank," she said. "Been drifting back and forth between Guatemala and Arizona for the last ten years. I've had too many lovers and too little love. You may have come across Mikey and Larch, my two kids. You see them horsing around up by Kasar Devi sometimes. You can't miss 'em – ponytails down to their asses. We've been up here in the mountains near on two years now. I can give you my SAT scores and menstrual cycle if you like."

I laughed. Her eyes twinkled. They were too clear to have smoked much *charas*. They had that lambency that was absent in the others. I asked her about the school.

"It's no great mystery," she said. "Just a little place for the kiddies at weekends, or the more unusual ones at any rate. The troublesome ones, you know? I brought Mikey out here when he was diagnosed ADD and put straight on 50mg Ritalin. No way was I gonna just accept that. So, I had heard of some guy in Delhi with a good record of sorting out kids and I came. I was coming over anyway for a conference actually, but the guy – Swami Caruther, a black man from Boston, living in Delhi – told me there was nothing wrong with my kid. Just saw things different, that's all. He saw colours and heard sounds that most of us couldn't pick up even if you shoved our eyes and ears right into them. It was confusing him – mixing him up. I sort of guessed as much. There was another mom there, also had a Ritalin kid – a little girl with some syndrome or other, Asperger's, sensory integration, whatever. She had been able to read her mom's mind since she was two – could actually speak the words her mom was reading in another room!

"It was obvious there was nothing wrong with these kids; they were just different. So, to cut a long story real short, we teamed up and started these classes. One of the moms was able to get funding from a programme in Colorado – a university that wanted to map the kids for genetic discrepancies, as if they're goddamn mutants or whatever! Anyway, we kept *stum*, just took the money and smiled, *thank you*. Now every few months I send a report back, and they're happy as pigs in the proverbial. For them, it's hard data; for me it's a future for my son. That's worth it in my book, yeah?

"We set up here in Almora because of Vivekananda, of course! You know his idea of *tat tvam asi*. Wild, yeah? It turns out that one of the local officials has an empathic child, and he was able to draw down more funds. Poor man's a devout Hindu, had been doing his best to deny there was anything weird about his girl until, at age four, she cured her granny of arthritis by just wishing it away. Suddenly, he had sick people camped all round his house. It got to the point he would have done anything to make the problem go away. Suki is the girl's name – a sweet kid, just a bit intense, a bit high strung."

I wanted to ask what this *tat tvam asi* meant, but Marylyn just ploughed right on.

"We have a dozen kids," she said, "and they vary. Some are just quiet, distracted – the sort teachers mark out as daydreamers or borderline artsy. Others are practically autistic. But they are all amazing – some of the cognitive and sensory stuff they can do is just . . . not supernatural or anything – they don't levitate or bend spoons, you know. They're just somehow more advanced. They don't fit in. They aren't designed for conventional systems.

"What's weird is how the hippies and New Agers seem to have more of these kids than ordinary folk. I haven't figured that one out yet. It's like they're choosing to come into families as chaotic as themselves. Or maybe the hippies just let them do their own thing more; don't try and impose too much control. Control is the last thing they need. It really warps them – turns them into zombies or psychos."

"I see," I said lamely. I didn't know what else to say. I had met enough Americans with unconventional ideas to know to tread carefully.

"So, you wanna visit the school sometime?" she asked.

"Sure," I replied.

"Tomorrow?" she suggested. "I'll tell Suria to show you the way."

I went to bed that night not sure what to make of Marylyn. I liked her, even if I wasn't sure I understand what she was on about all the time. I liked how positive she was, the way she talked about children with such reverence, and I was conscious of what Witlauf had said about trail-blazers – you had to see beyond the weirdness. Like how people never appreciated William Blake during his life, but were blinded by his priapic self-indulgence.

Suria came by my cabin next morning and led me a few miles through the pine forest to a clearing which I must have come across at some point before in my daily wanderings in the forest, but I had never noticed it. During most of those long walks I was so lost in thought that I hardly ever looked around me. In the centre of the clearing was a large round stack of logs, and as we walked around it, to my surprise I saw a little gap in the logs at the bottom with a heavy plank above it by way of a lintel. Suria walked through the gap and, by crouching down, I was able to follow him.

Inside I realised that the logs were actually stacked like a wall, and within them was an igloo-shaped building made from aluminium cans set in mortar. Their grey steel bottoms poked out through the concrete, making it look like a dome shelter in a Sci-Fi movie. In fact, it may well have been based on a *Star Wars* design. It was about the size of a domestic garage, but its circular plan made it seem larger. At the base of the dome was another small opening, and by bending down I was able to crawl through it also. Inside, I found a cosy room with a dozen eager faces sitting cross-legged on the floor and staring up at me inquisitively.

Marylyn was in the centre of the room, and as I stepped over the children and made my way to her, she bent forward and gave me a gentle squeeze. There was just enough headroom in the centre for the two of us to stand without having to crouch. It was a bit stuffy, but brighter than I expected. In among the cans were some coloured jars and bottles which channelled beams of light into the room like in a Turkish bath. On a semi-circular shelf above the children, there was a bank of computer terminals. Marylyn was in the middle of a lesson, and after introducing me, she got me to sit down on the floor and she continued teaching. They were discussing the rain cycle and weather systems.

"I think clouds are not just for rain," a little boy called Marshall said. "Also they are writing in the sky. From other worlds to this world."

"I see," said Marylyn.

"Sometimes they're messages for the rocks or animals or spirits, but other times they are for us, and sometimes even the actual person who is meant to see them gets to. They're not always saying something – sometimes it's just to make you smile or remember or cry when I need to . . ."

"I don't think clouds are the best way of sending messages," a girl with pigtails interrupted. "Email is far better. It's the fastest there is."

"What about dreams?" Suria said.

"Yeah, they're fast, too," the girl conceded. "Maybe even faster."

"This is just some of my knowing stuff" Marshall said. "I think it is important to share."

"In Seattle they have more clouds than here because of Mount Olympus," Marylyn's son, Mikey, added. "The moisture comes off the Pacific and then it drops. Sometimes I sit with a brick sitting in my stomach and icy sweats and blood pumping, and I get so sad about the hatred, and then I look at the clouds and I feel okay.

"It's why I don't wear polyester – because the clouds bang together, and I feel sticky and have shocks. Cotton is better."

"I like cotton, if it's blue," said another, "but only with no stripes."

"Stripes make you dizzy," Marylyn said. "Don't they, Paulie?"

"Uh-huh," he said.

Marylyn began handing back essays festooned with gold stars and bright red ticks. One little boy asked could he read his, and Marylyn agreed. Either he had it learnt off or somehow he was able to read between all the stars and ticks. At one point, two of the little girls got bored; one went outside and began spinning like a whirling dervish between the trees, while the other stuck her eye up to one of the portholes in the wall and stared at the sky humming to herself. She didn't budge for a long time, and I went over to check she was okay. I could hear her whispering and murmuring to herself, and I asked her what was up.

She said, "It's like a ship in a bottle from here. Maybe the classroom is a kaleidoscope, and we get to see different things, and then we climb back inside and see it different . . ."

Marylyn came over and said, "You know, sometimes I see them as being like little Martians, trying to figure out how the world works. They don't fit in – like there is somewhere else they ought to be. Maybe it's just that they are born with all of the light switches turned on. *Knowing*, that's the difference. Or maybe we all come in with the lights turned on, but then we turn them off."

She let out a great roaring belly laugh that belied her thin frame, before continuing, "These kids come in and say, 'You're not gonna turn my lights off. I want them on.' They're wired different. I'm the first to admit they can be a handful. Take my Mikey even; he was a real loner in the States except for another ADHD kid. He claimed the others were only interested in winning dumb trophies and kissing girls. They claimed he was retarded. I have to admit, I was prepared to deal with girl issues, not this! But the more I see of them, the more I realise . . . I dunno . . . when you hear of a little girl like Suki curing her granny's arthritis just by wishing it away, you have to wake up and smell the beans."

Marylyn was interrupted by a little boy who said, "I want to be on my own now."

"Sure, Ramsha, go. Skedaddle," Marylyn purred. "Who else wants to go play?"

Most of the class ran out the door. A few went over to the computers and logged on.

Marylyn turned to me and said, "You've gotta listen to them. Most need loads of time out. They need outside; it helps keep 'em grounded. They have a real feel for nature. One of the boys, Ramsha, can actually tune his heartbeat in rhythm with a cricket – wild!"

She looked over at the three children on the computers.

"Although that lot would be happy never to step out again," she said. "They'd swap their mom for a motherboard if they could!"

I was surprised to see so many top-of-the-range computers.

"They're thanks to Colorado State," Marylyn said. "They wanted to test neural processing skills, so I said, "Sure, no problem, give us computers." There's no better way. I realised early on that there was little I could teach these kids, anyway – they are far beyond me in everything but years. Just give them a computer, and they'll end up teaching us. We had to get solar panels put up in the trees to power them – that was hard, I tell you."

I thought of Sugata Mitra and his computers in the slums. Was this all it took – a few computers and a room made of coke cans? Marylyn had no special qualification or expertise, just hope. Of the twelve children, only three were locals; the rest were children of the New Agers. I wished

Tara could have gone to such a school – I felt sure he would have thrived. The stigma of leprosy and homosexuality would never have arisen. They would have accepted him for who he was.

"Basically, I'm trying to create the school of my dreams for Mikey," Marylyn said. "When he began causing trouble back home, the teachers took away his privileges. But he just switched off and decided not to care. First they didn't allow him wear his favourite hat, then they stopped him walking around during class. They even took away his favourite yoyo, which he was obsessed with. He simply stopped caring, so that in the end it was they who were being disciplined – by being forced to punish my innocent child. I suddenly decided that I'd take away all their privileges instead, by pulling him out of school. And then, they sure did care. They set social services after me and the cops, too, but I was prepared to protect Mikey whatever it took. They shut me down when I was a kid; they sure as hell weren't going to get to him, too. He started the good fight, and I just took up his standard and charged on. It was a Christian school, too! It's like, Jesus was the ultimate square peg – can you imagine him fitting into one of those places?"

Suki, the official's daughter, was sitting under a pine tree, digging through the earth with her fingers. She looked over at us and waved. She had a pink dot in the centre of her forehead.

"Hi, Suk," Marylyn called.

Suki waved some more.

"She's probably our most . . . ehh . . . intense child," Marylyn said. "Her mom sent her to different therapists, who diagnosed everything from ADHD to ADD to bipolar to obsessive/compulsive. She likes to press your buttons, won't tolerate any deception, any BS."

Suki sensed we were talking about her and came over. She stood toe to toe with me, staring up disconcertingly, her eyes darting back and forth as if she might be reading my thoughts. She reached out and took my hand, and the only way she could stop shaking it was by manually pulling her arm away with her other hand.

"I used to have songs stuck in my head," she spewed, spitting the words out like rifle fire and scuffing her shoes furiously as she talked. "Now there's been nothing in years. Sometimes I like choosing the ideas I like and let them in, and then if I try to feel happy, they come in closer and become my ideas. I don't really know how, it just happens. If some-one glances at me from a hundred yards away, I'll look up to meet their eyes, because I'm watching them in my mind. I feel them in my belly."

"That's right, you do," Marylyn cooed.

"I have dreams, too," Suki continued.

"Okay, so maybe she's a bit hyper now that she's off the methamphet-amines," Marylyn said, stroking her hair. "But she's coherent, and that's important. All that passion and spontaneity were coiling up inside her, making her neurotic. When I met her, she was on the verge of Tourette's."

"I wasn't able to be myself," Suki said, little bits of spit spraying out of her mouth.

"You weren't," Marylyn agreed. "And yourself is pretty awesome."

"Uh-huh," muttered Suki distractedly.

"Did you really make your granny better?" I asked.

"I guess," she said as she shrugged.

I thought it was a pity that the Tiger wasn't still around to record this place. It would definitely have been more interesting than the leper sta-tion. It captured an element of what the drop-outs were striving for here and was possibly more appropriate for early evening television than hir-sute men tickling naked women.

Chapter 23

S EEING AS HOW we didn't know about the school and didn't manage to film the full-moon party, all that was left for us in Almora was the leper station – hardly the most edifying topic to end a series on. I was reluctant to go near the place until I had made contact with Tara again to find out what he wanted me to say about him. They were sure to want the full low-down, and I had to have something ready. It was even more important to be prepared in case I met his parents. I had already had a disquieting incident the previous day when I had gone into town to phone the ticket office to confirm the Tiger's flight home. There had been a long queue in the telephone exchange, so I went outside to an unlicenced phone-*wallah* on the street. A young girl selling trail mix surreptitiously revealed a mobile phone from the folds of her *sari* and offered it to me, quoting a price that was double what the public exchange charged, but she guaranteed a clearer line and immediate service.

I made the call, and when I was handing the phone back, she said, "Where is he now?"

"Here it is – five rupees," I said, thinking her English poor.

"No," she said. "My brother."

"I don't know," I said kindly, presuming that she had mixed me up with some other Westerner. We all looked the same. I knew she couldn't be Tara's sister as he didn't have any.

"Yes, you do," she said determinedly. "Where is he?"

"Really, I don't know," I said.

"He was friend of Tara," she said.

"Oh," I said, it suddenly dawning on me. She must be one of Sangev's sisters.

"I heard he'd gone north," I said, flustered, "up to the Nepali border."

She wiped her nose and stared.

"You have cousins up there, don't you?" I said.

She wiped her snotty fingers on her *sari* and winced defiantly.

"I really don't know any more," I said. "You should ask your parents."

She appeared suddenly deflated, and to perk her up I asked could I use the phone again, which immediately turned her radiant.

"To where are you calling: local, trunk, national, international?" she chimed in a sing-song voice, scrunching her eyes to check the battery level against the harsh glare of the sun.

There was no one I really needed to call, but in the end I thought, to hell with it, and said, "International."

At this, she turned ecstatic and began to spit and polish the phone with her scarf before handing it back to me, saying, "Inter-nation-al, *sahib*" with a formality bordering on veneration. Meanwhile, I was thinking who I could possibly ring and what the Tiger would say when he heard I had wasted yet more of the budget. In the end, I tried my mother at home in Dublin, but she was out, and I had to leave a message on her machine.

The girl told me that her name was Indira and that she had been born the same year the dictator Indira Gandhi died. She was one of seven daughters and had one brother, Sangev, whom she didn't consider a real brother as he had leprosy and was never around. Their father was a trades-man and did reasonably well, but Indira wanted more for herself, and so every day after school she sold snacks on the street, just so that she could get a licence to be a street vendor. Her real business was as a public tele-phone. Her Motorola phone could make up to five calls a day before the battery went flat, and then it took almost the whole night to charge because of the weak and sporadic power supply at home. But even these few calls were earning her far more than the trail mix, and she had almost saved enough for a computer course. Her dream was to buy a PC and set up an internet kiosk on the street, so that Almora would be linked to the whole world. I found it staggering that such a young girl could already have formed so solid an economic plan. In India, economics was about more than stocks and shares; it was about pulling oneself out of the past; being able to put *chapattis* on the table – and then later Pepsi and later still Perrier.

She was by no means the first Indian I had come across to aspire towards computer literacy: the G-NIIT diploma, earned after a four-year computer course, was the dream of every upwardly mobile Indian. It was said that a bride with a G-NIIT required no dowry, and the diploma was frequently cited in the matrimonial ads of Sunday newspapers. What was amazing was that Indira was still so young – she could hardly have been over thirteen.

I thought it best not to call Tara using her phone, and so I went back to my friendly fax man on the main street and asked him would he mind making the call. He was a bit upset that I hadn't been around to chat since arriving back with the Tiger. I told him that I had been busy and that I would have more time once the Tiger had gone home. When I had been living there alone, I used to find, to my surprise, that I became rather loquacious on my weekly visits into town, as if my mind needed the occasional brush with reality to keep itself rooted in sanity. It grasped any opportunity to claw its way back from the wonderful realms of freedom I was leading it towards, scurrying back into the suffocating, dreary cage of reality like a timid wimp. As long as people in town didn't ask too many question or threaten to come and visit, I rather enjoyed chatting with them occasionally.

When the fax man had heard about the possibility of a television series, I remember, he had had to restrain his bafflement that a scruffy-haired, sandalled waster like me could get such a job. I think that Ireland went down in his estimation after that. If I was the best they could come up with, what sort of country must it be? But he had been unfailingly supportive at the time and had helped to send faxes back and forth to the Irish embassy in Delhi for me. Now, when I told him I wanted to ring Tara, he grimaced as though I had just stabbed him. He shook his head determinedly from side to side. It was a well-known rule that he didn't allow his fax machine to be used for phone calls. Ever. It was pointless even to ask. He regarded such a thing as beneath his dignity, an insult to the capabilities of his great machine.

"No, no, no, no, no," he would say to anyone who had the gall to ask. "I am a facsimile service provider, not a common phone-*wallah*."

I looked beseechingly at him on this occasion. I couldn't go back to Indira, and the telephone exchange was sure to take all day. Even then, the operators had a tendency to eavesdrop and would have spread the news about Tara around town like wildfire. And yet I didn't want to approach another phone-*wallah* in case Indira would see me and be offended.

"It is completely out of the question, my friend," the fax man said again. "Completely so. There is no way I could be blocking my lines with common telephony."

"But I'll pay the full fax price," I said.

"Out of the question, I am very afraid. Look! Down there – phone-*wallahs*, so many phone-*wallahs*, too many. They will be helping you only for the asking."

He tucked the antimacassar under and around the fax machine with great delicacy, sealing it away from my unseemly request. Finally, I was forced to go to another phone-*wallah* and just hope that Indira didn't get to hear about it.

I rang the burger bar. It was Donald who answered. Unfortunately, neither Tara nor Reg was in.

"You're still in Delhi?" I asked.

"What does it look like to you, Columbo?" he said.

"I thought you were only staying another week."

"Yeah, well, things change, yeah? I got my grant extended by the college. The stuff I'm turning up here is way too important to rush. I secured another six months' funding; but that's not the big story . . ."

His pregnant pause was designed to lure me in, but I didn't want to waste my money talking.

"Aren't you curious?" he said.

"About what?"

"The big story!" he said.

"I suppose," I said wearily.

"Well, it's for me to know and you to find out," he said. "Anyway, tell me how it's going for you guys. Have you met up with any really holy *swamis*? Have you asked them the big questions? Prada or Gucci? Is black the new black? Do stilettos have a role to play? Merc or BMW? Is Tom Ford really the reincarnation of Christian Dior . . . ?"

"Look," I interrupted, "I'll call back when Tara's there."

"What's your hurry, honey?" he said. "I can tell you all you need to know. Me and Reg are like this . . . like two snails entwined. We're going on a trip, right?"

He left another tiresome pause, and so I asked diligently, "Where?"

"Seattle," he trumpeted. "We're going to Seattle! And guess what's there?"

"The Space Needle?" I ventured.

"Other than that," he said irritably.

I was determined not to waste any more of TnaG's budget, and I was about to hang up when Donald said, "An inter-gender conference, actually. In a big swanky hotel downtown. All the leading doctors and scientists will be there. It's a biannual thing."

"Great," I said, disinterestedly.

"We're bringing Tara."

"To America?" I yelled.

"Yeah, it's all organised. The university is picking up the tab – they're even considering bringing a few more *hijras* over; that is, if I can find any of them with good enough English who aren't totally hooked on opium."

"Slow down!" I said. "Tell me this again. Tara is going to America?"

"Sure," he said. "In a few weeks."

"You're serious?" I said.

"Ask him yourself. Reg is coming, too, and maybe Niishraah if we can get her a visa in time."

"The princess?" I said, feeling my old devotion flooding back.

"Of course, who else?" he said. "How many fucking Niishraahs do you know?"

I was silent, trying to process all this.

"Why her?" I said. "She's not transgender, is she?"

"She speaks great English, and she doesn't take drugs."

Tara going to America! This was too wild. I had to talk to him. I told Donald I'd ring again in an hour and asked him to make sure that Tara was in when I did. Meanwhile, I went up the road to get a cup of *chai*.

Across from the *chai* shop, I caught sight of a backpacker just off the overnight bus from the south. He was binding his rucksack to his chest like a mutant marsupial and glancing around regretfully, as though realising that Almora was a step too far off the banana-pancake circuit. The town rarely featured in guidebooks any more; it had lost the cachet of its hill-station years. Its currency among backpackers was now so low that this boy would find it hard to get much value from his time here when swapping stories in the well-known traveller hangouts. Compared to the big bucks of McLoud Ganges, Srinigar or Auroville, this place was paltry pesetas. None of its notable inhabitants – Sri Vivekananda, Gandhi, D. H. Lawrence, Timothy Leary – was sufficiently in vogue to warrant a pilgrimage. These days, only washed-out stoners came.

I could see him trying to catch my eye, no doubt wanting advice, tips for the best guesthouse or a restaurant that sold passable spaghetti or edible pizza, but I had enough on my mind as it was. The implications of Tara going to America were boggling. The backpacker gave a tentative wave, but I averted my eyes and ordered tea from the Nepalese man who owned the *chai* stall. He was in a threadbare flannel blazer and was busily scraping the soot off the grate of his baked-earth stove. Beside me in the spit-strewn dust that formed the dining area, a group of *sherpas* squatted on their heels eating off stainless steel platters into which indentations had been hammered for every portion of the meal – *idlies, dhal, chapatti* and *subji*. There was even a stainless-steel groove into which slotted a stainless-steel water beaker. These platters were common across India, reminiscent of 1970s TV dinners or airline food, as though the nation ate its meals ready at all times for a sudden bout of turbulence.

I looked up to see a pariah dog chasing a sewer rat down a drain and noticed the backpacker adding a sterilising tab to his water before slugging it back, careful not to let the bottle touch his lips. My impatience with him rose to the point of contempt, but in truth it was directed as much at my former self as at him. I recognised the two conflicting desires fighting for dominance: the wish to puncture through the wall of alienation surrounding him and the equal and opposite desire to protect himself from it. He had just spent ten hours on a long-distance bus; no doubt having had his face pressed into somebody's rank armpit; having been stroked in places he regarded as off-limits; been befriended and interrogated many times by many people. It was understandable that he might now seek some *space*. Or at least, from a Western perspective it was understandable; for an Indian, everybody is one, there is no separation; so why would you try and create the illusion?

In a moment of weakness, I found myself beckoning him over, insisting he join me for tea, and the kitchen boy, spotting the new customer, came tripping out with a dripping dishcloth to wipe first the chair and then the table, in that order, and went off to fetch us two gold-rimmed shot-glasses of industrial strength *chai*. I spent the hour sharing whatever tips I had about the place with him, and we talked about the creeping influence of Indian spirituality on the West, and in particular on Hollywood. He said that the gooey, soft-focus, Buddhist/Hindu mentality that nowadays infused so many American movies was one of the most remarkable and least expected cultural metamorphoses of the late twentieth century, and that each backpacker was like a stitch knitting the two hemispheres closer together. I liked that idea a lot, that we were threads through space and time. I had been a thread in danger of being swallowed up by the fabric until my brother, the tailor, had come to unpick the seams.

When I finally got through to Tara later in the day, he explained, "All these doctors and professors coming together to make their studies, it's amazing. All looking at diddlies and making studies and writing reports."

He sounded as if he were still a bit overawed by the whole thing, and didn't quite understand what it was all about.

"Are you not worried it could be a bit of a freak show," I said. "You realise, they'll probably want to examine you?"

"Yes, my diddly will be famous! Donald says it will be on big movie screen, and they might poke at me with very shiny metal things, but it won't hurt. They all very expert. And I will be meeting with American *hijras* and we share our stories of having big diddlies or little diddlies or even no diddlies at all. Donald says these are very interesting people – very nice and kindly."

"Good for you," I said.

"Yes, yes, very good for me," he said gleefully and then turned solemn. "What about Sangev? Have you heard anything?"

I lied and said no.

Having met Indira, I had asked Khim Singh whether he had heard anything more about her brother. He said that there was talk that maybe he would make the journey down with the other shepherds to the Uttraini sheep fair at Bageshwer next January, that was if he had managed to survive the almost arctic conditions of the high Himalayan winter. No one knew for sure. The high mountains were cut off during the worst months, and nobody had had news from there for weeks. It wasn't even certain that Sangev was still healthy. If the cold hadn't got him, the leprosy could well have. It was unlikely that he had been able to get the right drugs up in his little *Bhotiya* village. The matron had told me that she had tried to give him a whole case of multi-drug therapy to take away with him, but there wasn't enough room on the donkeys. Leprosy was particularly virulent up in the mountain villages, and if he wasn't taking his medicine, there was every chance he'd suffer a relapse. I thought it best not to mention any of this to Tara and instead turned the subject to his own family.

"I saw your grandad in the bazaar," I said. "Do you want me to pass on a message to him or to your mum if I see her? I'm sure she must be worried, keen to know how you are getting on."

"Bugger her," Tara said bitterly. "Bugger them all. Why should I care? I have a new family now. Better – far better than ever. My real family never knew me. I was secret shame. Now they wouldn't even recognise the new me. Only Sangev would. I had the best lover-boy in the whole world, Mocha. Why did I have to lose him? It's not fair. I worry about him so much, you know, up there in the mountains all alone with his sheep and goats. What happens if a wolf or a *kukuriya bagh* attacks?"

"I'm sure he's fine," I said.

"You know about the *Bhotiya* dogs?" he said. "They are so fierce and strong, but they only protect the sheep and goats. Who will protect my Sangev? This is what I am asking. I miss him so much, Mocha. I miss him like a limb."

"I know, Tara. I know."

"When I was in Nizamuddin, I used to go to bed every night and dream of bringing our dancing troupe up to his stupid goat village, and we would all dance for him in the dirt outside his house. I think if he saw our beautiful dancing, he would fall in love with it, you know? Under our spell. And he would come away with us. And his stupid relations would be crying because it is so beautiful, our dancing. And they would want to give us lots of good money for good luck. And I would say, 'No, we don't take your money. And we don't give you our luck. Instead we curse you for seven years, for seven times seven years on the grave of Mata Bahuchara.'"

He was spluttering with passion as he spoke, and to relieve his anguish I changed the subject.

"Donald said he might be bringing more of the *hijras* to the States," I said.

"Yes, maybe," he replied, grumpily. "That would be okay – I miss them sometimes. And the dancing, too. You should have seen me, Mocha, I was such a beautiful dancer. Jemdanee said I was like the wind. I could be dancing queen of all *hijras* if I practised. Maybe we will all dance together in America!"

"Donald also said Niishraah might be coming?" I said.

"Yes, yes!" he said. "It's still only maybe, but it would be so wonderful. She is beautiful dancer. Sometimes still she comes here to Reg's. She asks about you, Mocha."

"Really?" I said, trying to maintain an even keel. "Will you make sure and tell her next time that I was asking for her, too?"

A three-legged cow ambling across the road began nosing too close to a vegetable stall and was beaten back viciously by the stall owner. It let out a tortured wail that drowned out my words.

"What, Mocha?" Tara shouted. "I cannot hear with all this caterwauling. What do you say?"

"Just tell her I was . . . ," I shouted, but the cow fell silent again and I was left shouting down the street.

Flustered, I found myself asking a question I hadn't dared ask before. Suddenly I needed to know.

"Tara, if I ask you something, will you promise to tell me the truth – it's about Niishraah . . ."

"Holy God and Shiva, too, I am promising faithfully . . ." he began.

"Okay, okay," I said. "Niishraah, she *is* female, isn't she?"

The moment I had asked I regretted it. Tara fell uncharacteristically silent. I could hear the hum down the line to Delhi and could imagine his brow puckering.

He cleared his throat and infused his voice with a sensitivity that was touching, "She's very nice. Very, very nice."

"Yes," I managed.

"And kind, too."

"Yes, that, too," I said.

"Yes," he agreed.

It was clear he was playing for time. Trying to spare me. I felt such fondness for him at that moment – that after all I'd put him through he still wanted to protect me. Suddenly, I realised I didn't actually need to know any longer. Of course she was female. I didn't need anyone else telling me.

"I'm so sorry, Mocha-ji," Tara continued before I could stop him. "It was a most excellent operation, and she is *so* female now. Not boggy and bloody like poor Gilia. No swelling like gourd, but soft and plump. So sweet and nice. Niishraah is so sweet and nice."

"You're lying!" I said, more ardently than I had intended. "She was never male! No way!"

"Yes!" he insisted. "This I am saying to you. Niishraah never had diddly, I am sure of this. Even little tiny one. But now she is even more female. Hundred-twenty percent. The cutting just made things clearer. She is very beautiful woman. Like Buffy's friend Cordelia – not like that Willow girl. Small, sweet, juicy bosoms like the mangos that are still only young and not falling from the tree."

A truck tearing by spewed dust into my face and brought me suddenly back to Almora main street. Looking around, I noticed a clutch of men brushing their teeth under a municipal tap, staring straight at me. I was reminded of that first phone call I had got from the Tiger all those months before and how it had started this whole crazy charade. I bid a quick goodbye to Tara and hung up.

I wasn't any closer to deciding what I should say to his parents, but I concluded that the best plan was to steer clear of them if at all possible. The whole situation was too big. Far bigger than me. There were no pat answers. Khim had told me that Tara's father was still disgusted by his son, and that he blamed me for everything. As far as he was concerned, I had stolen his boy.

As for Niishraah, I didn't know what to think. Ultimately, what did it matter if she was boy, girl or something in between? She was beautiful and kind. When it comes down to love, gender becomes more or less irrelevant. It was not about glands or valves, but mind and spirit. About the soul. And her soul was definitely female. Maybe not completely so, not 100 per cent out and out – but definitely tending towards it. The Western desire to force everyone into neat categories was so crude. In reality, gender had little to do with simplistic duality. It was a continuum, in which no one could be categorised as precisely either-or. Limiting it simply to a penis or a vagina was like limiting the beauty, fury and passion of a fire to the lump of coal that created it. Gender is about essence – far more significant than the mere mechanism that makes use of polarity points in the body to create biological life. This process – sacred and all as it is – is little more than a chemical reaction. The act of bacteria souring milk or high pressure causing rain.

Admittedly, there are the odd exceptions – people who fall clearly into the chiaroscuro of bright certainty on either side and serve further to illuminate the nebulous mass of the rest of us. What is certain is that all the truly great characters of humanity occupied the intermediary zone: from Cleopatra to Odysseus, from Gandhi to Mother Teresa. And that now more than ever was a time for balance, for melding. I tried to tell myself that to stand astride the sexes was no perverse or disgraceful thing. Not monstrous, but honourable. I put out of my mind all my previous unedifying thoughts of chickens plucked and trussed and stuffed with their own giblets. Donald had told me that among many native tribes, including Tahitians, Mojave Indians, Chukchee Eskimos and Andean sorcerers, a person who successfully bridged the sexes was highly regarded. It was only our Western thinking that had debased it. Maybe the *hijras* were the only sensible ones after all: if it took hacking off a superfluous piece of meat, the offending slug, to clarify the situation, perhaps it was a price worth paying. Or was I raving again? Was I desperately trying to justify my warped feelings for Niishraah?

Chapter 24

THE FOLLOWING DAY, we brought the camera equipment down to the leper station to film. It was the first really sunny day we'd had in the mountains, which pleased me as I wanted to make it look its best for Wolf. Just walking into it made me realise how badly I had let him down, and I felt genuinely guilty. He had asked me to keep an eye on the medical regime while I was there – just to oversee that the patients took their medicines once a week. It was a simple request, and yet now seeing the lepers, no nearer to being cured than on that first day when I had met them while stoned on Khim's *charas*, I could see how little I had done. It wasn't all my fault, of course; the lepers themselves were partly to blame. They didn't want to be cured. Some of them saw leprosy as their *karma* and didn't want to anger the gods by sneakily circumventing it with modern magic potions; others saw it as a good source of income as it attracted a disproportionate amount of alms because it was mentioned in all the holy books; while others again enjoyed the secure and easy life at the leper station and didn't want to risk being booted out when cured. But the biggest problem of all was that the station manager, who had somehow taken over the running of the place when Wolf left, wasn't eager to see the lepers leave.

Let me try to explain it: the problem all stemmed from Wolf's initial idea to teach the lepers a trade while curing them. He figured it would increase the likelihood of their families and communities accepting them back once they were no longer infectious. I suppose it was a trailblazing idea at the time. The community would be given an economic incentive to overlook the stigma that some believed could never be wiped clean by mere drugs alone.

In each station that Wolf set up, they focused on a different set of trades or crafts for the lepers: weaving, carpentry, cobbling, tailoring, iron work, and so on. It was intended that once the patients were cured, they would be sent home with the tools of their trade: a sewing machine, a loom or a last. To the few really acute lepers who had lost too much of their hands to be of much use, he gave goats which they were able to milk and breed. Don't ask me how they were meant to squeeze the teats – I never thought to enquire.

In Baldoti station, where the main trade being taught was weaving, Wolf had had a series of wooden looms made and acquired basic equipment to card, spin and hand-dye the wool in the traditional manner. It was an impressive set-up. Simple and effective. The problem was that it was too effective. Over time, the lepers had become skilled weavers and were producing such excellent high-quality tweed that the haute couture fashion houses of Italy became interested. Georgio Armani was a real fan, although it is likely that his interest stemmed as much from the shock-value of leper-made cloth as from any intrinsic quality of the stuff itself. I could imagine the black-clad Beardsley-esque designers in the fashion houses gloating smugly about their philanthropic beneficence and joking amongst themselves about the possibility of finding slivers of human flesh woven through the material. Either way, the station was said to be earning more money than it could cope with now, and rumour had it that the station manager was determined to hold on to the current crop of lepers for as long as possible, as they had all become master weavers, and he didn't want the trouble of having to train in a new set, and thereby suffer a fall in quality and profits.

It was a classic example of how trailblazing ideas can get bogged down in the duplicity of human machination. In theory, the idea was so simple, so logical – dole out the multi-drug therapy for nine months, cure the lepers and set them up with a trade for life. Unfortunately, in India things are never logical; its uniquely inverted perspective on the world makes everything topsy-turvy.

I decided it would be unfair on Wolf to focus on any of these aspects in the television series. Instead we chose to highlight his enlightened idea to build the leper station near a town instead of out in the wilderness as had always been done previously – neatly skimming over the fact that this plan hadn't worked out as expected either. The townspeople had chosen simply to bypass the station, crossing its perimeter only when absolutely necessary. In fact, so unwelcome were the lepers in the Almora bazaar that they had had to start growing their own food to guarantee a steady supply. And, as I mentioned earlier, even *I* was seen as an outcast by some traders because of my contact with the station. Nevertheless, despite these shortcomings, the station's location no doubt was having subtle influence on the locals; and after all, it is in the nature of pioneering ideas that they take time to filter through.

I'm not sure whether or not we succeeded in presenting the station in a good light. Despite my best efforts, it was hard to make the drab concrete rooms full of arthritic-looking men and women weaving on medieval looms appear as trailblazing as they truly were. I was also conscious of the fact that if we over-lionised Wolf's efforts, I risked drawing the wrath of other Westerners I knew who also had charities in India. For many, like Madame Singh Guli, it was almost a status symbol to have a dependent group of destitutes, and I knew that she and others would not be pleased that I had singled out Wolf for special attention.

As the Tiger filmed the open sores and blood-stained dressings of the lepers, I tried to assuage my guilt at having failed Wolf so miserably with the thought that at least I had been somewhat responsible for the first two patients to have left Baldoti in many months. Tara and Sangev might not have been the most seriously infected patients, and they both had been taking their medicine regularly enough beforehand, but at least their departure had freed up two beds. They were no longer a burden on resources, and this was definitely a good thing – although I doubted if Wolf would have been pleased to know of the trade I suspected Tara to be involved in now in Delhi.

Dani Ram, the station compounder, an honest and hapless victim of the machiavellian station manager, showed us around the dispensary and the wool stores, waiting patiently as the Tiger filmed a silhouetted shot of an old man working away at his spinning wheel. It struck me that this shot alone would make the trip to the leper station worthwhile – you couldn't have a programme about India without featuring a spinning wheel at some point. It reminded me of Miranda Singh Guli's exercise bike and how that was perhaps becoming now a more fitting symbol for the nation. In the papers, I was seeing more and more columns devoted to diets, exercise regimes and other Western fads spreading through the newly affluent classes. People were turning away from *ghee* and squeezing into bicycle shorts to tone their abs in mimicry of the bodies being beamed to them on satellite TV. Ganesh, the reassuringly podgy elephant deity, was fast becoming a figure of fun. The terms "work out" and "eat dirt" were taking on whole new meanings in this famine-beset land as fitness trainers bellowed orders at their fledgling charges.

With great pride, Dani Ram showed us the Maruti Gypsy jeep which the station used in its outreach programme. This was another of Wolf's big ideas, to go out into the countryside with a loudhailer and educate people about the early signs of leprosy. The Tiger asked could we come along on one of these trips to film it, but Dani Ram said he had just taken the loud hailer off as he was preparing for the once yearly trip up to the Nepalese border to arrange a supply of yak and camel wool for the weavers. He gestured up into the mountains, pointing to where he was going – up where the nomadic *Bhotiya* people herded their goats and yaks in the no man's land between Tibet, Nepal and India.

The Tiger and I looked at each other, the exact same thought striking us both in that eerie fraternal way; the excitement in his eyes matching my own. We had been talking about how great it would be to end the series in the high Himalayas: cutting to some ravishingly dramatic shot of me with a backdrop of soaring snow peaks behind. It seemed we had come upon the ideal opportunity. We asked Dani Ram could we join him, but he insisted there was no way he'd have enough room in the jeep. We looked so dejected that he promised he'd look into the possibility of getting us a second jeep for ourselves. The Tiger and I took another look at each other and knew that, one way or another, we were going. We'd end the series on the roof of the world looking back down over the subcontinent.

Two days later, we were back outside the leper station with two vehicles parked outside surrounded by a solid throng of people gathered to see us off. Unfortunately, the vehicle Dani Ram managed to find wasn't a jeep but an effete Maruti minivan with an 800cc motorbike engine. It was all he could find at such short notice. I tried not to think back to the difficulties we had already experienced trying to climb up to Almora in one of these leaf blowers. At least its tyres had a modicum more tread than the previous one; but grip alone wouldn't be enough to get us to where we were going.

The lepers had all come out to wish us well, and many of the local merchants had come, too, to give Dani Ram items to trade with the *Bhotiyas* or to ask him to keep an eye out for some rare herb or Russian tool or Chinese cloth that could be got only up there at the crossroads of central Asia. This yearly trip was always a big occasion. Without it the weaving couldn't continue.

The one-armed knife sharpener, whom I had often seen around town, was picking through the camera equipment, making admiring hissing sounds. He asked Dani Ram for a particular type of whetstone found only in Tibet. The baker boy had come with some secret request from his master and had hung around, staring at me and the Tiger, swishing his horsehair switch instinctively over an empty tray of pastries. The village paraplegic was there, too. He tended to turn up most places. He was cycling back and forth, moving like a yacht beating into the wind, tacking laboriously at each curb, and gritting his teeth with the sheer effort of propelling the tricycle uphill with one hand.

The route we would be taking into the mountains had been part of an international trading route between Nepal, China, Tibet, Kazakhstan and Russia for thousands of years. Heinrich Harrar, a friend of Wolf's whose life was portrayed by Brad Pitt in the movie *Seven Years in Tibet,* escaped to Lhasa along the route sixty years ago. Tibetan salt caravans had been using it since prehistory right up until 1962, when the Chinese invaded Tibet and all the borders were closed during the Indo-China war. In late August of each year, caravans would bring rock salt principally, but also Tibetan wool, gold dust and borax down to the Indian plains, and then return with silk, spices and palm sugar. The continuous line of thousand-year-old trade had come to an end with the Indo-Chinese unrest. Both sides blocked their borders and built military outposts.

Today the borders between Nepal, India and China are mostly open again, but trade has never returned to its pre-war levels. The only traders left are the nomadic *Bhotiya* tribesmen, who were known ostensibly as sheep and goat herders, but who now tend to earn most of their income as middlemen for traders based in China, Russia and India. You placed your order with them whenever they arrived in your area on their herding migration, and when they reached a Chinese, Russian or Indian contact in a town along their routes, they would convey it to the relevant trader, who eventually prepared the goods and sent them to you by way of the nearest mountain border. The *Bhotiyas* would arrange to have the cargo hauled down the mountain to you in goat panniers or by jeep.

The leper station had ordered their wool from the *Bhotiyas* a few months before – both the crude mountain wool of their own sheep and also some rare camel wool from Kazakhstan and pashmina goat wool fur from Nepal. Word had come through that the delivery had now reached the Nepalese-Indian border, and Dani Ram was going up to check its quality before escorting it down the mountain.

We had arranged to set off at dawn, but it was noon by the time we got everything together and had a quick snack of *dhal* and rice served on leaves and eaten with our fingers. It was great to be on the move again, winding our way up into the mountains, seeing the rhododendron trees become gradually wilder and more gargantuan and the pine trees more stunted and gnarled. The air got thinner, farms sparser, and every now and then the nausea of swerving up back and forth along the switchback roads was dissipated by the sight of high-altitude meadows embroidered with alpine flowers. The water in the tracery of streams that crisscrossed the road became ever purer and bluer, so that eventually they were rivulets of liquid crystal that shimmered like shards across the tarmac. As we ascended ever higher into the Himalayas, I realised just how low in the foothills Almora was, and how temperate by comparison. The chill was noticeable. The driver had brought blankets, and we wrapped ourselves as best we could. The world seemed to extend upwards and onwards for ever; the higher you went, the more beautiful it became and the fewer people it held. For hour after hour we didn't see another car or person. This perfect tarmac road didn't go anywhere and had been built by the army purely to service the military installation. I had to admire their handiwork, the sheer indomitability of the military machine which had created this elegant notch of black ribbon that wound its way ever upwards, as though the mountain had been put on a lathe and the tiniest sliver of spiral carved out of its flank.

I was reminded of Kipling's *Kim* and its account of how this place was once crawling with spies and assassins as China, India and Russia all vied with each other in the "Great Game" of international intrigue.

As night fell, my thoughts turned nearer to hand, to the sheer precipices that plunged back down to earth around each hairpin bend. I had plenty of experience of how ill-equipped Maruti minivans were at handling such terrain, and I knew that one false move and we were gone, hurtling downwards into the rocky abyss. But the driver was careful and somehow managed, by carving his way through each bend, to maintain maximum hold. The air grew icy, and the feeble Maruti heater was inadequate to combat it. We tried piling more blankets over us, but they couldn't stop the gnawing cold, and we grew gradually more numb and uneasy.

Around ten at night, we came upon an old British surveyors' bunga-low on a low brow, and having roused the watchman from his go-down, we unpacked our bags, lit a fire and went straight to sleep on the draughty floor. At dawn we were up again, stamping our feet to bring life back to our bones, amazed at the thick plumes of vapour steaming from our mouths. We had been reduced to sources of thermal energy which the air was deter-mined to steal. While I packed the car and Dani Ram heated some *chapat-tis* on the cooling coals, the Tiger filmed the sun rising and carving its way through the peaks, setting each mountain blushing in turn. Dani Ram was concerned to see snow on the slopes just above us. They should have been bare by this time of year, but the changing seasons were affecting every-thing. We still had to cross the highest pass at 3,000 metres, and if that, too, was snowed under, it would make the journey next to impossible.

We drove on, noticing with increasing foreboding that that the snow-line was far lower than anticipated. After an hour's further climbing, we were driving through a thick blanket of fresh snow with the tyres spitting and spinning as they tried to contend with conditions they were never meant to face. Dani Ram's Gypsy ploughed through it easily, but our little motorbike engine was thoroughly outclassed. The driver pulled over and tried deflating the tyres and rigging up some improvised snow-chains from old rope. We managed to crawl on for another hour, but the snow was growing ever thicker, and the van kept skidding precariously towards the precipice. After a while, the Tiger and I got out and helped push the little box-car around each bend. I had only sandals on, and I could feel the snow biting into my toes, gnawing at them. The whole thing was madness, and after about an hour of it the Tiger called a halt. It was just too dangerous. Finding a worthwhile location to end the series on wasn't worth this. We told Dani Ram to go on ahead in the jeep and that we would head back to Almora on our own, but he wouldn't hear of it. He said we couldn't come this far and not see the roof of the world. He offered to tie the Gypsy to the minivan and pull us up, but that was madder still.

We were about to head back down again when Dani Ram suddenly remembered a lower pass through the mountains that would definitely be clear of snow. It was more a trail than a road, a part of a network of pilgrimages routes that crisscrossed the mountains. If we wanted to, Dan Rami said, the minivan could drop us near by and we could hike across the pass. From there it wasn't far to Munsyari. He could come down and pick us up on the far side once he had dropped his load in town.

It seemed a shame to have to head back now after we had come so far, and so we agreed to the plan, turning the van around and heading off back down to a lower valley which intercepted the pilgrim path. Descending was even more treacherous than coming up. Whatever hold the tyres had managed up till this was now gone and we were dependent solely on the brakes, which smoked furiously the whole way. In a moment of real weakness, I reached out to whatever was at hand – an old Hitachi cassette player in the dashboard – and I turned it on hoping for some relief. There was nothing but static and military interference, and then I spotted it. A bootleg Phil Collins. His Greatest Hits. There's really no excuse, but in my weakened state I succumbed. I was scared and nauseous from the leaky petrol tank and was convinced that frostbite was setting in. We played both sides of the cassette, hit after odious hit: *And I can feel it, coming in the air tonight, Oh Lord, Oh Lord . . . How can you just walk away from me, when all I can do is watch you leave . . . Oh, think twice, it's another day for you and me in paradise . . .*

Anyway, we got down in one piece, and once we had packed up our tripod and camera into backpacks, we bade farewell to the driver. He pointed us towards a lush upland green meadow with a shining black buffalo grazing its edge and told us to walk straight through the meadow and follow the trail beyond. By nightfall it should bring us to a temple with a hostel where we could spend the night, and from there it was only a few hours' walk around to the other side of the mountain where Dani Ram would meet us. He assured us we'd have no trouble finding our way – the route was still used by many pilgrims and tribal people. We were bound to come across others along the way.

The Tiger and I looked at each other dubiously, wondering whether we were mad even to consider going to such trouble; but the place was so beautiful that actually we were rather excited to have the chance to go hiking in it. I knew that my feet would stay warm as long as I kept walking – they always did – but I piled on extra pairs of socks just in case. There was less pressure on us to film constantly now. We had more than enough in the can and would be editing a lot out as it was; anything extra was a bonus. Of course, carrying the tripod and camera would be a pain, but it would be more than rewarded if we got some perfect shots along the way.

The driver was right about the route: it was well marked, snow-free and easy to walk. It had to be, as pilgrims in India tend to be frail. The most devout Buddhist pilgrims don't actually walk at all; they crawl on their hands and knees – not like chimpanzees but like caterpillars, rising up in the air and then prostrating themselves back into the dirt. The region was sacred to both Hindus and Buddhists. The Himalayas had always been a lodestar for religions; temples and sacred sites were everywhere. For Hindus, the source of the Ganges, called the Cow's Mouth, which lies high in the Central Himalayas near the Tibetan border, is their *axis mundi*. While Buddhists call Mount Kailash in Tibet the navel of the Earth – its four shimmering facets of quartz, gold, ruby and lapis lazuli can cleanse one of all *karma*. The devout of both persuasions dream of spending their last years wandering from temple to temple, and so no matter where you are in the mountains, you're never far from a pilgrim.

The Tiger and I had walked only a mile or two when we came upon a *sadhu* dressed in swirling saffron robes and smelling of incense and urine. His eyes were glazed and blissful and he was limping badly. I wondered whether it was as a self-imposed penance or because he had injured his leg. I had already come across *sadhus* walking backwards and rolling on the ground as forms of devotion in Varanasi; and in Delhi once I had seen a *sadhu* tie his penis to a plank and stretch it down to his ankles as a means of currying favour with the gods. (I realised later that I was wrong to see these practices as penance – which is a Christian notion. They were instead expressions of devotion to the gods who guided them and bestowed on them their cherished existence.) Although they seemed excessive to me at first, they also made me more tolerant of the flagellantist tendencies of Irish Catholics, and it relieved me to see that the *sadhu* with the stretched penis did seem to derive pleasure from his devotion. Overall I approved of Hinduism's obsession with the male member; it seemed to be in many ways healthier than the insipid chastity of Catholicism, or the contempt for the organ among the *hijras*. Even if, as Reg had pointed out on our first meeting, there was an element of depravity about some Hindu religious iconography that went beyond mere erotica, I regarded it as a depravity based on pleasure, which was markedly different from Western pornography which was focused principally on violation. In India the purpose of life is liberation rather than redemption, and it is in this central difference that our diametrically opposed views of both this world and the next are most evident. That said, I'm not sure how exactly it liberates one to tie one's penis to a plank and stretch it to the ground.

At the other extreme from the suffering *sadhus* on the pilgrim trails were the luxury pilgrimage trips organised by five-star hotels where one paid large amounts to be carried to holy sites on wooden palanquins or even whisked by helicopter to all the holiest Himalayan sites in one day and back in time for a champagne reception that evening.

At the brow of the first hill, we met a family from Udaipur tucking into the contents of a stack of tiffin tins – as sure a sign of a family on the move as the tarnished copper pots were of *sadhus*. The mother of the family was squeezing rice and *dhal* into balls and handing it to the father, a regal man with a white turban and embroidered smock. Their son ran over to shake my hand, and as usual I was taken aback by the sheer untrammelled delight Indians can radiate to strangers. A gleam in his eye was saying, "We are, after all, not strangers, but separate expressions of the single entity." His white short-sleeved shirt shone against his lustrous skin. Although his sister was shyer and hid in the folds of her mother's frothy yellow *sari*, she did look up and flash me a winning smile.

I asked their father what they were doing so far from home. Were they on holiday?

"Yes and no," he said.

They had got a grant from a philanthropic foundation in the United States to convert their house for wheelchair use for his eldest daughter – a gifted linguist crippled with multiple sclerosis. But he knew that the money would be better spent on a trip to Lord Shiva's abode at Kedarnath.

"Every year people from my district come here to pray, and, each time, their prayers are answered. I just regret I haven't had the money to come before now. My daughter has had to suffer for too long, but not much longer. Only Lord Shiva can take care of her – my little petal."

I told him what we were doing in the area, and he asked me to make sure I thanked the American charity on his behalf once I got back to the West.

Walking in the pristine air was heavenly. As the sun drew overhead, the temperature grew quite pleasant. If God had to live somewhere, I supposed it might as well be here. Above us, jagged sheets of snow rose triumphantly onwards, but my attention was drawn to the ground and the tiny wild strawberries and orchids beneath our feet and the bruise-blue columbines knocking against our knees. We walked all day, stopping once or twice to film the hills and to record some wild-track of birds and insects and the general pervasive sense of fevered serenity. Having carried the camera for most of the day, I was struck by the feat of technology that had allowed something so complex become so small. I thought of movies like *Fitzcaraldo* and *Apocalypse Now* and the enormous expense and effort filming on location used to involve. Now the camera, lenses, microphones and cables could all fit into a rucksack. The tripod was the only thing that was still unwieldy. Its function was simply to stand up, yet somehow it hadn't developed at all in the century since cinema was invented.

As evening began to fall, we came upon a simple stone temple in a grove of trees. There was a barn out the back which had been converted into a hostel. An old woman led us to a patch of floor and rolled out heavy yak-hair blankets for us to sleep on. Sitting cross-legged on the bed beside me was a holy *baba* wearing a scrupulously clean, threadbare *dothi*. He was the best-groomed *baba* I had seen. Even his dreadlocks were neatly plaited. I wondered why the others always looked so filthy. Was there something holy about filth? Was that why I had allowed myself to become so dishevelled in my hut?

Mr Clean laid down his prayer beads and *namasted* us both graciously. We in turn acknowledged the god in him with bowed heads and hands aloft and allowed ourselves be parsed by name, nationality, marital status, etc., as we had a hundred times before. This man actually knew where Ireland was for a change, and he had heard about our language.

"Yes," he announced. "It is one of the 3,000 that soon will no longer exist."

He seemed somewhat different from all the other *yogis* and *babas* I had come across, and when he'd exhausted his questions I turned them on him.

"I have been wandering only eighteen months," he said. "Before that I was with Nivea, the cosmetics multinational. I led their marketing team for two years, but when they started talking of promotion and sending me to head office in Bombay, I got jitters. I saw my future as a corporate nothing and knew I couldn't do it. I left. Broke up with my fiancée – a real beauty: an NRI from Sacremento with white capped teeth. Quit the firm and walked to Varanasi. By the time I got there, my suit was in shreds, and I gave it away. I went to an ashram, and they gave me this *dhothi*. In return I gave them all my worldly possessions, although I don't know what good my laptop was to them. My father still gets letters from the company wondering when I'm coming back.

"It's funny, you know, because my *guru* set me to follow the Goddess Lakshmi, the Hindu goddess of beauty and cleanliness!"

I found it odd to learn there was a goddess of cleanliness, but I suppose if you have 333 million gods and goddesses, there's bound to be one for most things. Only a country of a billion people could handle a religion of 300 million gods. (India's profligate sense of pluralism was one of its most endearing characteristics and may yet prove to be its most valuable – a key to survival in the global village.)

"Not cleanliness as in soap or shampoo," Mr Clean continued. "But more as in purity – a clean heart. Some of the *gurus* I met before were really filthy. My first *guru* collected so much in alms he had his own private chef and swimming pool. Another was a *komat-panthi*; you know what this is? A *yoga* jock who is rigorously celibate and doesn't even allow himself be touched by anyone, but still sucks off his young *chelas*. He believes their semen makes him immortal. He boasted that he had blown over a hundred of his devotees. I heard of another who was bulimic; he would gorge on food and then stick his fingers down his throat to maintain the wiry, ascetic look."

"Do you enjoy the life?" I asked.

"Mostly, yes," he replied. "Sometimes when I've been walking for days without food, I get weary and think of my home and family, but then I look around me at the beauty of the people and the mountains, and I know there is nowhere else I could be. Goddess Lakshmi lifts my spirit. I could never allow anything distract me from her again. It's just me and her, and my blanket and water pot."

I asked Mr Clean would he mind if we interviewed him in the morning when there was more light, but he said he'd rather not.

"A *sadhu*'s life is about escaping this world and connecting to the divine," he said. "Television is the opposite. It stuffs you in a box and connects you to illusion."

I kind of knew he'd refuse. Of course, I was disappointed, but I didn't press him. I had been having similar doubts about the medium myself, and it was only the Tiger's reassurance about its merits that kept me going. He insisted that television was only as good as those who made it. A camera was like a pen, he said. It could be used to write great literature or depraved trash. He insisted that all we were doing in these programmes was documenting the world around us so that others could see it and make up their own minds. He said that people had to know about the world before deciding whether to cherish or discard it. He had a point. My primary concern was that we could never hope to encompass the infinite facets of the Indian world within two half-hour programmes. Whatever we managed to document would never be enough.

The *baba* handed me a small polished shell as a gift and then, wrapping a yak blanket around his flimsy *dhoti*, he lay down to sleep. While we had been talking, a string of weary, walked-out *sadhus* had come into the dorm and laid their long bronze tridents down beside them and gone to sleep. The room had become a *sadhu* barracks. The Tiger was kicking himself that he hadn't brought the floodlight so we could film it. He tried capturing the scene in the meagre glow of the candlelight but it was no good.

Within months of our returning home, the first 3-chip cameras would be launched with enough processing power to lap up the scene easily.

I had only just settled down to sleep when Mr Clean let out a great roar of laughter that quite unsettled a few of the other *sadhus* who seemed to be of a nervous disposition. He lent up on his elbows and whispered to me, "You know the one thing I really do miss?"

"What?" I asked, smiling instinctively in reaction to his beaming leer.

"You'll appreciate this – my Rupert the Bear books!" he said and let out another great belly laugh. "My father translated them into Hindi. Alfred Edmeades Bestall was a genius. I have all his books. Or, I had . . ."

He fell quiet for a moment. The *sadhu* on the mat next to him glanced over. He was busily grinding his teeth and alternately closing one eye and then the other with intense concentration. He waved his fingers at me mischievously when he caught me looking.

"There is no one quite like Rupert," Mr Clean said dreamily. "The yellow check trousers, the red sweater, and Podgy the Pig in plus-fours. A bear with anthropomorphic paws – what a wonder! I loved all his cunning ploys – swimming with seahorses, talking to birds. I love Pong-Ping the Peke the most. What about you?"

I didn't want to tell him that I was more of a Paddington man.

"He lived in Surbiton in Surrey," he said. "Have you ever been? I think it must be just like a hill station."

I told him I never had, although I had made my own pilgrimage to Paddington Station on one occasion.

"Some day I'll get there," he murmured dreamily before putting his head back down to sleep.

Chapter 25

I WOKE AT dawn the next morning after a fitful night's sleep. Mr Clean's tales about the weird proclivities of *sadhus* had left me feeling uneasy about my sleeping companions. I got up and splashed water on my face, genuflecting to the great mountain gods who were once again being licked by the first rays of sunshine. When I went to the kitchen to get a cup of *chai*, I was amazed to see a lanky Western backpacker crouched over the fire. It wasn't until he turned around that I recognised him. It was Lans Okalsom. He was smiling broadly as he rose to greet me.

"Ah, Mocha, I was wondering when you'd wake. I've been waiting for you."

I was staggered to see him. I half feared I might bump into Sangev, Tara's lover, up here, but had never even thought about Lans.

"How the hell did you know I was here?" I cried.

"I live just over the hill," he said. "You don't think you could trample through the mountains with a camera and tripod and not attract attention. Everyone here is talking."

I was wondering how to break it to him about Bhartrihari – about failing to see him, and about the man from Alwar on the train who said that we were all going to turn into Bhartrihari in the end. To my surprise, he said, "Yeah, so I heard you failed to find Bhartrihari?"

"How do you know?" I said.

He just smirked.

"We didn't really fail, Lans," I said. "I tried very hard; it just didn't work out. I don't think he was there anyway."

"He was there if you *believed* he was," Lans said coldly. "That's all it took: belief – I tried explaining that to you."

I wasn't in the mood for this. I had done my best.

"With all respect, Lans," I said, "belief isn't enough. We're making television – we need images."

He smirked again.

"You believe in Bhartrihari," I continued. "But you've never seen him, have you? Belief will get you only so far. I did what I could, Lans. I'm sorry it didn't work out."

He shrugged.

To goad him more than anything I said, "Lans, have you ever seen an immortal *yogi* anyway?"

"Of course," he replied, his voice prickling with excitement.

"You have?" I cried.

He nodded triumphantly. It was obviously the wrong question. His eyes looked like they had hit the jackpot.

"In fact, it was only last week!" he gloated. "Of course, I haven't been fortunate enough to meet Bhartrihari, but Sumatara is an immortal *yogi* who has been here a thousand years already. In fact, that's why I'm here. I was going to ask if you wanted to interview him."

"You've really found one?" I said.

I had been thinking since arriving in the mountains that maybe I had been too harsh on Lans. Witlauf's talk of cutting-edge ideas had made me more wary of dismissing any notion, no matter how daft. I didn't want hindsight to see me as a flat-earther; as closed-minded as Tara's family was about him; or as the Vatican had been about Galileo. Furthermore, Donald had said something that made me re-evaluate the whole notion of immortality. It was about a study they were doing in his university on microbes living under the methane shelf hundreds of feet below the sea. These microbes, which had just recently been discovered, had been alive since the time of the dinosaurs. I don't mean their off-spring – these were the actual selfsame microbes that existed in the time of the dinosaurs. They lived in a place with no light, no food and phe-nomenally high levels of pressure. They had survived simply by doing without a metabolism – the process of intake of energy and voiding waste. And so, if it was possible for them to survive for hundreds of thousands of years in such a hostile environment, then who's to say the odd *yogi* couldn't manage to hang around in a comparatively cosy cave for a thousand years?

"Go on," I said to Lans warily. "Tell me about this bloke."

"I've just told you," Lans said cockily. "His name is Sumatara. I met him only last week. It was extraordinary. It's changed everything!"

My mind began stoking up again. I felt the thrill of it. What if he really meant it this time? What better way to end the series?

"And you say we can film him?" I asked, just to make sure.

"Yeah, sure," he said nonchalantly. "That's what I came to tell you."

"Well, where is he?" I asked.

"He's everywhere."

"Okay," I said amenably. "But where exactly did you meet him?"

"Oh, on the vital plane."

"The what?"

"The vital plane."

"You mean, as opposed to the physical plane?"

"It was the vital plane superimposed on the physical."

With every passing week, I felt I had grown gradually more sane and balanced, mostly due to the Tiger's stabilising influence and my own conviction that I didn't want to drift too far from shore again. I'm not saying I was on dry land yet; I could still sail off on odd tangents, but I didn't mind that, as long as I could find my way back again. Lans, on the other hand, seemed to have let himself drift entirely and was surfing out on a current which seemed destined to end in doom.

"Could you touch him, Lans?" I asked.

"He's a god; why would I want to touch him?"

"Well, let's just say you wanted to – could you?"

"No, not actually touch him physically, but there was, like, this parallel . . . to get to the vital plane you've got to shift focus and open your third eye – it's hard to explain."

I could appreciate that. I asked him how he expected us to film him if he wasn't actually there, and he went quiet, his face gradually darkening.

"You're so stupid, you know?" he snapped suddenly. "You have no idea! You're so blind! What if you had never seen the sea, only a child's cartoon of it? How could you know what it really looked like?"

"Right," I said.

I could see him trying to get a hold of himself. He knew he had to keep calm if he was to convince me. I pointed out with quiet composure that a camera works by absorbing the light bouncing off physical objects – it needs something to be manifested physically before it can interpret it.

"Well, that's the brilliant part," he said with strained brightness, "because I'm here and I'm physical and I can hear him, so I can tell you what he is saying."

"Do you mean there's actually a voice that you can hear? Something we could pick up on a microphone?" I asked, clasping at straws.

"*Of course* there's a voice," he said. "Just not an audible one. You hear it inside. Sumatara has so much to say . . . He says that god is like chocolate – you can't explain how it tastes to another person, but you can share it with them, and they in turn can share it with someone else, and . . ."

"Lans . . !" I interrupted, but he was in full flight now.

". . . inside you he melts and cloaks your heart like a fondue . . ."

This was going nowhere. I was just glad the Tiger was still in bed and didn't need to witness it. I think Lans reckoned if he relayed enough of Sumatara's insights to me, I'd find some way to get him on to the television.

"And you know," he said, "Sumatara told me that god is no old fatty on a lotus leaf, or a Jew with a beard; he's more like a kid at a rave."

"A kid at a rave," I repeated.

"Yeah, he's young and vibrant and happy, just chilling out. He's like a field of vegetables – all green and full of energy – and he wants us all to become immortal. That's what the Beatles were doing here. They've become immortal through their music. He says you can see it all on the cover of *Sgt. Pepper*."

"Look, Lans," I said finally, "just stop this. You know I can't put an imaginary being on television. You've got to give it up. I think you might need help."

"But you can put *me* on television," Lans cried. "I'll tell you what Sumatara said. Please, I need this!"

Just then, the Tiger came out from the dormitory with Mr Clean. He had all our gear and sleeping bags clutched in his arms.

"Come on, we're off, Mocha," he said. "This *sadhu* here is going to show us a shortcut around the mountain. He says we can be at Dani Ram's place in time for a late breakfast."

The Tiger didn't wait for a reply, just dropped my bags at my feet and set off marching down the track after Mr Clean. I had no option but to follow them. I barely had time to wave goodbye to Lans before tearing off. I hated leaving him like that. He had told me that his wife had gone back to Oslo with their children, and the government had stopped paying his social welfare payments. It struck me how desperate he must have been to meet me that first morning in Almora, to have hiked the whole way down from here. It must have taken him at least fourteen hours, I reckoned, walking solidly right through the night. I wished I had more time to tell him about the man on the train who had known all about Bhartrihari and his recent burial. I should have found out from him if Bhartrihari had been reborn yet. But my head was in too much of a spin to think properly. Immortal *yogis* and Rupert-loving *babas* were all churning through my mind, and mixed with altitude sickness and the cold, they had given me a severe headache.

Just as he had promised, Dani Ram was waiting for us on the far side of the mountain. He was sitting on a three-legged stool at one of the *chai* stalls that seem to occupy every bend on an Indian road, no matter how remote. We got into his jeep and he drove us to Munsyari, a town near the Nepalese border, about fifty miles south of Tibet.

In truth, Munsyari was more of a village with pretensions than a real town, and existed only because the *Bhotiyas* had needed somewhere to settle when the borders closed during the Indo-China war and they could no longer roam. Their way of life ended. They had to shoot their pack ponies and sell off their goats; they could no longer weave their fabulous carpets as they couldn't get the wool. They were forced to turn for survival to shooting snow leopards and bears to sell on the black market.

Everyone presumed that they would be wiped out as a tribe – another genetic dead-end – until suddenly the borders opened again after thirty-five years of lockdown. Old trade routes were now being re-established, and they were managing to make contact with their former trading partners again. It was a shock how much had changed – most obviously in Tibet, where the monasteries and *gompas* that had marked the route through the wilderness were razed by the Red Army. Yet the local people were still as keen to trade as ever and were producing the same pashmina and fine camel wool as they had done for centuries. Trade was revived, but focused now more on cheap electronic and plastic goods from China than the rock salt, borax and gold dust of old.

Dani Ram pulled up outside a *chai* shack which he promised did great breakfast and had three smouldering braziers always blazing. We made our way through the heavy cloth door into a fug of cigarette smoke and steamy tea. We had just sat down at one of the braziers when a man in a uniform got up from beside us and asked for our passports. We were reluctant at first, but he insisted he was with Nepalese inland security. He studied them carefully in the half light and then asked what we were doing in his country without a visa. The Tiger flicked back a few pages, pointing confidently to his India visitor's visa, and saying, "India."

The official frowned and said that this was Nepal. I looked to Dani Ram, but he just shrugged.

"India," the Tiger and I said in unison.

"Munsyari," the official said. "Munsyari same-same Nepal."

"No, *India*," I insisted. I was quite sure of this. It isn't something you mistake.

The official just shook his head.

The Tiger told me to get out my map, and I showed him that Munsyari was clearly at least thirty miles on the Indian side of the border. He pointed to our camera equipment, demanding to know what country we were spying for – China or Russia?

I started calculating how much money we had for a bribe. We had long since exhausted the bottles of Johnny Walker bought for this purpose. The Tiger and I looked to Dani Ram, but he was studiously avoiding our gaze. It seemed that whatever was going on, he couldn't help. I looked at the map again. There was definitely only one Munsyari, and although the region had been squabbled over for many years and was as much Chinese in character as Indian, it was now clearly labelled as being within India's borders.

The official had taken the passports outside to his jeep with him, and when he came back his frown was slightly relaxed, but still suspicious.

"Irish?" he asked with a note of incredulity.

"Yes," we assured him.

"For sure?" he said.

We pointed at the golden harp on the passports, and his face broke into an uneasy smile.

"Maree Roobinson?" he enquired. "Your president?"

"Yes," we said, confused.

"Yes, yes!" he said in an accent more Chinese than Indian, laughing heartily. "Maree Roobinson comes India earthquake. Very wonderful woman."

We agreed.

"Drink to Maree!" he said and sent a man out to his jeep to bring in a case of Russian vodka which they had confiscated earlier.

"No drunking on duty," he said, "but this for internashnal reelaeshuns."

He had the restaurant owner bring out teacups and poured us both cupfuls of vodka, while he filled a jam jar for himself. Then having proposed a toast, he launched into a song which I guessed must have been the national anthem of Nepal or India or Tibet as everyone in the room stood up. When he finished, he gestured at us to sing our own, and the Tiger and I began a halting rendition of *Amhrán na bhFiann*. The response was so enthusiastic that we followed it with a folk song to which the official and his men responded with a brace of their own. We went on like that, alternating songs while bottles of vodka were passed around. The Tiger asked could he film the scene, and the official waved expansively. As the afternoon wore on, we tried out all the folk songs we knew, and then switching to pop songs that might be familiar to all of us. I suggested the Beatles and James Brown, but they hadn't heard of them, and we had never heard of the Chinese and Russian bands they mentioned. Finally, through their Babel of strange Mandarin-Hindi dialect, I was able to make out the words of one of the songs they sang, "Haw-kan-uu-jus-wuk-a-way-frum-mee, when-awl-aa-kan-doo-iz-waj-uu-leeve . . ."

At some point in the evening, looking around the little corrugated-iron shack at the villagers with their distinctive Tibetan features – tiny marble eyes and bulging cheeks, which made them look more Inuit than Indian – I thought of the unique prism this series had provided me with, allowing me see India in a completely new way. I just hoped that what I saw would be comprehensible to people at home. We had filmed 22 hours of footage – roughly 110,000 feet of film, about the same height as the snow-bound pass that had defeated the minivan. What did it amount to? Was this the start of something bigger? Could the Tiger and I go around the world documenting people and cultures? I realised that we hadn't made anything like a conventional documentary: we had failed to address the corruption, the chronic levels of illiteracy, the inequality and injustice. And yet we did so more or less consciously: we had no wish to impose our values on them. They didn't judge our obsession with justice, although in their traditional viewpoint it can never truly liberate. They didn't dismiss our obsession with equality, although again in their culture it was regarded as irrelevant since it couldn't help to enlighten. Everything about the way they traditionally saw the world was different: time was circular, not linear; the goal of human endeavour was liberation, not achievement. It was pointless judging it from our perspective.

We spent a freezing cold night in a room above the *chai* shack, and the following morning Dani Ram told us the snow had got so bad that the army was threatening to close the road. If we didn't get out soon, we'd be stuck here until early summer. He wanted to leave right away, but we begged him to wait a few hours so we could at least film a final scene. Reluctantly, he agreed to hold out until mid-afternoon. It gave us a chance to hike up into the mountains and film our grand finale.

As we tramped up through the snow, searching for the perfect location, we were spellbound by the allure of the ever-expanding mountain range that rolled up from the horizon the higher we went. I tried working out what to say in this final PTC. India had almost devoured me. It had changed who I was and how I saw the world, but it had clarified precious little. All I knew for certain was that the timely arrival of the Tiger had rescued me from the brink. I had been thrown a lifeline by him and by the Irish language – that superannuated carcass I had carried as a dead weight all my life – and now that I had hold of it, I was determined not to let go. To my surprise, I found I actually enjoyed presenting. I had always been most comfortable on the margins, and television presenting offered a perfect margin – an intermediary between the audience and the topic, like the *swamis* on the *ghats* in Varanasi, teetering on the cusp of the corporal and the divine, or the *hijras* and their nebulous gender existence for which no census tick-box existed.

We came to a brow above a sea of mist in which valleys and foothills were hiding below. The Tiger put me standing in a ray of light that made my cheeks golden, and spooled out the microphone cable between me and the camera. He checked the focus, adjusted the white balance and pressed the red button. I saw the blinking light come on and I began to talk.

"*Le teacht ar aon chinneadh deimhnitheach faoin áit seo . . .*" I began, then paused, taking a quick glance out at the black and white triangular crests of the youngest mountains on earth, shimmering as the orange fireball of morning set each peak alight one by one, before continuing.

". . . in which the levels of spirituality are as high as the living conditions are low, and in which the people are more fertile than the soil – a place in which God perversely appears to inflict hardship in direct correlation with the faith of its inhabitants . . ."

I continued like that, on and on, desperately trying to express the inexpressible, trying to weave together the sentiments in my heart and the confusion in my head, until suddenly I was interrupted by a tiny old man who appeared out of thin air. Literally he sprang from a hole in a rock – popping out like a genie. We were halfway up a mountain, and there was no one or nothing anywhere around. He was stark naked and was nodding vigorously at me, waving his hand towards me. I noticed something in his palm. Tiny snowflake-shaped mints. It was overflowing with them, and he smiled encouragingly as his head continued to bob merrily, exultantly. He was mouthing short cheep-cheep noises, as though we were birds and he was encouraging us to feed.

The Tiger switched off the camera, and I went over to accept the mints and followed the man as he gestured us through a narrow crevice into his tiny stinking cave. A meagre twig fire burnt hungrily on the ground. He signalled for us to sit down and we did, rather awkwardly; there was hardly enough room on the ground for the three of us cross-legged. He smiled at us again and, dipping his finger into the embers, rubbed ash on to our foreheads, whispering something to each of us as he did so. That seemed to be all he wanted. He gestured for us to leave again, throwing the remaining mints into the fire and shooing us back out through the crevice.

It was only on the way back down the mountain that the words he had said sunk home to me: "*Tat tvam asi*."

In the following weeks, I asked many people what it meant and was finally told that the best translation was "thou art that". It didn't help very much, and I went on searching until finally in a book on Swami Vivekananda I came across a longer translation of the term: "You are all God, O ye men and O ye animals, and living beings, you are all manifestations of the one living Deity."

Once we had crawled back out of the cave again, we packed up the gear in silence and staggered, bewildered and disorientated, down the mountain. We didn't even try to rerecord the monologue. The whole way back to Almora, we stayed silent. That evening, the Tiger took the night train to Delhi.

Chapter 26

A S I SAID, I stayed on for another few months after the Tiger had gone back, just reading my books and walking in the hills mostly. I didn't take up drinking my own urine again, and I managed more or less to keep my imagination under control. The choir of angels came forth now and again, but I let them recede into the background. My flight home was from Indira Gandhi airport, and I allowed myself a free day in Delhi before it. As soon as the train reached Delhi station, I dropped my bags in the hotel and went straight to the burger bar to meet up with Reg. Donald wasn't there. He had stayed on in Seattle after the conference. I was dying to know how things had gone for them.

Reg gestured me to a tractor stool, saying, "It was pretty mad . . . yeah? To be honest, it was more Donald's gig. I was like, gag-me-with-a-spoon at some of the stuff, but he thought it was all cool. All the boffins were excited at meeting the *hijras*. You could tell they had never seen anything like it in their lives."

"Who came with you in the end?" I said.

"In the end, it was just three: Tara, Kanna and Gilia. I don't think you know them. Kanna was part of Sajda's posse, you know? The millionaire gangster who was gunned down at the murder trial. And Gilia is from Nizamuddin – a real dweeb, with barely any English, but the doctors wanted someone just recently operated on. They wanted to examine the techniques."

"What about Niishraah?" I asked.

"No, not her sort of thing. To be honest, it was all a bit freaky. I've never been in a place so focused on genitals before – it was like a frat party sleepover. There was this French guy who was convinced that if we continue to obsess over our genitals they will eventually rise to our heads and our brains will sink to our groins.

"I was like, *kiss my grits!* at first. But actually, he was pretty convincing. Sex would become easier, as there'd be no awkward gymnastics or foreplay – just a quick shag through the car window as you wait in traffic, or on the bus, or in the supermarket checkout. A blow of your nose to clean up and you'd be off again. There would be no more brothels or porn cinemas, he said. Instead, you'd have underground libraries and seedy peep-show debating chambers. People would unzip their flies or pull down their panties to discuss serious issues . . . Yeah, like that's really going to happen! But it was a lot less freaky than some of the stuff they were talking about."

"What about Tara? How did he get on?" I asked.

"Fine, fine," Reg said, uninterestedly. "Oh yeah, that French guy also said you could see the change happening already in the way the testicles, which used to always be the crown jewels, were now just a backdrop to the penis."

"Tell me about Tara," I tried again.

"You know how it is with him," Reg said cagily. "He's a funny fish; you're never sure what he's thinking. I reckon he was happy overall. It was totally far out – the whole thing."

Shortly after, Tara himself came in the door, and I got to ask him directly.

"The church is definitely my favourite," he gushed. "You're so lucky, Mocha; you have your beautiful Jesus in a dress and his skin so white and beautiful. I spent all my time in St Mark's and St James' – the big temple with rocket tips all over it, right in the middle of the city. All the doctors were talking about hymens and semen sacs, but I was only thinking of the statues and holy pictures in 10th Avenue temple – so beautiful they are."

"You're a fan?" I said.

"Yes, but not only Jesus, also Virginny Mary – she has hymen, too, yes? She is so lovely. Like Mata Bahuchara, only thinner. But, yes, Jesus is the best – I wish I had a body like his, so strong and muscley – not like our fatty Vishnu and Ganesh. Although I don't like his chin grass – too bushy. Why can't he have simple moustache liked Indian way? Nice and oiled and neat. I want to wear a dress like he is, Mocha – it is very lovely."

"It's a *dishdasha*," I said. "Not a dress."

"Definitely a dress," he insisted.

I sighed and, pointing outside to a beggar, said, "Okay, what's he wearing? It's a *dishdasha*, Tara. It's an Arab thing."

"No, that is *kurta*," he scoffed. "Very different. I mean dress dresses."

I shook my head.

"Maybe nightie, so?" he said with a grin.

He hadn't lost his sense of humour anyway, but he did seem somewhat more demure, and the pretence at Americanisms had been largely dropped. I was surprised as I had thought the opposite would be the case. I thought he would have come back a fully fledged Yank.

"I am thinking I would like to be becoming a priest," he said. "I would wear the nightie, but not black – purple and pink and frilly like the bishops, I think."

He still had the ability to dissemble – to focus on anything but the issue at hand.

"Tell me more about Seattle," I said.

"It was good, but my diddly wasn't so interesting for them. There were many weirder examples than me. Most of all they wanted to know about being leper, what bits drop off and so on. It was interesting, I suppose. I see I am not so different now, you know? Yes, I have little bit still of leprosy and funny diddly, but everyone has something, hmm? Ringworm, rashes, big nose, small nose, hairy caterpillar eyebrows. It is not so important."

"Did the trip make things any clearer?" I said.

I was hoping that he might have formed a definite idea about what he wanted to do with himself. I suppose I was just being selfish, but I wanted to be able to go home knowing it was all settled. Before I left Almora, the fax-*wallah* had brought me a letter from the Tiger saying that TnaG had seen the rushes and liked them. They were prepared to pay me £800 and were keen for us to do more programmes for them. It was definitely the beginning of something. I wanted Tara to have a future, too.

"Maybe the army," Tara replied absentmindedly.

"The army!" I cried. "Are you off your head? You'll get beaten up far worse there than in Almora."

"No, they'll never know. I will keep myself wrapped up and do good training and shooting and spitting and killing, but also in the showers I can have beautiful secret lookings at my friends and they will all be sleeping beside me."

"You're joking?" I said.

"No, no. Maybe even I'll be put on guard duty up at Nepalese border and will find Sangev there and we can run away."

"Mmm," I said.

"I will be a subaltern – with badges and a bandolier and a beret, and even for special occasions a crimson cummerbund."

I sighed.

"Tell him about the *berdache*," Reg interrupted.

"Oh, yes," Tara said. "That was most interesting. They are Indians, but not like us: Red Indians. Not red in colour, just a little bit brown. They are *hijras* too."

"*Berdache?*" I said.

"There was a whole mini-conference going on within the bigger forum," Reg cut in. "They came from all different tribes – Lakota, Navajo, Mojave. They all have their own *hijras* – called *berdache*; it means two spirits. They weren't all hermaphrodite; some were, like, gays and trannies, too. As far as I could make out, in the old days they dressed as squaws and acted as some sort of bridge between the real world and the spiritual. There was a Crow elder there who said his people didn't waste humans the way white men did. He said they focused more on their spiritual aspect than the sexual. Although, from what I heard at the conference, the warriors used to be only too happy to get up on these *berdache* blokes and ride their asses when they were off together hunting or in battle raids. Anyhow, they only ever began considering it shameful when the white man came along and started jeering at them. Up to that they had believed that if nature makes you different, it also makes you stronger – like with a black swan or a white rabbit or whatever. It gives you power."

Tara was tracing his finger through sugar he had purposely spilled on the table.

"Tara struck up a real friendship with one of them," Reg continued. "Right?"

"Yes, a little," Tara said abashed. "He was Lakota. He lives on a plantation . . ."

"Reservation," Reg corrected.

"Yes, reservation," Tara said. "He looks after the children of drunk people in his tribe. He wants me to come visit him. They have a community centre and always like helpers."

"And would you?" I said.

"Maybe . . . He's nice, but I want to find Sangev."

I was surprised by his hesitancy. I thought he would jump at the chance of going to America.

"For sure, you'll go," Reg said. "Donald said he'd sort things."

Tara winced.

"Tara got a bit of a fright over there," Reg said. "It was totally Donald's fault. He figured out a way for him to earn a few bucks, but I think it freaked him out a bit."

Tara scowled at Reg.

"What? What happened?" I said.

"Oh nothing; it is not important," Tara said.

"No, tell me," I said.

"No, please, Mocha, it is really nothing. Maybe I will go to Lakota man – Mark is his name. I will live in the woods and wear his beautiful costume of a million feathers – all yellow and orange and gold. Maybe this is what I will do."

Tara wouldn't tell me what had happened, and Reg had to fill me in later. It seemed that Donald had introduced Tara to a photographer who had a suite in the hotel set up as a studio and was offering cash to anyone willing to pose for him. There was a big market in America for hermaphrodite porn, but most of it was faked. It was hard to find genuine hermaphrodites willing to pose, and this man was prepared to pay big money.

Tara had initially consented, as far as Reg could gather, but then he had been asked to do something on video that had frightened him. When he had tried to get them to stop, it ended messily, and he had fled from the room. I hoped to get the full story from Tara later on as he had agreed to come by the hotel that evening so say a final goodbye, but he never showed up.

Next morning, I flew home, and although I tried sending a few letters to him via the restaurant, he never replied. Reg kept in contact with him for another few months, but over time he gradually stopped turning up. Although there were rumours that he had arranged a fake passport and American visa stamp, Reg could never find out for sure. I wish I could say for certain that Tara managed to track Sangev down and bring him to the States. I like to think of them both hiding out on some Lakota reservation. But I suppose it's equally possible that he came to some sad end on the streets of Delhi and lay unclaimed in the Delhi morgue. What I'm hoping is that someday Tara will get to read this and be in touch. The Tiger and I are still making programmes, telling stories about people around the world. We'd love the chance to tell his.

Epilogue

I S THIS STORY completely true? To be honest, I don't know. On the flight home, a Buddhist *lama* sat beside me. He was escorting a group of young monks to a monastery in Switzerland. I told him about our journey and how we had filmed it, and he said it reminded him of Prince Siddhartha's journey through India, which was also later fashioned into stories. It might have lost some of its truth in the process, he said, but truth can never be a fixed entity; it is always evolving – despite what the law courts think – and the truest stories are always those about journeys. I told him that I was anxious that we hadn't done justice to the truth of India, and he told me that whenever you think that you have found the truth, you know it's time to move on, to delve deeper into the next layer.

This book definitely contains truth, but certain elements have been expanded, contracted and embellished. It is hard to pin down any experience, especially an Indian one. Life just isn't that stable. Consciousness is capricious and volatile, and even the very creation chamber of our continuum, in which the tiny nuclei are so coiled up in themselves, and the timeframe so contracted, that every moment of existence becomes a fickle and mercurial entity cloaked in the thinnest veneer of stability is fashioned by the determined focus of our rational minds. It's tricky.

I've tried my best to put down on paper what happened, but I admit at times I may have jumbled certain things to protect people, and some conversations may be more as I remember them than as they were. Yet the facts stand for themselves. Much of the journey was documented on film, and so it must be true, despite what Frau Doktor Lieberman would have us believe about the distorting capabilities of cameras. Other elements were recorded in my diary, so they, too, are likely to be accurate. As for the rest, I'm just not sure any more. I certainly haven't gone out of my way to lie, yet sometimes revealing the truth requires blurring the facts just a little.

MANCHÁN MAGAN

Angels and Rabies: A Journey Through the Americas

"[Magan's] writing is unashamedly sensual and he has an engagingly confessional narrative voice; his adventures are as poignant as they are hair-raising. And while exposing the chaotic workings of his own soul, Magan reveals the underbelly of the colourful cultural and sociological jigsaw of these two great continents."
Sunday Telegraph

"Frightening, funny and lovable." *The Sunday Times*

"A cross between Joseph Conrad and Frank Zappa." Gerry Ryan

"Somewhere between *Lost* and *Heart of Darkness*." Ryan Tubridy

"The charm of the book is that, no matter how wacky, the story is all about people. Faraway lands can be hard to visualise, even with detailed descriptions, but love and loneliness are things we can all relate to. Mocha's vulnerability and naivety make him likeable. Very strange, but very enjoyable." *Ireland on Sunday*

"Each chapter is gripping because truly insane things happen around the author: war breaks out in Ecuador; a famous Hollywood actress falls into his arms. Then there are the near death experiences... It is a warm, well written and entertaining book which will keep readers happy." *Village*

"His writing is intimate and immediate, perceptive and humorous."
Books Ireland

"This travelogue exudes an attitude that is unmistakably rock 'n' roll. Fuelled by the same wild abandon as Jack Kerouac, Magan journeys through the Americas with nothing but adventure on his mind." *Hot Press*

"This is never dull, and always genuine." *Irish Homes*

ISBN 9780863223495; paperback original

LARRY KIRWAN
Green Suede Shoes

The sparkling autobiography of the lead singer and songwriter of New York rock band, Black 47.

"Lively and always readable. He has wrought a refined tale of a raw existence, filled with colorful characters and vivid accounts." *Publishers Weekly*

ISBN 9780863223433; paperback original

SEAN O'CALLAGHAN
To Hell or Barbados
The ethnic cleansing of Ireland

"An illuminating insight into a neglected episode in Irish history... its main achievement is to situate the story of colonialism in Ireland in the much larger context of world-wide European imperialism." *Irish World*

ISBN 9780863222870; paperback

DENNIS COOKE
Persecuting Zeal: A Portrait of Ian Paisley

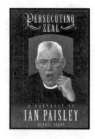

"This highly qualified author writes with an admirable mixture of clarity, charity and scholarship... I conclude with one word of advice: read this book." Tim Pat Coogan

ISBN 9780863222429; paperback

GERARD RONAN
'The Irish Zorro' The extraordinary adventures of William Lamport (1615–1659)

"Comprehensive and enthralling... Burned at the stake by the Mexican Inquisition at the age of 44, after a 17-year imprisonment, Lamport's story is truly extraordinary... Sometimes historical biography can be a dry read. Ronan's is anything but. He provides interesting insights into the lives of large Irish enclaves in France and Spain in the first half of the 17th century along with harrowing ones of those accused of heresy and subjected to the auto-da-fé of the Inquisition. Ronan's passion and sympathy for his subject shine through so it reads like a novel. A 'must read'." *Irish Independent*

ISBN 9780863223297; hardback

TOM HANAHOE
America Rules: US Foreign Policy, Globalization and Corporate USA

The disturbing, definitive account of globalization and the new American imperialism. Rather than serving as a global protector, the United States has shown contempt for the ideas of freedom, democracy and human rights.

ISBN 9780863223099; paperback original

FRANCIS J. COSTELLO
Enduring the Most
The Life and Death of Terence MacSwiney

"Francis J. Costello's comprehensive biography is most welcome... It will surely remain the definitive work." *Sunday Independent*

"Worth reading for several reasons: it is a transatlantic and fresh revision; it offers a psychology that explains a history; it illuminates an aspect of our present as well as our past." *The Irish Times*

ISBN 9780863222207; paperback

CHET RAYMO

Climbing Brandon

"[A] charming and thought-provoking book, equally accessible to the casual hill walker or those seeking meaning in today's hectic world." *Irish Independent*

ISBN 9780863223310; hardback

Honey From Stone

"A travel book about the world of ideas. Raymo uses the natural setting of Dingle as a place in which he asks you to explore with him through his own private universe ... a beautiful book that is well worth reading." *Irish Echo*

ISBN 9780863222320; paperback original

Valentine

"This atmospheric, lyrical and sensual tale of epic proportions... Raymo's interpretation may be controversial, but he is a gifted storyteller and philosopher." *Irish Independent*

"[A] vivid and lively account of how Valentine's life may have unfolded... Raymo has produced an imaginative and enjoyable read, sprinkled with plenty of food for philosophical thought." *Sunday Tribune*

ISBN 9780863223273; paperback original

In the Falcon's Claw

"[A] novel of never-ending pleasure ... superbly innovative. It is a work of rare and irreverent intelligence." *Le Figaro Litteraire*

"A metaphysical thriller comparable to Umberto Eco's *In the Name of the Rose*, but more poetic, more moving and more sensual." *Lire*

ISBN 9780863222047; paperback original

MÍCHEÁL Ó DUBHSHLÁINE
A Dark Day on the Blaskets

"A wonderful piece of drama-documentary... entertaining and captivating. It's an evocative story, a portrait of a young woman and her times, and an engrossing description of a beautiful place at a turning point in its history." *Ireland Magazine*

"A fascinating insight into Blasket Island life, life on the mainland, and life in Dublin in the early part of the last century." *Kerryman*

ISBN 9780863223372; paperback

GEORGE THOMSON
Island Home

"Imbued with Thomson's deep respect for the rich oral culture and his aspiration that the best of the past might be preserved in the future. It is when the deprived and the dispossessed take their future into their own hands, he concludes, that civilisation can be raised to a higher level." *Sunday Tribune*

ISBN 9780863221613; paperback

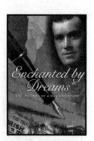

JOE GOOD
Enchanted by Dreams
The Journal of a Revolutionary

A fascinating first-hand account of the 1916 Rising and its aftermath by a Londoner who was a member of the Irish Volunteers who joined the garrison in the GPO.

ISBN 9780863222252; paperback original

STEVE MACDONOGH

The Dingle Peninsula

A comprehensive illustrated survey of the archaeology, folklore and history of one of Ireland's most fascinating regions.

"Far and away the best of the many books written about the area. A visitor who travels to Dingle without it is seriously deprived." *The Examiner*

ISBN 9780863222696; paperback original

Dingle in Pictures

"Wonderful colour photographs reproduced to perfection and with informative captions. All the text is printed in English, Irish, French and German. Gorgeous!" *Ireland of the Welcomes*

"A beautiful book... We stopped at many places featured in its pages and found that Steve MacDonogh's photographs wonderfully reflected the beauty that was there." *Irish Examiner*

"A stunning collection." *The Kingdom*

ISBN 9780863222795; paperback original

Open Book: One Publisher's War

"An intelligent, informative account of a life spent fighting for freedom of speech, a right which is still not adequately safeguarded." *Irish World*

"MacDonogh is without doubt the most adventurous and determined of the Irish publishers... This is an important book." *Phoenix*

"A fascinating and very important book." Brid Rosney, *Today FM*

ISBN 9780863222634; paperback original

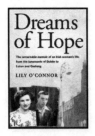

LILY O'CONNOR
Dreams of Hope

"It's a wonderful read from start to finish. Forced out of Ireland in the 1950s in search of a decent wage, with a young husband and very young family she lived first in Luton in England and later in a small town in Australia, some fifty miles from Melbourne. Hurrah for the likes of Lily O'Connor and the families associated with them – they make a lot of the bright spots in this world." *Ireland of the Welcomes*

ISBN 9780863223587; paperback original

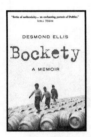

DESMOND ELLIS
Bockety

"The various adventures of a boy, living in less complicated times are recalled with humour and authenticity... The imagery is evocative and witty and Ellis' book is an easy read, avoiding sentimentality as it lilts through amusingly recounted, people-focused stories." *The Dubliner*

"Genuinely funny. It is enlightening to learn that, despite the censorious and tight-arsed approach of the Catholic Church and its lapdog politicians, working class people were quite subversive in their attitude to life back then. Straight-laced they certainly were not. *Verbal Magazine*

ISBN 9780863223648; paperback original

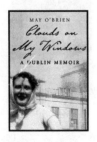

MAY O'BRIEN
Clouds on My Windows

"This is a wonderful book… May O'Brien says in her afterword that this is an ordinary book about Dublin life in the 40s. Maybe it is. But it's a story about an extraordinary woman, in any time." *Irish Independent*

ISBN 9780863223358; paperback original

DRAGO JANČAR
Joyce's Pupil

"Jančar writes powerful, complex stories with an unostentatious assurance, and has a gravity which makes the tricks of more self-consciously modern writers look cheap." *Times Literary Supplement*

"[A] stunning collection of short stories... Jančar writes ambitious, enjoyable and page turning fictions, which belie the precision of their execution." *Time Out*

"[E]legant, elliptical stories." *Financial Times*

"Powerful and arresting narratives." *Sunday Telegraph*

ISBN 9780863223402; paperback original

AGATA SCHWARTZ AND LUISE VON FLOTOW
The Third Shore: women's fiction from east central Europe.

"A treasure trove of quirky, funny, touching and insightful work by 25 women writers from 18 countries in the former communist bloc. Flipped open to any page, it offers a window into unique worlds – some political, all intensely imaginative and often unexpectedly funny." *Sunday Business Post*

"These stories are exciting, intriguing and never predictable. For all their startling narrative tricks and puzzles these stories will appeal for their wide range and honesty." *Books Ireland*

ISBN 9780863223624; paperback original

NENAD VELIČKOVIĆ
Lodgers

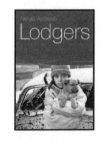

"[A] beautifully constructed account of the ridiculous nature of the Balkans conflict, and war in general, which even in moments of pure gallows humour retains a heartwarming affection for the individuals trying to survive in such horrific circumstances." *Metro*

ISBN 9780863223488; paperback original